WILDLIFE RESCUE

ANGELA WILKES

BROADCAST BOOKS · BRISTOL

© 2008 Angela Wilkes

Published by   Broadcast Books
7 Exeter Buildings
Bristol BS6 6TH
catherine@broadcastbooks.co.uk
www.broadcastbooks.co.uk
Tel: 0117 923 8891

ISBN: 9781874092896

Illustrations © 2007 Dru Marland
6 Belvedere Road
Bristol BS6 7JG

Cover illustration   David Sharrock

Designed by   Martin Laurie
martinlaurie@ukonline.co.uk
Tel: 01925 757 864

Printed and bound by   Henry Ling Ltd., at the Dorset
Press, Dorchester, DT1 1HD

CONTENTS

INTRODUCTION

First, there was the painfully skinny, hairless fox, its skin the colour of a bar of lavender soap, that slunk out of the disused dog kennel early one snowy morning. Cage-trapped the next night and taken off by an animal charity for mange treatment, it was an eye-opening introduction to the ills that can poleaxe wildlife in our midst.

Next came the woodmouse in my daughter's outstretched palm, prised from the cat's jaws. "He's not dead, Mummy, just unconscious." She was right and a few days of in-patient care – a plastic food container (punched with airholes) plus seeds, dried fruit, water and a guesswork dosage of broad-spectrum antibiotic powder wheedled from the vet – saw that one all right, fully recovered and released. Then there were the 200-plus frogs, hand-raised in a tank in the kitchen because we didn't want the goldfish to eat all the spawn and, anyway, weren't amphibians all dying off with some dreadful red-leg infection, or something? Or was it that the ponds were disappearing?

Hard on the heels of these narrowly-averted natural disasters came a crop-bound wood pigeon, a gull with a broken wing on the playing fields out the back, a catted starling and a young, fledged thrush crouching in the centre of a busy road in Peckham, rain-soaked and apparently waiting for death. A horn-honking traffic-jamming moment later and the thrush was heading towards becoming another house guest. Soon small branches jutted like a miniature Birnam Wood around the spare room and mealworms were marching across the bedspread.

South-east London isn't exactly the African plain or the dry forests of India, and its wildlife isn't as endangered or as high profile as the charismatic Big Cats. But it was becoming clear that much of the urban wildlife was getting into trouble for precisely the same reasons as the lions, tigers, big apes and whales the family were filling charity envelopes to save. Man-made interventions and destruction of natural habitats – via road traffic, powerlines, mega-scale cat ownership, modern fashions in gardening and building practice, to name but a few – were all piling on the pressure and putting local wildlife in peril. Come to think of it, we hadn't heard the sparrows clamouring outside the bedroom window since the new roof and loft conversion did away with those little nooks and crannies under the eaves…

Clearly, there was a problem, a clash of species' interests – and it wasn't going to get better. It was time to learn how to help properly. I became a one-day-a-week volunteer at a Wildlife Hospital for the next six years. As a car-owner, working from home, I was lucky enough to have the means and flexibility to do hands-on "rescues", too. That meant evolving a taxi-driver's internal roadmap of my area so that I could catch, collect and deliver wildlife casualties for medical attention as quickly as possible.

Not all of them survived. A few died in transit. Some had to be **euthanased** on arrival because their chances of recovery were considered hopeless or their condition was incompatible with release back to the wild.

But very many did make it, joining the hospital's annual output of several hundred successful "releases". Not only were they taken back to their original territories quickly, so that they could have a second (or sometimes third) renewed chance of life: often subsequent sightings showed that these former emergency patients were doing well, surviving long-term, and even reproducing.

My experience of animal rescue over the last few years has taught me that you can help wildlife quite easily, with a bit of thought and effort. You don't have to have a car, a home in the country, your own garden or a lot of expensive equipment to change the luck of a wildlife casualty – or even start to change the odds faced by a whole species that's got into trouble. Absolutely anyone can do it and you really can make a difference, if you set your mind and heart on it.

Is it worth it? Surely Nature looks after its own without us interfering? Would not a seriously injured bird or animal be best left to recover or get put out of its misery by a predator or car? Aren't there more than enough hedgehogs, or bats, or foxes around? It's not as though one individual is going to make a difference. Is it? I believe that there is a better way and that we owe it to our wildlife to give it a try. I hope that, when you have read this book, you will agree with me.

HOW TO USE THIS BOOK

The seven chapters that follow each deal with a commonly encountered animal or category of British wildlife. The chapters are organized into sections containing information about the animal's lifestyle, habitat and the major hazards, both natural and manmade, that threaten it today. There follow sections on how to help in an emergency, and through longer term conservation projects. At the back of the book there is a comprehensive Glossary which explains technical and biological terms in the text.

With heartfelt thanks for their advice, encouragement, patience and inspiring personal examples to: Sir Les Stocker, Founder and Director of the Wildlife Hospital Trust (St. Tiggywinkle's); Pauline Kidner, Founder & Director of Secret World; Ted Burden, Founder and Director of London Wildcare & London Wildlife Hospital and their staff and volunteers, especially my colleague Michael Salkend; Trevor Williams (the Fox Project); Mark Hemington (National Fox Welfare Society); Eddie Williams (Willow Wildlife Ambulance); staff and volunteers at the Swan Sanctuary, Egham; the Wildfowl and Wetlands Trust; Richard Thompson (RSPCA wildlife officer), D.C. Dave Flint of the Metropolitan Police Wildlife Crime Unit - and to my family for not minding the smells in the car and conservatory and not complaining about some very late mealtimes.

1

BARRY THE HEDGEHOG

*B*arry the hedgehog was curled into a ball, well hidden under dry leaves at the garden's edge. He was snoozing that sunny May afternoon, because that's what hedgehogs do in the daytime, when the strimmer struck. The gardener probably didn't even realise that the whirling wire had zig-zagged a slice off the top of the hedgehog's rounded, spiny back. But the sudden pain made the hedgehog unfurl – just in time for the strimmer to lift a flap of flesh from his forehead before moving on.

Several days later, Barry was seen wandering groggily in the grounds of a nearby children's hospital. Luckily for him, he was a healthy, strong young male with a sound immune system and he had been able to survive the initial trauma of his awful injuries. Not so fortunately, the weather was unusually warm for the time of year and his open wounds had attracted bluebottles. By the time a compassionate health worker stooped and picked him up, Barry was covered in wriggling maggots that were eating voraciously into his flesh. They would not drop off and leave him alone until they were fully grown. Barry's wounds had become infected. Harmful bacteria were releasing poisons. Even to the untrained eye, he was an obvious wildlife casualty – a hedgehog out and about during the day, confused, in toxic shock and dehydrated.

He wasn't a pretty sight and he smelled terrible, too. A hanging corner of skin was obscuring his line of vision and the glistening membrane that covered his skull was exposed. But despite his horror-film appearance, he was still keen to eat. Staff at the wildlife hospital where he was taken for help took this as a very good sign. First priority was replacing the water volume and body salts that Barry had lost. Many sick and injured animals die because they become dehydrated through bleeding (like Barry), because they are vomiting or suffering from diarrhoea, or they're simply too ill to eat and drink. Unless body fluids are rapidly replaced to make good the volume lost and correct metabolic

imbalances, the animal's kidneys will fail. Then other major organs, like the liver and heart, will fail, and coma and death are inevitable. Barry got his life-saving treatment as an injection under the skin, not by mouth or via a drip. This was partly because hedgehogs tend to roll up on drip-lines and pull the connection out, but also because his facial and head injuries would have made syringing liquids into his mouth painful and stressful.

Next, his wounds were gently flushed with warmed saline solution and all dead tissue was taken off. Then all the maggots were removed. Some were dug-in so deep that only their tail tips could be seen. Finally, the cleaned flesh wounds were packed with water-based gel and left open to the air to heal naturally. Stitching or stapling could have sealed infection in and a dressing wouldn't have stayed put on that roly-poly body. Throughout the treatment, he was given pain relief. Before long, patches of new healthy flesh began to appear where the strimmer had struck. Four weeks after the accident, he was released back to the wild. There were some bald patches (which would probably stay that way), but otherwise, Barry was as good as new. Missing prickles or not, after his gruelling ordeal, no one could call this small survivor "spineless".

Hedgehogs

1

HEDGEHOG FACTS

POPULATION AND DISTRIBUTION

Hedgehogs have lived in all parts of Britain since the Iron Age. The species found in Britain is genetically of European (or Western) stock, and is found from Portugal and Ireland to the west, the former Soviet Republic to the east, Scandinavia to the north, and the Mediterranean to the south. It coexists in several places with the similar-looking Eastern hedgehog. Hedgehogs continue to survive in these islands, but their future looks bleak. Since 2000, their numbers have halved in the UK from 1.5 million to c.750,000 in 2006. Whereas millions once milled around our towns and farms, modern landscape changes (grubbed-out hedgerows and orchards, loss of short-turfed horse-grazing areas) have made Britain a far less hedgehog-friendly place than it used to be. Every closed-up fence gap, blitz on garden pests and increase in road traffic turns the screw tighter.

HABITAT

Hedgehogs can live just about anywhere – provided it's not too wet. You'd expect to find them where you can see deciduous trees. Hedgehogs need dried leaf material and twiggy litter to make their nests warm and weatherproof. You don't have to go to the countryside to find hedgehogs, either. They can thrive alongside human dwellings. Untidy corners of gardens, parks, cemeteries and waste ground, the less manicured the better, provide hedgehog havens. Compost heaps, log piles, long grasses, are resting-up areas by day.

Hedgehogs tend to avoid one another's company, unless it's the **breeding season**, each normally sticking to its own home range (though these overlap). They usually rouse themselves around dusk to forage, but after heavy rain, they may start on the slug and snail harvest during daylight hours. Hedgehogs can travel a couple of miles every night looking for food. That's why filling in all the low gaps and holes in fencing is harmful, shrinking hedgehogs' territories in one fell swoop and cutting food supplies accordingly. It also limits their gene-pool breeding options, making for a less healthy population overall.

Hedgehogs forage in out-of-the-way places such as underneath hedges and overhanging vegetation because such secret corners yield plentiful supplies of their main foods – insects and other **invertebrates** such as slugs and **worms**. They rely on their highly developed senses of smell and touch to find food, hence all the snuffling and snorting they make while searching. You are more likely to hear a hedgehog in your garden than to see it!

Hedgehogs aren't very fussy feeders. They tend to run whatever they find in their path past their taste-buds. This can get them into real trouble (also see *Poisoning*, p. 14). But their normal diet is insect-based. It includes caterpillars and other insect larvae, earthworms, slugs – which they roll backwards to remove their sticky mucous coating – spiders, flies, butterflies and moths. Beetles are a favourite. A research project examining the stomach contents of hedgehogs killed on the road or exterminated by gamekeepers found beetle remains in three-quarters of them – and one animal had chomped through a staggering 75 for its last supper.

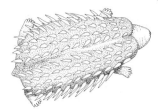

Given half a chance, hedgehogs over-eat. They need to do this as autumn approaches, or they won't build up sufficient fat stores to see them through winter **hibernation**. Also featured on the hedgehog menu are **carrion**, small **rodents** and their nestlings, some young of ground-nesting birds, lizards and the odd frog. Hedgehogs do eat snails, but not the big ones with tough shells. As they feed, little bits of grass and leaf get swallowed, too, so hedgehogs get a certain amount of "greens". If they live in an area of gritty soil, their teeth get very worn down.

In captivity, non-releasable, or convalescent animals are fed a mixture of meaty pet food and dried ground-up insects with vitamin and **mineral supplements** and occasional fresh fruit. The British Hedgehog Preservation Society sells a ready-made supplement containing dried meat, insects, nuts, berries, fruit, cereals and honey (also see *Useful Organisations*, p. 25). Some wildlife centres give hedgehog patients a few catfood or dogfood pellets to help keep their teeth clean, because a totally soft food diet provokes **calculus** build-up and gum problems. Clean, fresh water must be available daily – on no account give milk. Milk can give hedgehogs **enteritis**.

IDENTIFYING HEDGEHOGS

Hedgehogs must be the easiest of all British mammals to recognise, being the only ones covered in spiny prickles. Actually, the spines are just modified hairs and, like hairs, they can drop out and re-grow. Sick hedgehogs sometimes lose a lot of spines. When a hedgehog is born, its first spines are soft, pliable, off-white and covered in **membrane**. They are shed later and replaced by the longer, tougher brown-and-cream variety – around 7,000 2cm-long ones. Hedgehogs' coats also contain coarse hairs on their faces, legs and underbody.

British hedgehogs can be between 20 and 30cms long. Their weight may fluctuate according to age and time of year. A well-fed animal in the wild may weigh 1kg or more. Only the male is a "hog", females are "sows". Neither sex looks particularly like modern pigs. Perhaps their name arose from their snuffling food-searching habits just below the surface of a pile of leafmould or twigs. But it must have been the bristly brown wild boar of old, rather than the broad, bald-looking farm-reared modern porker that inspired the name hedgehog. In some parts of the country they are known by the older name, "urchins". Some people also call baby hedgehogs "urchins"; others refer to them as "hoglets".

Unless the male is in raunchy mood, telling the sexes apart isn't that obvious. Females are not invariably the smaller, lighter sex, although the fattest, heaviest hedgehogs tend to be older males. Look at an uncurled animal's underside, holding it against your midriff, its tummy facing outwards, to check which is which. A female hog will have two openings close together (vagina and anus) and both will be near the root of its tail. The male's anus will also be close to the start of its tail, but its penis will be located near the centre of its belly. Alternatively, gently put one hand around a hedgehog's middle (try while it is eating). If all you can feel at the centre of its belly is fur, it's a female!

Determining the sex of baby hedgehogs is not so easy. When very young, a male hog's penis is located,

One hour after birth, blind, deaf and covered in soft white prickles – but able to crawl.

Ten days old: a much sharper set of spines and getting the hang of curling up.

confusingly, far nearer the tail. Also, if a handler feels a lump in the middle of an infant's belly, it's quite likely to be the shrivelled remains of its **umbilical cord**. Even experienced wildlife rehabilitators have made mistakes when "sexing" young animals in captivity – and ended up with surprise litters later.

BREEDING

Hedgehogs are solitary for most of the year, the males dispersing in the spring when they emerge from hibernation, to find a mate to breed with. Adult males don't feature in hedgehog family life. After mating, the male makes a same-time-next-year date and exits. Female hedgehogs don't continue rearing after the young are weaned, at around two months. This doesn't, of course, make them "bad" mothers. Cases have been reported of injured sows making it back to the nest to suckle young before dying. It's just that parental dependency doesn't last long. Baby hoglets are initially very vulnerable, though, and cannot roll up until they're about two weeks old. They don't have the muscle power. The desired

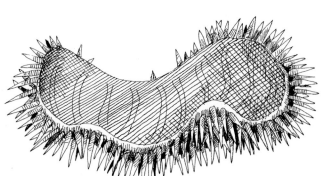

Only a badger or an occasional fox can unlock a curled-up hedgehog.

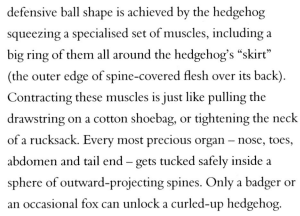

defensive ball shape is achieved by the hedgehog squeezing a specialised set of muscles, including a big ring of them all around the hedgehog's "skirt" (the outer edge of spine-covered flesh over its back). Contracting these muscles is just like pulling the drawstring on a cotton shoebag, or tightening the neck of a rucksack. Every most precious organ – nose, toes, abdomen and tail end – gets tucked safely inside a sphere of outward-projecting spines. Only a badger or an occasional fox can unlock a curled-up hedgehog.

Hedgehogs can live up to six or eight years in the wild (ten in captivity). They mature sexually at 8–12 months. Courtship is noisy and can take ages, the female adopting a spines-flattened posture, nose pointing in the air, for mating. She normally gives birth after 30 to 40 days' pregnancy, but this varies – perhaps as a survival strategy to counter very cold spells and food shortages in early spring. She can have up to eight young, although only two or three are likely, and may have one or two litters a year. Town litters tend to be bigger than country ones.

AVOID DISTURBING A HEDGEHOG'S NEST. If a mother is disturbed around the time of birth, she will probably desert or eat her young. Leaving human scent on hoglets – e.g. touching them with an ungloved hand – is liable to trigger such reactions.

HIBERNATING

Hedgehogs hibernate – the word comes from the Latin for "winter" – to conserve energy when the weather is cold and food resources are scarce.

They usually do so from around October (or January depending on temperatures) until March or

April, with the occasional "awakening" mid-term if **foraging** conditions are right, or if they wish to change sites. In autumn, hedgehogs instinctively gather grass and dry leaves in their mouths and build a special robust **hibernation** nest under brambles, brushwood or log piles. They'll also nest in compost heaps and ready-stacked bonfire heaps, so hibernating is a risky business. Youngsters that haven't put on enough stored fat to see them through this annual metabolic go-slow, or whose systems are weakened by disease or **toxins**, are among the hedgehogs who never "wake up" from their winter "sleep." Up to 70% of young hedgehogs may die in their first winter.

COMMON HAZARDS FOR HEDGEHOGS

ROAD ACCIDENTS

A hedgehog's tried-and-tested defence – rolling up in a ball and hoping the danger will go away – is not effective against today's motor traffic. The Mammal Research Unit at Bristol estimates that a minimum of 20,000 hedgehogs are killed each year on the roads. Along with rabbits, squirrels and rats, they're the most common British road-kill mammals. The effect of this slaughter, say researchers, is a "serious unknown". Occasionally, a hedgehog may be caught a glancing blow and spun out of the path of oncoming vehicles. If it can be found and treated before succumbing to dehydration, **flystrike** and attack by **corvids** and predators, it may survive such an accident.

SIGNS: These include hedgehog *moving around in daylight* in an abnormally slow, laboured manner; limping, holding its leg at an odd angle or other signs of fracture; flesh wounds which have become infected (ingrained dirt from road, fly eggs, etc.), dehydration (look for sunken eyes, skin that "tents" when gently pinched); the animal seems disorientated, weak, has a **faeces**-stained rear; **seizures**; a weaving or lop-sided walk which may indicate concussion and serious head injury; or it may be **collapsed**, hypo- or hyperthermic as result of exposure to weather. A Hedgehog lying "flat out" on a verge will be either dead or unconscious (sleeping or hibernating hogs curl up) so check, without causing safety problems for yourself or other motorists.

TREATMENT: First aid includes pain relief, veterinary treatment for **shock**, **rehydration**, **wound management** and fracture repairs – possibly **pinning** or **stabilisation** using external framework; then **rehabilitation**. Hedgehogs are prone to trying to cope with bone breaks, including crushed feet, so that by the time they are rescued, the limb or foot can no longer be saved. It is common to find a fracture has healed itself, but is twisted. Amputees are not released into the wild but are normally kept in sheltered conditions, such as a walled private garden.

Counting road-kill corpses, a standard way of estimating population size, has shown a huge, steady hedgehog decline.

GARDEN AND FARM MACHINERY

Getting caught by machinery and tools ranks alongside traffic accidents as the most common cause of hedghog injury and death. Strimmers are particularly life-threatening to hedgehogs sleeping, or hibernating unseen in nests, under long grass and overhanging fringes of vegetation. Hedgehogs often get impaled on garden forks, too.

> **SIGNS**: Serious injuries, as above for road traffic accidents, with frequent limb and nose losses; severe **trauma**.
> **TREATMENT**: Many animals are so severely injured that they are **euthanased**. If only one rear leg has been lost, the surviving machine-cut victim may be treated and retained in captivity. Surgical and drug treatment, is given, as above, for traumatic injuries from motor accidents. The spiny skin over the hedgehog's back heals slowly, because it has fewer blood vessels (to reduce heat loss) than furry skin.

Strimmers are particularly life-threatening to sleeping or hibernating hedgehogs

EXTERMINATION

Hedgehogs are the nation's most popular wildlife casualty – the creature that is most likely to get taken to a wildlife hospital for care when it is in trouble. But not everyone views hedgehogs in a kindly way. Gamekeepers have traditionally targeted them for extermination, in the belief that they kill the chicks of ground-nesting birds and steal eggs. But with their small, overshot jaws and rather blunt teeth, hedgehogs don't have the **oral** equipment to penetrate eggshells easily, nor have they evolved the mental equipment to use tools, like some other mammals and bird species. Loveable they may be, brainy they are not.

It's unlikely that a hedgehog would take a nestling with its parent around, too, although they would certainly eat a dead one. Perhaps hedgehogs have been taking the blame for gamebird damage mainly perpetrated by others (foxes, corvids, rodents and **mustelids**) these past centuries.

DOG ATTACKS AND BADGER PREDATION

Both working dogs and pets are capable of attacking hedgehogs, often fatally. Very young animals, or tame ones, don't curl up well, or quickly enough. They also fall victim to **predation** from rats, foxes and ferrets. Although hedgehogs can also run – quite fast over short distances – to avoid trouble, their instinctive response is to roll up. Badgers have very powerful claws and they have no trouble easing a hedgehog open and eating it, from the inside out. Badgers may also pose a significant problem for hedgehog populations when they share the same **territory**, because both animals compete for similar foods.

> **SIGNS**: These include serious snout injuries, broken facial or jaw bones.
> **TREATMENT**: Some fractures may be stabilised with stainless-steel wiring; other traumatic injuries would require hedgehog to be euthanased.

CRUELTY

Mistreatment, such as using the animal as a makeshift "football", results in multiple injuries and frequent deaths. One hedgehog rescued by a passer-by in London revealed the curled-up victim to be a more exotic species – a **pangolin** – but thanks to prompt intervention it survived, albeit with severe bruising.

Pangolin and hedgehog.

> **TREATMENT**: As for traumatic **RTA** injuries, above.

FALLING DOWN DRAINS, ETC.

Hedgehogs have an unfortunate flair for falling down holes and getting stuck. They may be unable to get out because a pit's sides are steep and slippery. Or if they've toppled in headfirst, their backward-pointing spines prevent them struggling back up. They will starve.

> **TREATMENT**: The victim may be pulled from a hole by gripping a generous portion of the spines on its back, otherwise you'll need tunnelling or engineering help! It must be given a proper health check, and any injuries examined and treated.

DROWNING

Steep-sided ponds with no overhanging vegetation to grip, and uncovered swimming pools, provide many a hedgehog with a watery grave. Hedgehogs can swim, but can't keep paddling indefinitely.

> **TREATMENT**: Never just fish a hedgehog out and let it go. It may have inhaled water and must be treated for potential **inhalation pneumonia**.

GETTING CAUGHT IN NETTING OR LITTER

Discarded garden or sports netting, fishing tackle and litter can all entangle a hedgehog, leading to blood-flow restriction, **tissue death** and starvation.

Looking for a meal in discarded litter can be a deadly mistake.

> **TREATMENT**: Never try to remove tight restrictions yourself unless you are far from help. The hedgehog must be cut free, along with a portion of netting, and taken to the vet immediately. The constriction may need to be removed under **anaesthetic**; surgery may be needed, as well as drug therapy to counter infection, and rehydration.

GETTING COVERED IN HARMFUL SUBSTANCES

Hedgehogs often inadvertently walk through corrosive or toxic substances such as oil, paint, battery acid, and then compound the mischief by trying to lick their stinging feet clean. Use strong, absorbent paper (newspaper would do) or a soft, dry towel to mop off the worst of the substance, then a little Swarfega hand cleaner gel and warm water to soften any tar clinging to the hedgehog's spines. Loosely wrap it in another clean towel (leaving the head free) to stop it ingesting or inhaling more while being taken for help. Retain nearby containers for identification.

SIGNS: The animal is found collapsed, or suffering bouts of vomiting and/or diarrhoea; with possible chemical burns, or paint, on its spines and feet.
TREATMENT: Vets or wildlife centres could contact the Veterinary Poisons Information Service (See Useful Organisations) for advice on treatment options for any substances that have been swallowed, inhaled or which have burned the skin. **Fluid therapy** may be tried, plus **activated charcoal** and/or sodium bicarbonate to absorb harmful stomach and gut contents.

POISONING

Pesticide poisoning is likely if agricultural pellets containing **methiocarb** are around. Hedgehogs that have eaten gardening slug pellets containing **metaldehyde** – which decomposes in dead slugs – may be poisoned, too. Five grammes can kill an adult animal.

A build-up of tiny amounts of pesticides, from many different encounters, can also cause a delayed reaction when stored fat is broken down and released to provide energy during hibernation. There are many sources of **poison** – rodent-killers, **insecticides**, etc. – and their **symptoms** may be confused with those of disease. Hedgehogs may even lick up antifreeze, because it has a sweet taste.

SIGNS: May include **nervous system** disturbance (e.g. **hypersensitivity** to sound, **tremors**, **paralysis**, fits); traces of blood or dye in the faeces, excessive **salivation**, multiple small bleeds, vomiting, diarrhoea, severe weight loss, breathing problems, depending on what has been ingested and how much was swallowed. **Herbicides** can produce **signs** identical to those of lung worm infestation or **bronchopneumonia**, etc., such as congested lungs, foaming at mouth, laboured breathing.
TREATMENT: Identifying a pesticide poison is difficult and there is no known **antidote**. Other poisons are also difficult to trace, unless the hedgehog is found near the source. But at the wildlife rescue centre, fluid therapy would be tried, activated charcoal used if ingestion is suspected, and if traces of the poison are found nearby, the Veterinary Poisons Information Service can be contacted for advice. A **Vitamin K injection** may be given if **Warfarin** (rat) poisoning has been diagnosed.

DISTURBANCE OF NEST

(Also see *Orphaned and Displaced Baby Hedgehogs*, pp. 23, 24)
Sometimes it may be possible to reposition a displaced **nursery** nest. If you find baby hedgehogs inside without their mother, you must not touch them or their mother may kill them on her return because they smell wrong. Try pushing the nest back gently with your shoe, then move away quietly. But if the nest lining has been damaged (e.g. with a garden fork) you will have to provide alternative shelter at the same site, then watch and wait to see if the mother returns to move them (to a safer nursery site). Throughout, you must be careful not to leave human scent on the youngsters. If the nest occupant is a hibernating adult, put it in a box lined with clean straw, hay or dry leaves. Place the box near where you found the nest. Make sure it is protected from weather and other hazards (people, dogs, foxes, badgers poking around). Try to disturb the hedgehog as little as possible. Call a wildlife hospital, the British Hedgehog Preservation Society or the RSPCA for advice.

SIGNS: If you see or hear very young hedgehogs which have come out of their nest, this may indicate that the nest has been abandoned (e.g. mother killed while out feeding). Seek expert advice quickly.
TREATMENT: Orphaned hoglets will have to be warmed, given fluids and hand-reared in captivity, and may not be released until next season.
(Also see *How They Are Cared For*, pp. 23, 24)

TOO LIGHTWEIGHT TO HIBERNATE

Up to 70% of hedgehogs can die during their first winter. Hibernation is more suspended animation than ordinary sleep pattern. The hedgehog's **metabolism** virtually shuts down in a kind of voluntary **hypothermia**, triggered by a drop in the air temperature (which is why hedgehogs in some parts of the species range don't hibernate at all – it never gets cold enough, or food does not become sufficiently scarce to warrant it).

The animal's heartbeat slows to just five beats a minute, while breathing stops for several minutes at a time. A hibernating hedgehog feels cold to the touch and it may look dead. (A hibernating hog will be curled up, a dead one won't.) During this time, the hedgehog has to live off its stored fat. One type of fat cell contains structures which can burn up the fat quickly to keep vital life processes going. But if the hedgehog has not put on enough weight in the preceding autumn, it will "run out of energy" while hibernating, and die. Late-born hoglets must weigh 500–550g before the start of winter to stand a chance of surviving.
AUTUMN BABIES: Orphans found weighing under 550gms after mid-October are housed indoors and hand-fed before being released to hibernate. If they do not put on weight sufficiently quickly, they are kept in until the following spring.

BONFIRE ACCIDENTS

Taking special precautions before lighting a stockpile of dried vegetation should be second nature at all times of year when hedgehogs (and other animals or

Late-born hoglets are often kept in captivity and reared until Spring

invertebrates) may seek shelter there. If the worst should happen, immediately wrap a burns victim in a wet towel, and take it to a vet.

> **TREATMENT**: Pain relief, treatment for shock and smoke inhalation. If injuries are considered survivable, supportive therapy is given, such as fluids, **oxygen therapy**, **topical** skin wound treatment and round-the-clock nursing.

WEATHER PROBLEMS

Resting and hibernating animals are vulnerable to floods, extreme cold and other natural disasters, such as fires. In drought conditions, they will find it extremely hard to find food. Warm weather also makes fly strike more likely in a hedgehog that is already sick or hurt.

HEDGEHOG ILLNESS AND HUMAN HEALTH

LEPTOSPIROSIS, SALMONELLA, RINGWORM

Follow customary veterinary hygiene practices to avoid contamination by micro-organisms such as those that cause **leptospirosis** or **salmonella**. Both are caused by **bacteria**. Hedgehogs and other wildlife appear to act as a reservoir for leptospirosis, which affects liver and kidney function and causes a potentially fatal human illness – **Weil's Disease**. This is spread by infectious bodily fluids, most usually ingestion of contaminated **urine**. Rats are commonly carriers. Leptospirosis used to be a serious health hazard to sewer and dock workers

Wrap a burns victim in a wet towel

in the days before **antibiotics**, but hedgehogs are not a significant source of transmission.

> **SIGNS OF LEPTOSPIROSIS IN PEOPLE (WEIL'S DISEASE)**: Flu-like symptoms, including sickly headache, joint stiffness, raised temperature. Anyone handling sick animals who experiences these should seek advice from their doctor immediately. Diagnosis is by blood tests.
> **TREATMENT**: Prompt antibiotics.

Salmonella-family bacteria cause unpleasant gastro-intestinal symptoms, leading to dehydration, and they can be life-threatening in the elderly, babies and young children and to anyone who has a compromised **immune system**. Most infections in people are from eating contaminated **poultry** products.

> **SIGNS**: **Malaise**, symptoms 12 to 24 hours after infection; nausea, headache, stomach pain, diarrhoea, sometimes shivering, **fever**.
> **TREATMENT**: Rehydration therapy. Antibiotics only if infection spreads to blood.

RABIES

Hedgehogs are not thought to play a role in potential spread of **rabies**, a disease that may affect any mammal.

RINGWORM

This fungal skin infection (also see *Fungal Infections*, p.19) can be passed to human handlers and would require treatment with **antifungal** drugs, topically and/or orally.

HEDGEHOG DISEASES

SALMONELLA INFECTION

In mammals, this can cause different diseases, according to the strain of bacterium involved. One type produces blood-poisoning. Another leads to **typhoid fever**, which in turn can trigger life-threatening gastro-intestinal bleeding. Hedgehogs may get infected by eating carrion, beetles or maggots or via **asymptomatic** carriers.

SIGNS: Include sudden outbreak of green diarrhoea; dehydration, collapse. If you find a hedgehog in the wild suffering from the effects of salmonella bacteria, its illness is likely to be advanced. It is potentially zoonotic.
TREATMENT: Aims to keep hedgehog warm; antibiotics and rehydration therapy administered through **vein**. But it would be unlikely to survive.

E-COLI

This infection may severely affect hoglets and can be fatal. Strict clinical hygiene is necessary when nursing very young animals.

SIGNS: Pale green diarrhoea, sometimes blood-streaked; dehydration. (Potentially zoonotic.)
TREATMENT: **Rehydration**; nursing in isolation.

LEPTOSPIROSIS

(Also see *Hedgehog Illness And Human Health*, opposite)
Different strains cause different effects, including cell destruction within the liver and small blood vessels, or in the kidneys – when it is caused by the body's own **immune reactions**.

SIGNS: **Jaundice** – yellowish gums and eye membranes indicate liver damage; **kidney failure**
TREATMENT: Leptospiral organisms in the environment are destroyed by drying, exposure to **ultraviolet light** and disinfection; strong sunlight renders **infective urine** harmless. Veterinary treatment includes antibiotics, fluid therapy and supportive nursing. Chances of recovery would depend on the degree of damage to the liver, which can repair itself to a certain extent, and kidneys, which cannot.

BACTERIAL RESPIRATORY INFECTIONS

These are often accompanied by lungworm infestation.

SIGNS: Catarrh, breathing difficulties; may progress to pneumonia.
TREATMENT: Includes anti-bacterials, **oxygen therapy** and **bronchodilator** drugs to ease breathing. Severe cases may be euthanased.

Pseudo-tuberculosis

This is another hedgehog disease, affecting liver and kidneys, and is commonly seen in young animals.

> **Signs**: **Chronic** weight loss, diarrhoea, weak back legs. **Post-mortems** may reveal greyish white cheesy spots on liver and **spleen**.
> **Treatment**: This is usually detected too late for effective intervention.

Other Serious Conditions That Affect Hedgehogs

There are many other conditions affecting hedgehogs, including **tumours** and abcesses, a susceptibility to **foot-and-mouth** (the **viral** disease which affects hooved animals), and a measles-like viral infection which causes nervous system symptoms such as circling and loss of co-ordination. In the wild, most of these illnesses will result in death, but occasionally a sick hedgehog may be found (e.g. awake in the daytime and not fully curled up) in time to benefit from treatment.

Teeth and Gum Problems

Gritty soil ingested with the earthworms a hedgehog eats wears its teeth down. This, in turn, can lead to serious root infection. Hedgehogs in the wild are also prone to getting a build-up of rock-hard calculus on their teeth, again triggering gum trouble. Infected teeth and jaws can kill an animal through **blood poisoning**.

Gum recession and attendant bone loss loosens teeth until they drop out. A hedgehog that can't eat properly won't survive.

> **Signs**: Only on close examination. A hedgehog will not stop trying to feed, no matter how painful mealtimes have become.
> **Treatment**: A dental MOT, follow-up **antibiotics**; possible visit from dental vet, who will use different drilling equipment because mammals' tooth enamel is harder than that of humans. Also possible extractions, descaling and polishing.

"Ballooning"

An unfortunate condition in which the hedgehog's body becomes inflated. This may be an after-affect of RTA (road traffic accident) trauma, a deep infection which has produced gas, or damage to the rib cage and respiratory system.

> **Signs**: The hedgehog's body is swollen with air, double its normal size.
> **Treatment**: This would entail diagnosis of the underlying condition, and repeated deflation of affected area as necessary, plus antibiotics.

"Popping Off"

The purse-string muscular structure which enables a hedgehog to roll up can sometimes become misplaced – a state of affairs that the hedgehog cannot rectify on its own, because the muscle goes into **spasm**.

SIGNS: The legs and **pelvis** visible, back's spiny skin in twisted position.

TREATMENT: Muscles are relaxed under general **anaesthetic** and eased back into position, then post-operative pain relief.

VITAMIN AND TRACE ELEMENT DEFICIENCY

A lack of these (e.g. **zinc**) in diet causes the hedgehog to lose spines, develop **rickets**, etc.

TREATMENT: Feeding correct diet, with mineral and **vitamin supplements**.

FUNGAL INFECTIONS AND EXTERNAL PARASITES

RINGWORM

Ringworm, a fungal skin infection, is quite common, affecting up to a quarter of hedgehogs in the wild. But although they may carry it, they don't appear to suffer great itchiness. Severe ringworm causes crusty scabbing, hair and spine loss. It seems to be worse among suburban hedgehogs, where the populations are denser. Fungal **spores** can survive in the environment (e.g. in nests) for a long time.

SIGNS: Dusty spines, cracked skin, dry flaky swollen ears, hair loss, especially from face and ➤

➤ head; missing or thickened spines, scabs which cause bleeding if removed. There is often secondary bacterial infection and **mite** infestation, too.

TREATMENT: Diagnosis is by culture or biopsy. It has been suggested that hedgehogs may recover spontaneously in the wild, although this has not been recorded. Treatment includes prolonged antifungal drugs, anti-bacterials for secondary infections; mite removal. Recovery is slow. Hedgehog ringworm is zoonotic and causes fast-spreading, very itchy skin blisters on people. Treated by antifungal drugs. It is the most common zoonotic illness of wildlife rehabilitators.

MITES

These tiny, spidery creatures live on or below the skin's surface. Some just cause scurfy skin, others burrow down and produce severe **mange** symptoms, including intense itchiness, loss of hair and spines. Mange can be fatal, particularly to young hedgehogs. **Microscopic examination** of skin flakes proves the presence of mites.

SIGNS: Mites may be visible to the naked eye as moving, powdery deposits around the hedgehog's ears, eyes and cheeks; crusty skin **lesions**.

TREATMENT: Depending on mite type and site, by injected **ivermectin** (a drug originally used as a cattle wormer), or topical mite-killer spray or wash. Eardrops. Drugs for bacterial infection.

A dental MOT may be necessary

ABOVE AND RIGHT
Engorged ticks look like tiny grapes or sultanas and must be removed delicately to avoid infection.

TICKS

More than one kind is prone to hitch a temporary ride on a passing hedgehog's ears or the undersides of its legs and feed on its blood. **Anaemia** is not usually a threat and a heavy tick burden is often a sign that the hedgehog already has another illness. But ticks can also transmit blood-borne diseases, including **Lyme Disease** (a **zoonosis**) and other illnesses which cause fevers and **paralysis**.

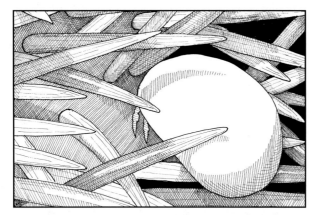

SIGNS: Possible local **inflammation**; a **tick** when full of ingested blood looks like a swollen grey sultana; there may be several in a cluster.
TREATMENT: The ticks are removed – the mouth parts are seldom left behind in the hedgehog's skin – by using a wire device or by applying a topical tick-killer solution.

FLEAS

They tend to breed in nests and other bedding. They are mainly **host-specific** and are an unavoidable part of life in the wild. In summer, one animal may inadvertently play host to 100 at a time.

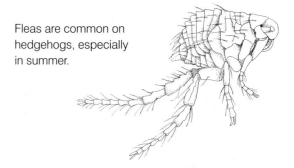

Fleas are common on hedgehogs, especially in summer.

SIGNS: Fleas seen moving amid spines and hairs. Put hedgehog on absorbent white paper to see if flea debris falls off as a dark powder if you lightly tap spines with pencil. If dust (dried blood in flea **faeces**) turns red when a drop of water is added, the hedgehog has fleas.
TREATMENT: If hedgehog's condition stable, by flea-killing compound, such as Frontline, but **insecticide** would not be used on baby hedgehogs.

MAGGOTS

Flystrike is a potentially fatal problem in warm weather, and the hedgehog's daytime snoozing lifestyle makes it vulnerable to **bluebottles** and other flies looking for somewhere to lay their eggs.

SIGNS: Small white eggs, maggots; rotten smell.
TREATMENT: Maggots are lightly dusted with **anti-larval powder**, dabbed with naturally antiseptic lavender essential oil or gently   ➤

➤ tweezered out and dropped into an animal-safe dilute antiseptic. Unhatched flies' eggs are flushed out with squirted **saline solution**, such as contact lens cleanser spray. A small watercolour paintbrush, or cotton bud moistened in clean water, is used to clear eggs from around eyes. **Chloramphenicol** (a topical antibiotic) eye ointment will smother remaining eggs or larvae; wounds are cleaned, **antibacterials** and non-steroidal anti-inflammatories given to counter **toxins** released by **bacterial action**.

INTERNAL PARASITES

WORMS IN LUNGS

These are quite common in hedgehogs. Lung **parasite** problems seem to peak in autumn, and particularly affect young hedgehogs. Many die as a result of the lung congestion caused by **worms** and their larvae, as well as the severe secondary bacterial chest infections that often accompany infestation. Older animals are thought to develop a degree of immunity. Different worm types may be picked up via slug, snail, beetle and earthworm intermediate **hosts**.

SIGNS: Rattly breathing, chesty cough, possible **nasal discharge**; weight loss, weakness; open-mouthed breathing; larvae (often coughed up and swallowed) may be passed in **faeces**; bronchial **pneumonia**; sudden **acute respiratory failure**. ➤

TREATMENT: Anthelmintic (worm-killer) drug, plus anti-inflammatories to counteract possible **toxic shock** response to dead **worms** in lungs; also a **broad-spectrum** antibiotic for **pneumonia**; **bronchodilators** of the kind **asthma** sufferers use, via a **nebuliser**, to help the hedgehog's breathing.

WORMS IN THE GUT

A range of **worm** types affect the hedgehog's digestive system, including **tapeworms** (for which beetles are intermediate **hosts**) and intestinal **flukes** (a flat kind of parasitic worm). Some cause considerable, even fatal, harm without producing much in the way of visible **signs**. Hedgehogs may also harbour microscopic blood parasites – to unknown clinical effect. Young and sick animals with a heavy fluke burden usually have many external parasites as well.

SIGNS: May include green, mucousy faeces; lethargy, weight loss; shed tapeworm egg segments (looking like small white grains of rice, often moving when fresh); faecal signs of blood loss from gut.
TREATMENT: May be by single injection of an appropriate wormer; fluids therapy, veterinary nursing care.

WHEN HEDGEHOGS NEED HELP

One woman rang a hedgehog charity because she was curious about a small hedgehog "sunbathing" on her rockery. Another reported little ones "playing" in her garden in winter. Both cases turned out to be of dangerously hypothermic young hedgehogs which were frantically trying to warm themselves on cold winter days. All were taken into care.

The good thing about having to decide if a hedgehog is a "rescue" emergency or not is that it doesn't much matter if your worry turns out to be ill-founded and a casualty turns out to be OK after all. It can simply be replaced the following evening at the spot where it was picked up and it won't be unduly upset by the break in its foraging routine. Hedgehogs are not easily put out. When startled, they will probably curl up (or at least twitch into ready-to-roll mode) but they aren't particularly nervous of people.

Seeing a hedgehog out in daylight can often be a sign that there is something wrong, such as concussion, disease or even blindness – but not invariably. You will have to watch it for a while and use your judgement. Healthy hedgehogs sometimes come out to forage on milder, wet winter days when slugs and snails are about, and a hibernating hog whose nest has been disturbed will also seek another haven in which to continue its winter rest. Generally, though, you would not expect to see a healthy hedgehog up and about in the day.

If you think the hedgehog is uninjured, healthy but hungry, or short of fluids, offer it clean fresh water and meaty catfood or dogfood. Monitor it to see if it eats and drinks and then makes its way back undercover. Make sure the hedgehog isn't hanging around in the same spot, hours later. Don't assume someone else will sort it out. Badly hurt, or very sick, hedgehogs often blunder around for days, trying to carry on as normal. But in this state, they are likely to encounter further dangers, or physically deteriorate to the point of no possible return.

STILL IN DOUBT? Take the hedgehog to a vet with an interest in wildlife, or to someone who's used to dealing with and treating hedgehogs. The British Hedgehog Preservation Society will put you in touch with knowledgable people in your area.

If you're worried that the casualty may be a nursing mother, she should still be seen promptly. Treatment may be carried out quickly, and the hedgehog returned to the site at dusk, or if longer-term care is required, it may be possible to find her nursery nest and bring the young into the wildlife hospital, too.

Some "rescues" will die despite your actions, or need to be put to sleep. But by intervening when you spot a problem, you will have kept the hedgehog's survival options open. You will save some lives. You will also reduce the suffering for all casualties, many of which would otherwise be run over (perhaps for a second time), die of dehydration and toxic shock, or be attacked by predators and carrion birds or by vandals.

TRANSPORTING

By law, a wildlife casualty must be contained when carried in a vehicle. A hedgehog isn't likely to disappear behind the dashboard or pose a driving hazard, but

Out and about in daylight often means something's wrong

rolling around inside a car won't improve its condition. Keep the casualty quiet. Prevent it being moved around, using a coiled-up cloth as a bolster inside its container. Ensure that it can breathe easily. It will feel less stressed if it can "hide" behind some crumpled paper inside a darkened container. Don't let other people keep disturbing it, or looking at it.

ORPHANS AND DISPLACED BABY HEDGEHOGS

Young hedgehogs in the nest normally keep quiet, to avoid being eaten by predators. If you hear their cries – small, cheeping birdlike distress calls – or see them out in the open at this stage, something is very wrong. They will have "blown their cover" because they are cold and hungry. Their mother may have been killed. Or she may have gone into hibernation before her young have been weaned. It's possible that the nest has been disturbed and the young have already been taken out and handled. They will not survive without your intervention and help.

If you accidentally disturb a football-sized grass-and-leaves nursery nest, however, and find young hoglets quietly curled inside and not apparently distressed, don't touch them. Watch from a distance to see if their mother returns, and seek advice. The adult will usually come back and move her young if the nest has been damaged.

How Old is It?

You may be able to calculate how old a baby hedgehog is from its appearance: newborns are pink and tiny, their soft spines covered by a big, fluid-filled sac of skin that looks like a blister. At around 11 days old, hoglets can curl up. Their eyes and ears open at about three weeks. They have all their milk teeth by five weeks or so. In the wild, they would be fully weaned at two months and leave the nest.

How They Are Cared For

Orphans, true or displaced, are usually hand-reared by volunteers, in **artificial litters** of roughly the same size and age, and barrier-nursed to prevent cross-contamination. They are released when they have attained a weight (about 600g) at which they can survive on their own.

Hoglets need food, fluids, warmth, TLC – and help with "toileting". This last service is just as important as all the others. Without being helped to empty their bowels and bladder, they would die.

ORAL REHYDRATION – very young babies may require **electrolytes** and other replacement fluids for their first one or two feeds.

FEEDING – two-hourly at first. Carers use needle-less 1ml. syringes, or puppy/kitten feeding bottles, and babies are encouraged to "burp" afterwards by having their backs rubbed while they are gently held against the handler's chest. Different wildlife centres use different kinds of formula milk, e.g. Esbilac, and some add goat's **colostrum**.

Feeding is a skilled business. Very young babies lack a strong sucking reflex. Carers must avoid allowing any liquid to trickle into lungs. Hedgehogs will learn to lap from a shallow dish at an early age.

Weaned hoglets move onto an adult diet of meaty dogfood or catfood, insect mix and water. Hoglets are weighed daily before feeding.

AMBIENT WARMTH – hypothermic youngsters are gradually warmed via a covered heat source (heated gel

Hoglets get weighed daily before feeds and are "burped" afterwards

pad, animal hot-water bottle) or overhead chick-rearing lamp. Very young hoglets have fewer spines than adults, but it is vital that they do not get overheated, either.

TOILETING – after feeds, a baby hedgehog's bottom must be wiped very gently with a warm, moistened cottonbud. This mimics the mother hedgehog's normal actions in the wild. Carers also look for any changes in the frequency and nature of what is passed, to monitor the animal's state of health. Newborns' **faeces** are naturally bright green, becoming gradually paler, and brown on weaning.

OVER-WINTERING JUVENILES & CARING FOR HOGS AT HOME

You may decide to give a temporary stop-over to young hedgehogs that have not put on enough fat to survive hibernation. A juvenile that weighs less than 550g as winter approaches (because it is the result of a late conception or rarer second litter) will need to come inside until the following spring. It must be kept warm – so that it doesn't go into hibernation – and well-fed. Or you may want to offer a permanent home to an adult that cannot go back to the wild. A non-releasable patient may be lacking a limb, unable to see or have some other permanent, though less obvious, disability which would make its life in the wild impossible or very difficult. Fortunately, there seems little likelihood of baby hedgehogs "**imprinting**" on humans and becoming too tame and dependent on their fosterers. Once they reach adulthood, hedgehogs appear to adopt a take-it-or-leave-it attitude to people – which is just what rehabilitators want. But some certainly turn out to be "characters", on closer acquaintance.

Hedgehogs in captivity need a correct and fully varied insect-based diet, clean water available daily, a secure environment from which they cannot stray – and into which predators such as rats, ferrets, etc. cannot penetrate, if outdoors. Provide a range of natural (or artificial) nesting sites under trees and hedges and potential bedding materials, such as clean, shredded paper, leaves and twigs (not hay or straw). If indoors, they will need an enclosure with high smooth sides they can't climb. Hedgehogs are not house-proud, so you need to try to keep bedding and food bowls apart, likewise separate droppings from both these zones. Cleaning must be done daily.

Check hedgehogs regularly for any health problems: you can encourage a hedgehog to uncurl by gently, rhythmically stroking its back from head to tail until it relaxes and pokes its nose out. A good time to take a look is when it is feeding. Finally, give hedgehogs their privacy.

They need to be able to hunker down at will under their bedding, well away from carers' prying eyes and poking fingers.

TIME FOR RELEASE? WHEN AND WHERE

Hedgehogs are usually released back to the wild around dusk, at suitable times of year, in areas where there is already a thriving hedgehog population. If possible, a recovered casualty would be put back in its original **territory**, at the spot where it was found. Ideally, this would be in warm weather when lots of insects would be around.

Support-feeding on site would be offered for a period – though few "releasees" return to take advantage of this. Research shows that hedgehog releases generally survive well, even those that have been artificially reared. Females unable to breed, any adult unable to roll up or a blind or deaf hedgehog would not go back to the wild.

Dogs attacking hedgehog, from Queen Mary Psalter c.1310. This heraldic beast looks as if it can look after itself…

Useful Organisations:

British Hedgehog Preservation Society (BHPS)
01584 890801; www.britishhedgehogs.org

People's Trust For Endangered Species
020 7498 4533; www.ptes.org/mammals

Royal Society for the Prevention of Cruelty to Animals (RSPCA)
cruelty line: 0300 1234 999
advice line: 0300 1234 555
www.rspca.org.uk

Veterinary Poisons Information Service via vet

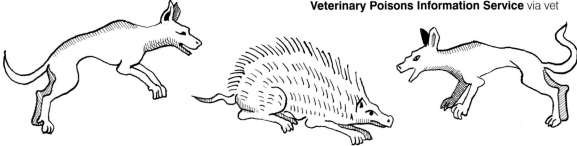

Did You Know?

◆ Hedgehogs have a thermostatically controlled **brown fat** zone around their neck and shoulders. When air temperature suddenly drops low, these fat cells produce heat double-quick, stopping the hedgehog dying of cold during hibernation.

◆ Adults' spines are ringed with 3 colours: dark brown, beige and cream.

◆ Hedgehogs' necks and bodies are shorter, in relation to their weight, than those of any other British mammal. Their legs are fairly short, too – but they can run and climb well.

◆ A hedgehog will not hibernate if the temperature is between 18–22°C.

◆ Hedgehogs like "living on the edge". Their favoured **habitat** is the zone between open land and dense vegetation.

◆ With their acute sense of smell, hedgehogs can detect prey up to three cm below the soil's surface.

◆ In fact, smell is so crucial to a hedgehog that any casualty whose illness or injury had deprived it of this vital sense would not be returned to its natural habitat even if it had fully recovered otherwise.

How Should I Handle a Hedgehog Casualty?

1 If removing a road traffic accident survivor, don't become a pedestrian casualty yourself or park in a way that endangers other road users. Ask someone else to slow, stop or warn oncoming traffic, or use a warning triangle. Walk towards oncoming traffic and make sure you are clearly visible.

2 If the hedgehog is mobile, stop it moving away by throwing a light cloth or garment over it, such as a teatowel or T-shirt. Hedgehogs can scamper quite fast over short distances, make for low vegetation cover if possible, and be hard to find. Use gloves, a towel or part of your clothing to muffle the hedgehog's spines when you pick it up. Use both hands to support the hedgehog and hold it close to your body to avoid dropping it. You can pick up a hedgehog in your bare hands without getting too prickled, if you keep your hands soft and flexible. It's likely that the hedgehog will curl up.

3 If the hedgehog is having an **epileptic fit**, don't move it until this has finished, then put it in a darkened, well-ventilated container and keep it very quiet before taking it to the vet or rescue centre.

4 Call the practice, or wildlife hospital, to let them know about the hedgehog you're bringing in. Describe its symptoms to the best of your ability. Make a note of the surroundings and circumstances in which you found it: e.g. mammal traps, paint cans, wire, broken glass, angling litter. Knowing that an animal has come into close contact with sharp litter, or chemical waste, will help direct its treatment.

▶▶ 10 Ways to Help ▶▶▶▶▶

◆ Drive with extra care at dusk and early morning – remember that hedgehogs (and many other creatures) are active and looking for a meal at these times.

◆ Hand-check vegetation before using gardening or agricultural mowing tools and machinery and ask staff in your local parks and green spaces to do the same.

◆ Leave part of your garden or cultivated land untidy, wild and undisturbed to help hedgehogs survive. Make log piles, compost heaps, leave areas of long grasses, plant native shrub hedges.

◆ Carry a First Aid kit in your car – and one for animals

◆ Keep open drains and deep narrow trenches covered over, or give hedgehogs an escape ramp.

◆ Give hedgehogs a ladder – trailing rope, chicken wire or vegetation – or steps of stones or house bricks to enable escape from a pond. Put a cover over the swimming pool.

◆ Put away netting – high up – when not in use, clear up litter and take broken fishing line home for disposal.

◆ Avoid using pesticides which harm hedgehogs directly and remove their food source. If you must use pellets, put them under low slates, so hedgehogs can't reach them.

◆ Restack and thoroughly search dried garden litter before you strike that match.

◆ Don't let your dog harass wildlife.

HEDGEHOG FIRST AID

Even if you are not a vet, just an ordinary member of the public with no relevant medical qualifications, the law allows you to carry out FIRST AID on an animal in order to keep it alive, alleviate suffering and keep it in a stable condition until expert help can be found.

Follow the A,B,C (and Ds) guide and don't do more than is necessary.

AIRWAYS. Gently clear debris, vomit, mucus or blood from around nostrils and mouth area. Don't attempt to investigate throat.

BREATHING. If the hedgehog has been immersed in water, hold it head-down for short while to help drain liquid from lungs. You're unlikely to give a hedgehog "the kiss of life", but if it has stopped breathing, but still has a heartbeat, you could gently blow a small amount of exhaled breath (which still has some oxygen in it) into its nostrils. Make a "tube" of your lightly clenched hand to avoid direct contact. Remember that the hedgehog's lung capacity is very small. Watch to see if its chest rises, then wait for it to fall again (count up to five slowly) before trying again.

CIRCULATION. If a fresh wound (e.g. from a gardening tool) is still bleeding, gentle finger pressure can stem fast-flowing arterial blood (bright red, spurts with some force). Blood from a vein is darker, plummier red and trickles more slowly. Never disturb an already-formed clot – it could be plugging a cut **artery**. **Clinical shock** is indicated by fast, weak pulse, confusion, restlessness or unconsciousness.

DO wrap a burns victim in a wet towel straight away, to help cool flesh as quickly as possible.

Do immobilise the casualty (a "doughnut" made from a twisted towel will hold it securely and stop it rolling around in box during transportation).

Do warm through a baby hedgehog that has become too cold **gradually**. A quick emergency measure: put it down your jumper (or inside your bra, if you wear one!) Sensing your heartbeat may help its survival, too (don't restrict airflow).

DON'T try forcing a hedgehog to uncurl. This will stress it. The vet will examine it after anaesthetising it. Never try to remove any foreign object jutting from body. Put a protective pad over it instead to stop it moving and triggering blood loss.

DON'T cut tightly embedded constrictions off, such as wire, string, nylon fishing line. Only remove what will come away easily. The rest will be removed under anaesthetic and drugs will be given to counter possible release of toxins when blood circulation is re-established.

DON'T try to drip liquid down hedgehog's throat, even if you think it is dangerously **dehydrated**. You could offer a conscious casualty oral rehydration fluid (available from chemists) to see if it wants to drink.

Casualty Kit

✔ Wire cutters, secateurs, heavy-duty scissors

✔ Thick gardening gloves

✔ Clean medium-sized towels (as "stretcher", bolster, or cover to darken container)

✔ Cat carrier, washable, or disposable cardboard shoebox with low-level, big ventilation holes

✔ Newspaper, brown paper, to line the carrier (don't throw away soiled paper until the vet or wildlife hospital staff have seen it)

✔ Mild liquid antiseptic (e.g. Hibiscrub handwash. It can be used undiluted, if necessary); saline solution and ordinary soap and water are also disinfective

✔ Rehydration powder sachets, from chemist (can mix with fresh bottled water on site)

✔ Screw-top animal-use hot-water bottle, covered to avoid burns (or fill a large empty plastic drinks bottle with warm tap-water)

✔ **Sterile** dressing pads

✔ Plastic tweezers

✔ Gauze bandage strips

✔ Cotton buds

✔ Petroleum jelly (for removing flies' eggs around eyes)

✔ Empty loo roll holder (for breathing tube)

TRUE OR FALSE?

1 If I put a hedgehog in my garden and feed it every night, it will stay there.

2 Hedgehogs are sound asleep all winter.

3 Hedgehogs go "scrumping", impaling ripe apples on their spines.

4 They aren't killed by poisonous snake bite.

5 They steal milk from resting cows' udders.

6 They make great combs!

7 Cooked hedgehogs are a wonderful cure for boils.

8 Like highwaymen, they used to have a price on their heads.

9 Healthy hogs sometimes foam at the mouth and roll around.

10 Best thing you can give a hedgehog is a saucer of milk.

ANSWERS

1 False. Not unless you wall it in. Radio-tracking shows that foraging hedgehogs can walk two-and-a-half miles in a night, and will climb (even 4ft slatted wooden fences) and dig past obstacles.

2 False. Hedgehogs hibernate from October-ish until frosts finish in March or April to save energy, but "wake up" to forage if there is a mild spell. In warmer climates, they do not hibernate at all.

3 False. Fanciful myth, immortalised in old woodcuts – though a squashed overripe fruit might get caught on spines. If they want to carry anything (bedding, etc.) hedgehogs use their mouths.

4 False. Britain's only poisonous snake, the adder, could harm a mammal the size of a hedgehog if its bite hit non-spiny skin and might kill it within hours. Scientific experiments have found that hibernating hedgehogs have some resistance to an array of poisonous substances in this state – e.g. they can live for up to half an hour in deadly carbon monoxide gas. Their tissues are better able to withstand trauma and, at lower temperatures, need less oxygen, too.

5 False, probably. With their small mouths, the most milk-mugging a hedgehog is likely to manage might be lapping up leaks, though reports of udder damage might suggest otherwise. Hedgehogs are probably more interested in invertebrates in the cow pats.

6 True. Dried hedgehog skins, nailed to wood, were once used to comb, or "card" wool and separate flax fibres in cloth-making. How hedgehogs must have blessed the start of the Industrial Revolution!

7 False. There is nothing in a hedgehog's body, boiled or otherwise, that can counter bacteria found in boils, although English apothecaries may once have sold such a "cure".

8 True. Snouts and tails handed in to country estates managers were worth handsome payouts in bygone centuries. Today, an estimated 5–10,000 hedgehogs a year are killed by gamekeepers in case they take ground-nesting eggs or chicks.

9 True. Self-anointing with flecks of saliva is an odd-looking pastime which might be mistaken for a fit. It's been suggested that it's a form of self-advertisement that spreads chemical messengers over the body. We humans can't smell them, but other hedgehogs can.
Hedgehogs tend to salivate excessively and lick unfamiliar objects they encounter for the first time, then cover themselves with spit.

10 False. Lactose intolerance means milk will give hedgehogs enteritis and diarrhoea. That could kill a hedgehog – especially if already ill or affected by parasites.

2

HOME ALONE

*T*he vet was puzzled. In front of him was a little cup made of what looked like papier-mâché, with two hungry baby birds inside. The man who had brought the nest in said he'd found it lying on the grass in the park. This was odd because, judging by the look of the nest and the shape of the birds' bluish-grey heads and short curved beaks, the nestlings were house martins and young martins don't fall out of trees. In urban settings, like this one in Greater London, they are nurtured in dried mud nests glued to a wall, high up under the eaves of a building or against a window frame. (A more natural nursery site would be a cliff or rocky outcrop.) It's probable that this nest had been dislodged from a wall during decorating or building work.

Young swallows, swifts and martins do not go anywhere near the ground, if they can help it, even when their feathers are grown. Their long wings and very short legs would make take-off from down there extremely difficult, even for a strong adult. Instead, these youngsters would launch themselves from the high-up nest, when they were ready, using a warm air thermal to spiral themselves upwards. They would be fed in the air by their parents, to begin with. As they matured, they would continue to live, eat, sleep and even mate on the wing, only landing at a nest-site when it was time for them to breed.

Even though they were in safe hands at the vet's, the nestlings' problems were far from over. It was a busy practice, midway through afternoon surgery. No one had the time to hand-feed these tiny babies once, let alone around the clock. Their diet would have to be carefully mixed to mimic the lump of flying insects a parent bird would diligently catch, then push down the youngsters' gaping throats – every few minutes, from dawn until dusk. If a specialist wildlife carer and rehabilitator could not be found in the next half-hour, the vet would have to put the nestlings to sleep.

Thankfully, one of the veterinary nurses managed to contact a small wildlife hospital a few miles away and an "ambulance" – a volunteer driver willing to criss-cross rush-hour city traffic in time to save the birds – was also alerted. Hungry baby birds cannot wait. If they are not fed as often as Nature intended, they die of shock and starvation very quickly.

Sylvie, whose flair for hand-rearing birds had prompted her to set up her own wildlife hospital unit for small mammals and garden birds at her suburban Surrey home, expertly examined the youngsters. Both appeared to be fit and healthy, their black eyes looked bright and alert, and there were no signs of cat damage.

Taking up a minuscule portion of the gritty, sloppy mixture of meaty petfood, ground-up insects, vitamin and mineral additives that serves as bird babyfood, she introduced a blob into each mouth in turn with a moistened orange stick. As soon as one round ended, it was time for a second helping. House martins are extremely hard to feed and it was a good job that Sylvie has sharp eyesight and a steady hand, not to say the patience of Job. Hand-rearing is full of potential pitfalls from giving the wrong diet to inadvertently choking the young birds, or allowing them to become imprinted. But, nine days later, the birds were ready to go back to the wild and were successfully released over the village pond.

GARDEN BIRD FACTS

POPULATION AND DISTRIBUTION

"Garden birds" are principally those species that tolerate a degree of human presence in order to find food and have learned to trust the reliability of such "takeaways". Some birds, whether full-time UK residents or migratory visitors, favour a particular part of the country. Or they might only appear in your garden or local park at certain times of year, when natural food sources get scarce and bird tables and hanging feeders offer a lifeline. But patterns change all the time. Not all common-or-garden birds are as "common" as people once thought. Some are worryingly scarce. Formerly familiar species, such as sparrows and starlings, have been gradually disappearing from the scene, while others are nudging in, such as the bright Indian ring-necked parakeets which are thriving in SE England.

Native bird populations in the UK, as yearly national Breeding Bird Surveys highlight, are far from static. Annual surveys of common birds by the British Trust for Ornithology, RSPB and Joint Nature Conservation Committee, highlight significant ups and downs which appear to form part of a long-term pattern of growth and decline. In a recent survey, 44 species were found to be increasing, 26 decreasing.

While some birds thrive, such as the 50% population increases among some types of geese in the previous eight years, others – notably house and tree sparrows, starlings and a range of farmland

The house sparrow: now declining at a disastrous rate.

and woodland birds – are vanishing at disastrous, accelerating rates. Destruction of **habitat** is one of the chief ways in which we put pressure on bird populations. Wide-scale grubbing up of hedgerows and orchards, overzealous "designer" landscaping and garden makeovers can remove, at a stroke, acres of tangled undergrowth and thick twiggy cover that would normally give birds somewhere to hide from their predators, shelter from the elements and safely rear their young.

Bird population graphs have a far-reaching story to tell, acting as markers for past historical, social, environmental and weather pattern changes in the UK. There are 16 species showing most significant decline on the conservation "red list", such as song thrushes, whose numbers have halved since the 1970s. The reasons for such dramatic drops are not always obvious, let alone remediable, although it is heartening to note that some "losers" earmarked for urgent conservation action have picked up in numbers very recently: song thrushes, tree sparrows and reed buntings, for instance.

Adding to such stressors, migratory birds have a hard time reaching their breeding grounds. Millions are killed while running the gauntlet of hunters' guns across southern Europe and the Mediterranean.

HABITAT

There are an estimated 16 million gardens in the UK. Many small bird casualties will be picked up in gardens (public or private), regardless of what their species' principle natural habitat might be. Woodland birds – siskins and goldcrests, in particular – are being seen more often in gardens now. Although gardens

are not ideal habitats for all birds and can never be a substitute for a healthy, biodiverse natural landscape, this patchwork of green oases plays an increasingly vital role in sustaining bird life as a result of changes to the "real" countryside.

Unfortunately, some gardens can hinder rather than help bird survival, despite providing the basics of food, nesting sites, shelter from the elements and water. A large domestic cat population (9m in the UK), widespread use of **pesticides** and **insecticides**, or feeders that aren't kept clean can all be detrimental to garden bird life. However it is increasingly clear that gardens definitely help some species, such as blackbirds, house sparrows and starlings, to produce more young. Some farmland birds, such as goldfinches and yellowhammers, have successfully fallen back on gardens as vital backup resources when times were hard and their populations faced particular stress.

IDENTIFYING GARDEN BIRDS

The kinds of birds likely to come to the attention of wildlife rescuers and rehabilitators are often small, urban species which have got used to living alongside people – "little brown jobs", in birdwatchers' shorthand. On closer inspection, many of these birds are more colourful than this tag would suggest. The Top Ten garden visitors are: *starlings, house sparrows, blackbirds, chaffinches, blue tits, robins, greenfinches, great tits, dunnocks* and *collared doves. Wood pigeons* are increasingly familiar, too.

If you're building up your visual identification skills from scratch, a colourful wall-chart picturing common species, a clean feeding station with predator-free flight paths, daily fresh water, seeds and kitchen scraps make a cheap and easy observers' starter kit. Check who's using your birdtable or feeder early in the morning and around dusk and you will soon learn to recognise different species, and individual birds, by sight. With the exception of young birds, whose plumage is incomplete and often differently coloured to that of adults, you should soon be able to tell your female blackbirds from your thrushes, your dunnocks from your wrens.

It is amazing how fearless regular visitors can be, as anyone who has ever dug soil under the beady gaze of a hungry robin will know. (One theory puts robins' tameness down to lack of persecution over past centuries.) If you are patient, you should be able to see many species, close up. Your garden birds soon learn to identify you, too, and will let you approach very near if they trust you.

Binoculars can be a boon and will certainly increase enjoyment if you take your birdwatching further afield, but they aren't essential to begin with. Buy secondhand; seriously "hooked" wildlife enthusiasts are forever upgrading. Avoid placing feeders close to large plate-glass windows. These may make it easier to gaze from your armchair but pose a hazard for birds, which can fly into the glass and fatally injure themselves.

BREEDING

Finding a mate, building a nest, producing eggs and nurturing nestlings is an extremely high-energy investment. There are many mouths to feed and the pace is urgent. Family size has to include a large margin for wastage. Young birds are inexperienced in the art of food-finding, predator evasion and other

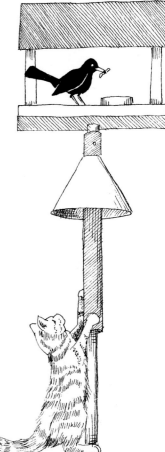

Site feeders away from rain, full sun and passing predators. You can squirrel-proof them, too.

survival techniques and many don't make it past their first winter. So breeding pairs of many garden bird species produce more offspring than are needed, statistically, to replace each parent with one surviving chick that will go on to breed in its turn.

Although it is usual for a pair to build and fill one nest in the spring, highly prolific breeders, like tits and sparrows, can have more than one clutch a year, if conditions are favourable. Each family may contain, not two or three, but seven or more chicks. Some birds of prey hedge their bets by bringing up "an heir and a spare". This is so that if the first-born, larger chick (one egg always hatches in advance of another) doesn't reach fledgling stage, its sibling can step into the breach to pass on parental genes. If the bigger chick thrives, though, the younger, smaller brother or sister still has a role – as a possible backup food resource.

It is thought that only 20% of birds hatched in any year live through their first winter. Out of 100 newly hatched garden birds, only a handful – around five – will still be alive three years later. Survival chances are statistically rosier after the first year, because the most vulnerable, inexperienced youngsters will have already died. Birds can be capable of surprisingly long lives: ringed birds (whose bodies were recovered after they had died) reveal some veteran record-holders: an 8-year-old robin, a 14-year-old blackbird and a starling of 16. One black-headed gull (strictly speaking a waterbird, but a common garden and playing fields visitor, too) was over 26.

Some birds of prey hedge their bets by bringing up "an heir and a spare".

But these are the exceptions. Predators and man-made hazards, disease, starvation and hostile extreme weather conditions mean most birds' lives are only one season long.

NESTLINGS AND FLEDGLINGS

Life begins as a fertilised, firm-shelled egg, laid by the female in a pre-constructed nest (or nesting hole), which is incubated by parental body heat. Hatched youngsters continue to need help in conserving warmth because their feathers take a while to grow. Their fast **metabolism** requires a high-energy protein diet, too, which is why even seed-eating varieties are fed meaty grubs and insects to fuel their rapid growth while in the nest. For these biological reasons, if a young bird needs to be rescued, *there must be no delay*. They cannot survive long once separated from sources of warmth and food for energy.

In the wild, raising nestlings entails a ceaseless parental routine of "shopping trips". Insects and grubs are pushed into gaping, clamouring beaks every few minutes during daylight hours. According to avian ethics, the biggest, loudest, strongest gapers get the lion's share of food. Small, weak, meek babies tend to drop off the edge of the world. If a parent bird suspects that a youngster is sick or abnormal, she may eject it from the nest. Many a young bird "rescue" is one of "Nature's rejects" – though many take full advantage of a second chance of survival to confound fate.

Nature never intended for all young birds to survive, of course. If all the annual UK resident hatchlings were around to compete for limited winter food resources, most would perish. A small bird uses

up to a fifth of its body fat just staying alive overnight in extremely cold weather and, if it cannot replenish that quickly the following morning, it will not survive another night at similar temperatures. But the balance of nature in many parts of the UK has been disturbed, putting extra pressures on bird populations. With so many man-made hazards and human lifestyle fashions that damage or remove bird habitats tightening the screw, a helping hand for nestlings and fledglings is in order. It may be as basic as providing birds with a place to be hatched.

FEEDING HABITS

The shape of a bird's beak gives a rough clue as to what it eats. The short, chunky beaks of sparrows and finches are good for crunching husks off seeds. Long, slender, poky beaks such as those of a woodpecker or curlew are ideal tools for winkling out invertebrates from leaf litter, mud, or crevices in tree bark. Birds that eat a wide range of foods, including both grains and insects as well as fruits, will have beaks somewhere between these two shapes, i.e. long and thick. Sharp-edged, curved beaks (eagles, falcons) are efficient for tearing up meat.

But even though some species may have a preference for a particular diet, birds have to be flexible feeders to survive, and all species of garden bird are meat-eaters while still nestlings.

Apart from opportunistic snacks snatched throughout the day, main mealtimes for most garden birds are early morning, when they must stoke up on body fuel to make up for energy lost keeping warm during the night, and dusk, just before they settle for the night. Some birds of prey that use gardens, parks or farm buildings are nocturnal and feed during the night. Those that aren't may come to gardens at particular times of day, targeting smaller birds when they flock in to eat and drink.

If you want to boost a small garden bird's feeding opportunities, be sure that you don't introduce deadly dangers by mistake, such as disease and predator opportunity. Offer a suitable range of foods avoiding those that can harm, such as desiccated coconut, whole or half peanuts, salty snacks, hard dry bread, and milk. Keep food and surfaces scrupulously clean, avoiding build-ups of faecal debris, moulds, etc., which spread diseases that are fatal to birds. Move the table or feeder to different positions.

BIRDS AND THE LAW

All our wild birds are protected by law. "Wild", as defined by the Wildlife and Countryside Act, 1981, is any type that is ordinarily resident in, or a visitor to, Great Britain. This protection does not apply to game birds, such as pheasants (except during the closed season), **poultry**, or to any bird which has been bred in captivity from an egg. It is an offence to "take, injure, kill or sell a protected species", to possess one or to disturb a bird in its nest or place of shelter.

Starlings use strong muscles attached to their beaks to yank earthworms out of the soil.

Urban sparrows once relied on grain spilt from horses' nosebags.

Blue tits will tunnel through windfall apples to reach the pips.

Robins follow large animals, and digging gardeners, for any invertebrates they disturb.

35

Rules also apply to the release of particular birds, such as barn owls (which need a Defra licence) and it is against the law to release non-native species into the wild. Consideration must be given to the release of any species if it is, or is likely to become, a pest in that area.

It is also an offence to keep any bird in a cage too small to allow it to stretch its wings freely (unless it is being transported, exhibited or receiving veterinary treatment).

COMMON HAZARDS FOR GARDEN BIRDS

Birds face many natural perils, from predation to weather extremes and sudden food shortages. But many problems are man-made: damage to the environment that leaves birds nowhere to feed, shelter or breed and acts of deliberate destruction, such as shooting or poisoning.

COLLISIONS AND WINDOW STRIKES

A huge number of bird casualties are the result of vehicle hits and window strikes. Other injuries and deaths are caused by colliding with powerlines, wind turbines and other man-made hazards which birds have either not seen, because of mist, rain or failing light, or were helpless to avoid being blown into during stormy weather conditions.

According to the British Trust for Ornithology, up to 100 million birds are crashing into windows in the UK each year, with up to a third of them dying. Bright sunlight can turn an expanse of plate glass into a giant mirror, reflecting only further expanses of sky.

In other light, glass may create the illusion that a building may be flown right through, unless visual markers indicate that there is a solid surface. Kestrels and peregrines, which often nest in urban areas, are prone to smack into the windows of high-rise buildings. Smaller birds ricochet off domestic picture windows and end up, unconscious, on the patio. They may also enter large buildings by mistake, then crash into windows in their panic. It used to be thought that window-strike fatalities were caused by birds breaking their necks. Now it is understood that the chief damage is brain swelling and retinal detachment.

Birds trapped in buildings during daylight hours will be able to exit unharmed if internal lighting is switched off and doors and windows left open. If chased, the bird will inevitably hit glass.

> **SIGNS**: The bird is unconscious or drowsy, uncoordinated, confused. Various effects of head trauma, such as brain haemorrhage, plus multiple fractures and other possible damage to wings, beak, eyes (the last may not be immediately obvious and needs specialist examination).
> **TREATMENT**: As for Traumatic Injury (p.38).

ROAD ACCIDENTS

An estimated 10 million birds are killed or maimed on roads in the UK each year. Barn owls fly low and slow over roads at night and are attracted to feed on small, road-kill mammals by car headlights. Gamebirds are prone to run out in front of traffic and small, light birds can get drawn into speeding vehicles' slipstreams

as they criss-cross their own territorial flightpaths. Birds also eat grit and insects from roads, the insects having been killed by traffic.

The last forty years of research have shown that roads have a serious impact on local birds. In one farmland area, 4% of the locally produced sparrow population, 11% of song thrushes, 12% of blackbirds and 3% of linnets were killed by traffic. But because birds hitting cars can cause people to have accidents, attention has been paid to minimising bird-use "hot spots" and making roads less attractive as flight paths and feeding areas. The highest bird deaths are on roads bordered by trees and shrubs, so new measures include siting vegetation some way back from the verge.

SIGNS: Most victims are killed outright, others are run over by other vehicles. Head trauma is likely among survivors. The damaged bird may be in undergrowth at the roadside, unconscious, or drowsy and disorientated; injuries include fractures and abrasions, with broken or missing feathers.

If you're not sure whether an accident victim is dead or unconscious, remove it to safety. Put it in a well-ventilated container e.g. with holes punched around the *base* of cardboard box, until you or the wildlife rehabilitator can take a closer look. Prop the bird upright, on its breastbone, so that it can't roll over.

TREATMENT: As for Traumatic Injury (p.38).

BARBED WIRE

Fencing regularly traps tawny and little owls.

SIGNS: Severe **lacerations** or fractures, as the bird tries to escape.

TREATMENT: As for Traumatic Injury (p.38).

WIND TURBINES

These pose a grave threat to birds of prey (and mute swans), say conservationists. Thousands of birds, including hundreds of golden eagles, have been killed after flying into the blades in the US and continental Europe. In the UK, wind farms in high, remote areas such as in Scotland can pose a hazard to rare birds such as sea eagles, which will be particularly vulnerable on account of their huge wing span and fearless nature. On the other hand, environmentalists argue that the numbers of annual bird fatalities are in the thousands and therefore statistically tiny in comparison with the millions of birds dying in traffic accidents or through flying into windows.

PREDATION

Garden birds are caught and eaten by rodents, birds of prey, dogs, foxes and a range of mustelids from badgers to weasels – and by cats. The last predator is probably the only one in this list at all likely to leave enough of its victim to be "rescued", and some pets regularly bring live birds into the house, uninjured.

A bird's automatic responses when seized by a predator include expansion of its blood vessels, a

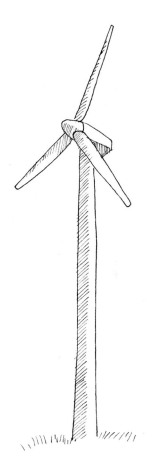

Wind turbines can pose a hazard to large birds of prey, such as sea eagles.

slowing of its heartbeat and a drop in blood pressure. In other words, it goes into a state of extreme **cardiovascular shock**. The biochemical imbalance may be enough to kill the bird, even if it hasn't lost much blood from wounds.

SIGNS OF TRAUMATIC INJURY (window strikes, road accidents, collisions, wire snagging, etc.): These include skin **lacerations**, as a bird's skin tears easily, open wounds, bloodied feathers, a broken beak, broken feathers and bone fractures. A broken leg or wing will hang uselessly below the site of the break and may be out of alignment. Wing fractures are more common than leg breaks among bird casualties brought into wildlife hospitals. Most involve soft **tissue** injury (e.g. to air sacs) as well as bone damage.

SIGNS OF CAT-ATTACK INJURIES: Some **signs** may escape notice, as there may only be pinprick entry wounds, with very little blood, and they're likely to be hidden by feathers. But the wound channels will run deep into tissue, where they will introduce **infection**. Look for specks of blood and get the bird examined by a vet. The so-called "48-hour syndrome" that mysteriously killed so many (especially young) bird casualties with no evident signs of injury is now identified as **septicaemia** (**blood poisoning**). It is triggered by the **bacteria** found on cats' teeth. Only **antibiotics** are likely to save a "catted" bird's life – if given in time.

Signs of cat attack injury may go unnoticed

TREATMENT OF TRAUMA CASUALTIES

The bird's wings must be immediately immobilised (kept closed, by its sides) to prevent further injury. Great care must be taken not to put pressure on a bird's abdomen. Because of the position of its lungs (which work differently and are sited differently to those of mammals), this would restrict its breathing.

Treat a window-strike casualty as above. A vet will prescribe specific treatment for head injuries and brain swelling and retinal damage. Some birds may survive with the loss of sight of one eye, but birds of prey cannot be released with less-than-perfect binocular vision because they would not be able to hunt.

Apart from emergency treatment, bird casualties would be handled as little as possible, to avoid worsening the effects of shock. The casualty would be put in a well-ventilated, indirectly warmed environment such as a hospital bird-cage, away from lights and noise, and propped into an upright position to aid its breathing.

The bird *may* die while in this initial recovery cage. However, wild-living birds are surprisingly tough. If a trauma victim can survive the immediate aftermath of its injuries and its condition can be stabilised, it will then be in the best possible position to benefit from supportive treatment and nursing care. Antibiotics will probably be a decisive factor in its chances of recovery.

ANTIBIOTICS

These are usually given **prophylactically**, on the assumption that cat-injury is highly likely in any bird casualty you may pick up. They are usually injected into the muscle in the breastbone area (single **injections** are less stressful for small birds than a continuous course). A recommended dosage* is 15mg for a sparrow or robin-sized bird, 30mg for starling or blackbird. Ideally, drugs are given within 4 hours of suspected or known cat attack. These will be supplemented by **steroids** to boost healing and **antifungal** drugs to counter possible lung problems. **Spores** that have been tolerated by a bird while it was in good health can suddenly overwhelm its system when it is under stress.

REHYDRATION

An injured bird will also require **rehydration** to replace lost body fluid volume and to biochemically rebalance its blood. If its condition was stable, a bird might be given **sterile** crystalloid fluids (like Hartmann's solution with 10% Duphalyte, which contains **amino acids** and B vitamins) injected under its skin or into cavities inside limb bones. Birds' bones, apart from being hollow in places, are very rich in blood vessels which would transport these injected fluids. Dosage would be calculated according to bodyweight.

A concussed bird would never be given anything to eat or drink directly. But a conscious bird that wasn't severely **dehydrated** might be encouraged to drink for itself by having its beak gently dipped into liquid once or twice. This can be done in an emergency by a rescuer using over-the-counter rehydration sachets, sold in powder form, made up with boiled, cooled water to correct proportions, or mixing up an International Isotonic Rehydration Fluid.

---

*as recommended by St Tiggywinkle's Wildlife Teaching Hospital

---

> **INTERNATIONAL ISOTONIC REHYDRATION FLUID**
> - 1 tablespoon sugar
> - 1 teaspoon salt
> - 1 litre lukewarm water
>   (cooled from boiled, or bottled)
>
> The mixture must be thrown away after 24 hours and made afresh.

An unconscious bird must never be left in a cage next to an open-top container of water – it could roll in and drown. A water fountain is safer than an open dish for a conscious bird that can drink for itself, too.

REHYDRATION FOR HEAD-INJURED BIRDS

It used to be thought that replacement fluids should be withheld in order to minimise fluid build-up and pressure inside the brain. But specialists now advocate maintaining normal fluid balances in the bird's body, despite any head injury.**

WOUND MANAGEMENT

If surgical stitching is required, this would be done under an anaesthetic suitable for birds (e.g. isoflurane) administered through a customised face mask, such as a finger stool or plastic connector glued to narrow

---

** The International Zoo Veterinary Group has drawn up a detailed head trauma management programme for a comatose bird that includes early oxygen therapy via a mask, or oxygen chamber. On admission, the bird would be kept very still, checked for brain bleeds or leakage of cerebrospinal fluid, then given anti-shock treatment. Skull x-ray is recommended.

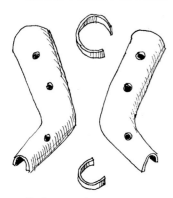

Splints can be custom-made, like these plastic ones for pigeons…

tubing and slid over the beak and nostrils (**nares**). Care has to be taken so that gas is not trapped in the air sacs which supplement the birds' lungs, resulting in an anaesthetic overdose. Along with their honeycombed bone structure, air sacs enable birds to take on board the large oxygen supplies needed to fuel flight energy. Sacs often get punctured by cat attack, showing up as swellings under the skin. Most heal of their own accord while the bird receives treatment to counteract bacterial infection.

BROKEN BONES

Bones can only be mended if they are not badly shattered – hence the importance of not allowing an injured bird to flap or try to run. With a mammal casualty, **stabilisation** of fractures would not start until an animal had been rehydrated and given 24 hours to recuperate in a hospital cage. But birds' bones are so brittle that emergency stabilisation must be taken right away to prevent further movement and damage. A broken leg must be quickly **splinted** or otherwise immobilised and its wings restrained (also see *How Should I Handle a Bird Casualty*, p. 61) or the bird will have no chance of recovery.

Bone fracture stabilising methods include metal pins, external frameworks, strong bandaging (hard to keep clean and in place with bird casualties) and **splints**. Leg splints can be very simple, if the fracture itself isn't complicated. One method uses small sections of adhesive masking tape, stuck face to face with any excess trimmed away, to splint simple leg breaks in small garden birds. The area around the break will have formed a hard callous within two or three

…or as simple and cheap as a clean, recycled ice-lolly stick, used here on a broken leg.

weeks and the splint may be cut away, allowing the bird to use its limb again. Wings are strapped in the closed position while bones heal – the correct alignment is very important.

Slings (as used by pigeon fanciers) may be used to keep the bird temporarily suspended. (A bird thus immobilised must be helped to pass body wastes.)

Complicated fractures, involving skin breakage, nerve and blood vessel damage and exposure of the bones, require more complex measures, including wound cleansing and possible suturing. Pain relief, antibiotics and anti-inflammatories make the bird more comfortable, offset infection and boost healing.

The timing of fracture repairs is complicated by the fact that birds' bones, fed by rich blood supplies, heal remarkably fast. Bones can begin to reknit within five days of hospital admission. They may have started to set naturally in the wrong position by the time an

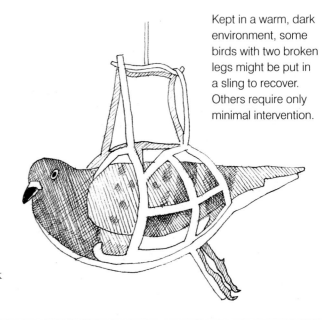

Kept in a warm, dark environment, some birds with two broken legs might be put in a sling to recover. Others require only minimal intervention.

injured bird is taken into care (and there is no question of re-breaking them, under anaesthetic, and resetting). If the natural repair process spreads to nearby joints, fusing results. This reduces mobility (a permanently locked wing section might preclude flight) so that a bird would be unable to survive in the wild.

Amputation of one limb may be considered, according to species. One-legged birds are seen in the wild but a wildlife hospital would be unlikely to release a surgical amputee. Removal of a damaged eye may be considered, provided the casualty was not a bird of prey. No convalescent bird would be released without a flight trial and period of careful assessment in an outside aviary.

Broken Beaks

These are often the result of a collision.

> **Signs**: The beak looks twisted or a section is partially hanging off.
> **Treatment**: The fracture is stabilised straight away by the beak being temporarily taped shut *once the casualty has been secured*. (It can be stabilised in a semi-open position, using a small piece of smooth wood, to facilitate breathing.) Treatment options would depend on whether a bird had broken the jawbone (inner skeletal section) of its upper or lower beak, or just the **keratin** sheath of either part. It would also depend which half of the beak was damaged – top or bottom. In some cases, jawbone breaks can be stabilised with wire **sutures** until they repair themselves. The lightweight outer sheath ➤

> ➤ of a beak can be replaced by an artificial one (recent repair work has successfully used dental acrylics and glues). But whereas a bird could survive *in captivity* with a missing upper beak, it could not manage if it had lost the lower one, because there would be nothing to support its tongue.

Broken Primary Feathers

These may need finger-pressure to halt bleeding. Plucked feathers tend to regrow, but a large feather that has been broken must wait until the moult to be replaced naturally.

> **Signs**: May include continued bleeding from a large feather stub.
> **Treatment**: Primary feathers can sometimes be repaired using a glued-on extension made from another feather tip – not necessarily from the same species! Otherwise, a bird will have to be kept in captivity until it has grown new flight feathers. For some species, such as swifts and hawks, every feather must be in perfect condition if the bird is to be released back to the wild. This raises the problems of long-term housing in captivity.

Shooting

Conservationists calculate that 500 million migrating birds have, until recently, been shot every year in the Mediterranean as a whole, from Gibraltar to the Middle East. In the 1970s, around five billion birds were estimated to be using this major **migration** pathway every year. More recently, the numbers of birds killed while running the gauntlet along this route may have been dropping – simply through depletion. But wildlife organisations are concerned that the slaughter continues at the same high, one-in-ten, rate, with France, Italy, Greece, Spain, Malta and Belgium being identified as the worst offenders.

The EU Birds Directive that should protect birds is widely flouted by European hunting groups, as are national laws and international conventions. Calculations based on numbers of cartridges used (five per dead bird) suggest that Italy alone shoots 100–150 million birds annually, a tenth of its migrants. France shoots another 55 million. Its laws give hunters the longest season in Europe (July 14th to February 28th) and allow 50 species of migratory birds to be shot and killed.

In the UK, the shooting casualties you are likely to come across will probably have been victims of airgun attack. A single airgun pellet can cause considerable distress and injury (e.g. loss of eyesight), even if the bird is not killed by it. The RSPCA investigated 800 airgun attacks on birds and animals in England and Wales during the last quarter of 2000, and it is thought that this figure represents only a fraction of the actual total of living creatures, pets and wildlife, being attacked "for kicks".

Gamebirds, some of which are native to the UK and some of which are introduced species, are bred here specifically and legally for sport shooting, under licence from Defra. Other birds may be shot, under licence, if they are considered to be farmland pests.

Paradoxically, the same bird species (such as sparrows and starlings) may feature on conservation priority alert and perceived pest lists at the same time.

SIGNS: Air gun pellet injuries may not be visible, or they may include obvious wing and leg fractures and eye injuries; the bird may look listless and its movements be impaired. Or a bird may have recovered naturally from an old injury. Birds' blood clots faster than that of mammals and their slightly higher body temperature gives them a higher resistance to infection. Lodged pellets may only become evident if the bird is x-rayed as a result of another health problem.

TREATMENT: Pellets are not removed if they are securely lodged and unlikely to cause further trouble. Otherwise, surgery is performed under **anaesthetic** and drugs are given to prevent infection and aid healing.

NETTING

Fruit and vegetable netting and other garden hazards can entangle birds, leading to wing and bone breaks and the loss of all, or part, of a wing, limb or foot. The result can be fatal blood loss or **blood poisoning**.

SIGNS: The bird may still be imprisoned in netting, or moving around with fragments tightly wound around part of its body, cutting off its blood supply. The bird may have already lost a necrotised foot or wing.

TREATMENT: Ligatures are carefully teased off (bird given anaesthetic pain relief and relaxant) and the casualty is kept in captivity for a week. It will be observed for signs of pressure **necrosis (tissue death)**. A ligature, such as nylon netting, digs into flesh and acts as a too-tight **tourniquet**. It cuts off the blood supply to any part of the body beyond it, until the flesh dies. Antibiotics may be injected to offset infection. Yeast cell extract and shark liver oil may be massaged into damaged tissue to try to help restore circulation. In some cases, **amputation** of a single limb may be carried out (depending on bird species) or the bird is put to sleep if limb damage is too severe to enable it to survive in the wild.

POISONING

Agricultural or gardening pesticides harm birds through direct ingestion of a caterpillar, slug or insect that has been contaminated with a chemical.

Harmful corrosive and/or toxic substances can get absorbed when a bird **preens** contaminated feathers. Birds can walk through, or fall into, paint, oil and other liquids if they are illegally discarded or carelessly left around. Pigeons and starlings are also damaged by a non-setting, sticky gel designed to keep building ledges free of roosting birds.

Some birds are deliberately targeted with poisoned bait, to lure them to their deaths. It is within the law for gamekeepers, farmers and landowners to poison "pests", under special licence from Defra. They must do this away from footpaths likely to be used by the public. (There is no guarantee which birds, or mammals, will actually eat the bait, of course. Some corn-eating birds may eat bait intended for squirrels.)

SIGNS: These include sorry-looking birds with oily, sticky feathers; they may be strong-smelling, or have muscular **spasms**; if you find dead or dying **corvids** around a piece of meat or broken eggshells, don't touch them or let children do so – such bait will have been injected or otherwise "doctored" with **poisonous** liquid or powder.

TREATMENT: There is no **antidote** to any of the above "poisons" (a poison is *any* substance taken in by the body in such quantities that the metabolism cannot cope with it and excrete it). So only warmth and fluids support therapy will be possible. A tube-fed mixture, including **kaolin** (clay) and **activated charcoal**, may absorb some of the internal **toxins** from the gut. But **pesticides** usually pass so quickly through birds' systems that any flushing-through will come too late. Contaminated feathers will need specialised cleaning to remove all traces and prevent chemicals further burning the skin. Delicate **membranes** around a bird's eyes, nose area and beak would be wiped clean on site and some of the contaminant absorbed (e.g. by paper or cotton towel).

CROP TEARS

The crop is an expanded muscular section of the bird's oesophagus. It acts as a kind of first-stage stomach along the digestive route. Food is stored in it and may

Garden and farm pesticides harm birds

be partially broken down by tiny stones that the bird has swallowed to help act as extra "teeth". Torn crops are often seen in pigeon-family casualties. Tearing can occur if foodstuffs have expanded after having been swallowed or if a bird has been attacked by a predator.

> **SIGNS**: Layers of muscle and delicate skin in upper chest area are split, and corn, seeds, etc., may be spilling out. The bird may be extremely dehydrated because it cannot retain any swallowed liquid.
>
> **TREATMENT**: Wound cleaning; the crop is repaired and reattached by surgical stitching, once bruising and tissue die-off has resolved and the bird's condition has stabilised; rehydration therapy; **broad-spectrum antibiotics**, convalescent care, hand-feeding by tube into stomach.

DEFORMITIES

Some bone deformities may be the result of an old injury that has healed crookedly. Others may have been present from birth but allowed the bird to survive until now. Disease and infection can also cause swellings, distortions or bone loss (e.g. part of a leg or a foot). Other deformities can be the result of man's interference. An example is the incorrect feeding of hand-reared birds, such as giving a young bird of prey only lean meat, not a natural-prey diet that includes bones and feathers. That mistake would lead to a calcium-phosphorus imbalance in the young bird, causing its bones to be soft and prone to break for no reason.

> **SIGNS**: Visible deformities include (unfractured) crossed-over beaks (crossbills have them naturally for opening nuts!), curved legs, permanently clenched feet. It is surprising how some birds are able to survive such physical handicaps for a while.
>
> **TREATMENT**: This is possible in some cases, and includes beak-trimming (although the bird would have to remain in captivity), diet changes, minor surgery. But euthanasia would be recommended if the bird's long-term outlook in the wild and quality of life was thought to be poor.

AVIAN DISEASES AND HUMAN HEALTH

All evidently sick bird casualties should be treated as potentially infectious until a vet has given you a diagnosis. They should be kept where they cannot infect other birds, or transmit a *zoonotic* (passable to people) illness. Bird welfare organisations advise that there is little chance that highly contagious bird flu can be passed directly from wild birds to humans. But, if handling birds, sensible hygiene precautions should be taken. (Also see *Avian Influenza Viruses*, p. 46).

ORNITHOSIS AND TUBERCULOSIS

Bird illnesses that can cross over to humans include an avian **tuberculosis** sometimes found in pigeons, and **ornithosis**, which affects different species including birds of prey, pigeons and doves, gamebirds and seabirds. Caused by strains of **chlamydia** organisms,

ornithosis affects the lungs and may be passed to human bird handlers via inhaled dried, dusty droppings from infected birds. (Also see *Avian Tuberculosis*, p. 47)

PREVENTION

Transmission is more of a hazard to those working regularly with caged birds, but wearing a cyclist's air pollution mask over your mouth and nose is a good idea if you clean out wild bird casualty cages. You should not get into close contact with wildlife casualties if you are immuno-compromised.

SALMONELLA, E-COLI AND CAMPYLOBACTER

Other zoonotic illnesses that can affect birds, humans (and other mammals) include those caused by **salmonella**, **e-coli** and campylobacter micro-organisms. In birds, the illnesses they cause often prove fatal. In humans, they cause headache, nausea, gastric pain and diarrhoea and can result in dangerous, even fatal, illness in very young children, the elderly and anyone whose **immune system** is not in good shape (e.g. someone receiving cancer treatment).

PREVENTION

Use **antibacterial** handwash and clean any equipment, housing and utensils used for garden bird, pigeon or bird of prey rescue and **rehabilitation** with appropriate bird-safe, veterinary-use disinfectant daily. If you feed birds in your garden, make sure you are not spreading death along with the birdseed and kindness. Keep tables and feeders free of harmful **bacteria** by washing them regularly with soap and very hot water, or a little dilute bird-safe disinfectant or dilute bleach (rinsed off thoroughly). Regularly move feeders to fresh sites to avoid debris and excreta build-up.

COMMON BIRD DISEASES AND GARDEN BIRDS

Illnesses in wild birds are often hard to identify. This isn't surprising, because the evidence is hard to come by. Small garden birds that fall ill tend to hide. Most die unnoticed, their corpses soon scavenged. Unlike pets and farmed birds, wild-living species are seldom examined to find out what killed them. Most data on bird illnesses has come via owners and breeders of pet caged species. With the exception of studies into influenza epidemics that pass between poultry or waterfowl and humans – bird illnesses that are of great interest to people – the public remains relatively ignorant about what makes birds ill.

Definite diagnosis of a living patient is often impossible, even if an ailing bird gets taken to the vet or to a wildlife rescue centre. Sick birds are kept apart from others in temperature-regulated isolation cages to prevent cross-infection. Later, depending on its species and disease status, a patient will be housed with others of its own or a compatible species. (Birds such as robins or birds of prey would be accommodated in solitary splendour, to avoid fights.)

On admission, signs of illness can be confusingly interchangeable. Parasitic **worms** living in the gullet, a fungal invasion of the lungs and a **viral** chest infection may all produce similar breathing difficulties, for example. The bird may be seen panting, with a partially opened beak. But any bird will breathe like this if it is highly stressed or feeling too hot.

Weak, white feathers on this young crow can hinder flight and may be caused by deficient nutrition or by agrochemicals.

The cause of its misery may be hard to pinpoint, but a bird that feels groggy will not be hard to identify. It will probably be sitting apart from its fellows, in a hunched position, reluctant to feed. Its eyes may be partially shut (the nictating **membrane**, the inner or "third" eyelid, may have moved across the iris of each eye). Its feathers are likely to look in poor condition, unpreened or very greasy-looking. They may be fluffed up. If you touch the bird, its body will feel cold. You may be able to feel its breastbone as a sharp edge.

RESPIRATORY TRACT INFECTIONS

These may have a variety of causes – **infection** by a virus, **chlamydia** micro-organisms (also see *Ornithosis*, p.48, and its zoonotic form) or secondary infection by bacteria. Birds that have been in contact with harmful substances, like oil, and ingested it while preening are vulnerable to viral and secondary bacterial infections because their immunity is compromised.

AVIAN INFLUENZA VIRUSES

There are over 140 strains, many of which circulate in wild birds at low levels. Most of these viruses are benign, but some are rapidly fatal to birds. Transmission can occur to domestic poultry and waterfowl via infective faecal and other secretions. The highly pathogenic (disease-causing) H5N1 type appears to have spread back to wild birds, from poultry, through mutation. But it is highly unlikely that it can be passed from wild birds directly to people. You are unlikely to find a live garden bird suffering from H5N1 bird 'flu.

INHALATION PNEUMONIA

This is one of the chief killers of young birds being hand-raised in captivity. It is caused by inexpert feeding that allows liquid to seep into lungs accidentally. Reservoirs of fluid in the wrong place are fertile breeding grounds for harmful bacteria. **Inhalation pneumonia** is not infectious to other birds. (See *Orphans and Displaced Baby Birds*, p. 55).

SIGNS: Breathing that you can hear, runny nose and eyes, open-beaked breathing. If this could be caused by stress, stop handling the bird immediately and put it in a darkened, quiet container to recover. A bird admitted to a wildlife hospital with breathing difficulties would be isolated and treated as if its condition were infectious (and possibly zoonotic).

TREATMENT: A **virus** producing breathing difficulties will have multiplied to such an extent that antiviral drugs would have little effect. Drugs may be given for **secondary bacterial infections**.

INFECTED SINUSES

This is a serious condition in birds and may need surgery to clear solidly blocked air pockets. Birds need to be rehydrated and hand-fed for a while.

PARAMYXO VIRUS INFECTION IN PIGEONS

A highly-contagious infection in birds, it seems to have spread to feral birds from the racing pigeon population. It is spread chiefly by direct contact with the **faeces** and other body fluid discharges of infected birds, and via dried particles of the same, floating in the air. By the time **symptoms** show, a bird may have already infected many others.

SIGNS: Breathing problems, eye discharge, watery or bloodstained diarrhoea. Neurological signs may appear later, including **spasm** of head and neck (bird may hold its head upside-down), **paralysis**, loss of balance and co-ordination. The bird cannot peck up food.

TREATMENT: Strict **barrier-nursing**. Treatment focuses on keeping the pigeon alive by artifically feeding it liquid food, squirted by a large, needle-less syringe directly into its crop. Most birds make a full recovery, although they remain infectious for weeks, and the twisted-round head position may last a long time. A vaccine is available against paramyxo and some wildlife centres administer this to existing in-patient birds that may be vulnerable to incoming infection (either on the hospital bird ward or in a pre-release aviary visited by wild-living feral pigeons). Where conditions did not permit long-term, isolated barrier-nursing, euthanasia of the infectious bird would be likely. A bird that shows no signs of infection may be shedding virus in large quantities.

BIRD POX

Another virus, commonly found in pigeons, birds of prey and seabirds. It is highly contagious to other birds, although many make a full recovery in care.

SIGNS: **Lesions** in the throat or scaly, brownish scabs on the skin (most noticeable around featherless zones, e.g. beak, nose, feet).

TREATMENT: Barrier-nursing; supportive care in captivity to alleviate symptoms, **topical** treatment of any dislodged scab site that starts to bleed (haemostatic liquid or powder). But euthanasia may to be recommended because of risk of cross-infection to other birds. Some lesions may leave permanent scarring.

AVIAN TUBERCULOSIS

This is a contagious illness seen by wildlife hospitals in pheasants, wood pigeons, starlings and sparrows. **Tuberculosis**, caused by a myco-bacterial infection, is a **zoonosis**. Although previous BCG vaccination may provide some immunity, anyone handling any kind of wildlife should be aware of essential hygienic practices. Potential avian-to-person spread is via the infective bird's faeces.

In humans, TB is treated by a cocktail of anti-tuberculous drugs, similar to antibiotics, that will directly kill infective organisms or stop them multiplying. Progress of the illness may be halted for a number of years, too, by the body's own immune system. Unchecked, TB goes on to affect other organs and permanently destroy tissue. But there are key differences between human and bird TB infections. Whereas tuberculosis in people is usually spread by airborne infective droplets which are inhaled and infect a lung, in birds these primary lesions are usually in the intestines following ingestion of organisms (e.g. from food contaminated by infective faeces).

> **SIGNS**: Weight loss, poor overall health, possible breathing problems, and usually diarrhoea.
>
> **TREATMENT**: Euthanasia of the infected bird is likely to be recommended. Barrier-nursing and treatment with anti-mycobacterial therapies may be tried, but the success rates are poor. Strict hospital hygiene is required because massive amounts of **bacteria** are shed in infected birds' faeces.

ORNITHOSIS

This can lead to a zoonotic **pneumonia**-like infection in humans, its symptoms ranging from **fever** and cough to severe headaches and tiredness. **Ornithosis** is caused by certain kinds of Chlamydia micro-organisms. It triggers illness in birds such as pigeons, doves, pheasants and wild raptors that is occasionally fatal. But, in its **chronic** form, the infection may result in lesser symptoms, such as lethargy. Bird handlers are advised to follow strict hygiene protocol and wear disposable surgical gloves, in particular when handling pigeon casualties. The disease is spread in dry faeces. Infection may be contracted via the eye membrane.

> **SIGNS**: A discharge from the bird's eyes or nostrils, shortness of breath, "clicky" or otherwise noisy breathing, gastro-intestinal symptoms such as loose droppings. Laboratory tests confirm diagnosis, but healthy birds can be **asymptomatic** carriers.

> **TREATMENT**: This is possible, following positive diagnosis, with anti-bacterial drugs, bird kept in isolation and barrier-nursed, but euthanasia is probable in view of illness's zoonotic potential.

SALMONELLOSIS, COLIBACILLOSIS (CAUSED BY E-COLI ORGANISMS) AND CAMPYLOBACTERIOSIS

These are bacterially-spread illnesses that affect wild bird populations, peaking in warm, damp weather. Many birds are fatally infected as a result of poor bird-table and garden feeder hygiene that allows food and water to become contaminated with bird saliva or faeces. Healthy birds can be **asymptomatic** carriers. Varieties of these micro-organisms cause illness in people, but usually as a result of eating infected food.

> **SIGNS**: Smelly loose droppings (healthy bird droppings are not runny, excessively green or malodorous). They should normally contain two distinct portions, white urates excreted by the kidneys and brownish-black faeces. **Enteritis** causes rapid dehydration.

A small needle-less syringe is used to rehydrate a young sick bird, using an anti-toxic liquid formula.

> **TREATMENT**: Rehydration and **gavaging** (force-feeding) of anti-toxic liquid (e.g. 10g activated charcoal, 5g kaolin, 5g light magnesium oxide, 5g tannic acid, made up with water to 500ml). Broad-spectrum antibiotics by injection into muscle, to counteract the effects of poisons released into the bloodstream by actions of bacteria.

BOTULISM

Although this is usually linked to deaths of waterbirds, *any* wild bird may fall victim. Birds become fatally paralysed if they accidentally ingest toxic bacteria from partially caked mud and rotting vegetation around ponds on very hot, sunny days. The organism responsible, *clostridium botulinum*, flourishes in anaerobic conditions.

> **SIGNS**: Many dead and dying birds on site. Those still alive may be showing signs of paralysis, e.g. floppy legs; birds unable to stand or get away. Victims are killed when paralysis extends to their breathing mechanism. Explosive, projectile diarrhoea (but not foul-smelling like that linked to salmonella poisoning).
>
> **TREATMENT**: Tube-feeding with liquid containing kaolin and activated charcoal, aimed at absorbing toxins and washing them out of body, but success rates vary according to the speed with which help is given. Once the bird's condition is stable, it may be started on liquid food.

OTHER SERIOUS PHYSICAL CONDITIONS AFFECTING BIRDS

CONSTIPATION

This is highly distressing for a bird that has been unable to stand for a while, perhaps due to the restrictions of the hospital cage, rest or fracture treatment (e.g. being supported in a racing pigeon-style sling). Mineralised waste deposits will tend to form a hard plug.

> **SIGNS**: A hard, internal lump that can be felt just in front of the bird's cloaca (its body's single-opening "waste disposal unit").
>
> **TREATMENT**: Paraffin, at blood temperature, gently syringed into the cloaca will enable softening and removal of the blockage.

EGG-BINDING

A dangerous condition which occurs when an egg gets trapped inside the female's oviduct (egg-passing tube). It may be caused by spasms or by a duct failing to contract normally.

> **SIGNS**: A jammed egg may be gently felt, lodged in bird's abdomen. It is vital not to break the egg.
>
> **TREATMENT**: A little syringed paraffin may enable the egg to be eased out, or the vet may give an injection of oxytocin and calcium.

CROP BLOCKAGE

This often occurs when a bird has been fed the wrong diet. Food remains in its crop, undigested.

SIGNS: The bird repeatedly trying to swallow; the crop feels hard and distended at top of chest.
TREATMENT: The crop contents are squeezed back up the throat and removed with blunt-ended tweezers. This must be done very gently to minimize the bird's discomfort and to avoid tearing fragile crop skin.

HYPERTHERMIA (BIRD TOO HOT)

Featherless baby birds are particularly prone to overheating if the nest (or hospital cage) is in direct sun. Recovering trauma victims need ambient warmth, carefully controlled. The bird must be able to move away from a heat source.

SIGNS: Open-beaked breathing, panting.
TREATMENT: Immediate action to lower body temperature, e.g. moving the bird to a cooler place, giving **rehydration** fluids. Plant-spray with lukewarm water, or use a fan, as emergency measures. Site garden nestboxes where they will not be subjected to temperature extremes.

HYPOTHERMIA

On cold winter nights, a sleeping garden bird burns up 15–20% of its total body fat, just keeping itself alive

A sleeping bird uses 15–20% of its body fat on a cold night, just staying alive

until daybreak. If it can quickly find enough food when it wakes up to replenish that lost energy store, it will survive another night outdoors – provided its feathers stay in good condition. If they get wet or damaged, their insulation value has gone.

The bird's blood circulation retrenches. It pulls back from the outermost network of fine capillaries and concentrates on keeping major organs going. Meanwhile, the body's peripheral cells begin to shut down and the bird starts to die, from the outside in.

SIGNS: The skin feels very cold to the touch; the bird becomes increasingly lethargic and eventually loses consciousness.
TREATMENT: This has the aim of reopening closed small blood vessels, but it must be done very gradually. It may entail warming the bird's immediate environment (but not its body) with radiant heat. Other methods include administering warmed fluids via artificial feeding or through a **vein**, the gentle use of a hairdryer on a low setting, or wrapping the bird in layer of bubblewrap without restricting breathing. It is important to conserve vital body heat while transporting a bird casualty.

FUNGAL INFECTIONS

ASPERGILLOSIS

A very serious disease caused by fungal spores invading the lungs. It affects several types of wild bird, including pigeons and birds of prey, waterbirds and seagoing species. Infection is via airborne spores which get breathed in. Birds whose airsacs are damaged (also see *Predation*, pp. 37, 38) are particularly vulnerable. The spores settle in tiny cavities along the **airways** and multiply. The fungus thrives in damp or mouldy hay, but its spores are easily spread in dry, dusty conditions, such as floors of inadequately cleaned cages and aviaries.

Some birds can carry **pathogens** with no evident ill-effect. But the stress of an injury, capture or captivity, a poor diet or severe environmental pressures can trigger dormant fungal invasion into full-blown disease. Other birds may become chronically infected, but stay alive for weeks or months. Diagnosis is by laboratory test.

SIGNS: A runny discharge from nostrils and eyes, open-beaked, audible breathing, **depression**, hunched posture, half-closed eyelids, aerated feathers. Severe weight loss (sharp "keel" breastbone). An **acutely** affected bird may die suddenly, without showing any signs.

TREATMENT: Lung fungal infections are hard to remedy and prevention remains the best cure. **Systemic** anti-fungal drugs may be given **orally** or misted into airways via a **nebuliser**. **Bronchodilators** and **oxygen therapy** are given to ease difficult breathing. Infections may take months to respond to treatment. Oiled seabirds are given anti-fungals prophylactically, before they show any signs of the illness, because they are known to be prone to develop full-blown aspergillosis after being contaminated (see *chapter 3: Water Birds*).

PARASITES – EXTERNAL

FEATHER LICE

Common and found most often in young or sick birds. **Lice** can weaken feathers. In large numbers, they cause irritation and possible self-inflicted wounds through scratching. Some lice cause **anaemia** by blood-sucking.

SIGNS: The bird scratches itself all the time. **Lice** are seen amid feathers as tiny dust-like flakes that move. Large numbers may indicate the bird is generally debilitated.

TREATMENT: Dusting with bird-safe powder to control lice, e.g. Rid-Mite, from pet shops.

BITING FLAT FLIES: (ALSO CALLED LOUSE FLIES)

These have tiny vestigial wings, but don't fly. Instead, they appear to hop sideways. They are troublesome for nestlings and are host-specific. One type lives in the nests of swifts and swallows, crawling onto birds during the annual breeding season. Such pests might look small to us, but to a young swallow, they are the size of a big crab. They suck blood and may cause **anaemia**. 20 flat flies have been found on one bird.

SIGNS: A flat-looking insect with sucker-like feet, 3mm long, crawling among feathers; irritation; weak, anaemic nestlings. Flat flies may play a role in blood-borne disease transmission.

TREATMENT: Bird-safe insecticide powder.

FEATHER MITES

Seen particularly on **corvids**, such as crows, these **mites** feed on skin cells and feather particles. ("Red" mites, found on domestic chickens, feed on blood.) Feather mites spend their entire life-cycle on a bird's skin surface, clinging on with suckers. Lung mites cause breathing difficulties.

> **SIGNS**: Feather mites are minute, spider-like creatures which can be seen with the naked eye.
> **TREATMENT**: For feather mites, a **topical** dab of liquid **ivermectin** on skin at the back of the neck, or Rid-Mite powder.
> Some vets use Frontline for external **parasites** on birds. This is an injected anti-parasitic drug derived from established cattle and horse wormers, used for internal (e.g. lung) mite infestation.

TICKS

Another spider-like species of **mite**, ticks are found on birds as well as mammals. They feed on blood and their saliva is toxic. One **tick** bite can kill a bird. Ticks can transport bloodborne diseases, such as **Lyme disease**, which is zoonotic.

> **SIGNS**: **Ticks** become visible when swollen with ingested blood. They look like a small grey-brown sultana. They are often attached to the head and provoke intense localised and **systemic** reactions in birds.

> **TREATMENT**: The **tick** is removed and killed to prevent it reattaching itself to another bird or mammal where it could potentially spread disease. Removal may be by a proprietary wire hook (from a pet shop), by a dab of a topical **acaricide**, or after suffocation with petroleum jelly or olive oil. It's vital for birds to be given prompt systemic treatment (broad-spectrum, long-acting antibiotics, anti-inflammatories) plus supportive therapy.

PARASITES – INTERNAL

"TRICK", OR CANKER – TRICHOMONIASIS

This will kill the bird if left untreated. It is caused by primitive swimming micro-organisms (**protozoa**) and it produces airway-blocking, unpleasant-smelling, yellowish brown lesions, chiefly around the throat area. It is spread by direct contact. Young members of the pigeon family, which feed directly from a parent's throat, are particularly vulnerable. The condition is also found among birds of prey which have eaten affected doves or pigeons. Birds starve, or suffer respiratory distress, when canker lesions totally fill the throat.

> **SIGNS**: Raw sores, cheesy growth inside throat, thick saliva, foul smell. "Trick" may also invade the head and respiratory system, eating away the beak, skull or eye socket. Lesions may sometimes be felt inside the crop as a solid, immovable mass. Dead and damaged tissue blocks airways or interferes ➤

> ➤ with the flap that separates digestive and breathing tubes, leading to inhalation pneumonia.
> **TREATMENT**: Veterinary diagnosis (signs may be initially similar to those caused by virus). Euthanasia by **anaesthetic** overdose of severely affected birds. Removal of infected flesh *after* medication with antiprotozoal drugs to kill invading micro-organisms, antibiotics to counter secondary bacterial infection. Great care would be taken to avoid heavy bleeding (overgrowths may involve major blood vessels). Rehydration, artificial feeding. Some dead tissue may come away naturally and be harmlessly swallowed.

GAPEWORMS: (SYNGAMIASIS)

Infection is via an intermediary host that a bird has eaten, such as a snail or worm. Gapeworms live in the windpipe, causing breathing difficulties.

> **SIGNS**: Shortness of breath, open-beak breathing; red, threadlike worms may be seen attached to the airway lining when glottis flap opens and closes, as bird breathes. **Microscopic examination** of saliva and **faeces** will show worm eggs.
> **TREATMENT**: A broad-spectrum wormer given by mouth or by injection under skin.

OTHER WORMS

These may be present, including intestinal ones, and some are so common as to be considered normal.

Many parasites will only cause severe, noticeable health problems when the bird is debilitated by illness, injury or environmental pressures.

MAGGOTS

The result of **flystrike**, maggots begin as an external problem when blowflies lay eggs in open wounds, or on the body of a bird that has been unable to clean itself. The problem shifts below the surface when hatched larvae eat into the bird's flesh. The bacteria they introduce release toxins which soon cause fatal **septicaemia** (blood-poisoning).

WHEN TO INTERVENE (AND WHEN NOT TO!)

Wildlife hospital staff are often handed a small cardboard box containing a bird that should have been rescued hours, if not days, sooner or one that should have been left entirely alone!

When to intervene is not always an easy decision. We are told to leave helpless-looking, not-quite-ready-to-wing-it fledglings on the ground because parent birds will be nearby and many bird species naturally go through this vulnerable, halfway-house survival test without our help. We may be afraid that an obviously injured bird will "die of shock" if we try to touch it. If we do decide to pick it up, but do so tentatively, it will escape. If we hold it too tightly and in the wrong place (the abdomen) we could stop it breathing.

People often try to do their best for birds in trouble, looking after them at home, with the best of intentions. But they may end up putting the bird's life on the line by doing the wrong things. One leading vet, who specialises in birds-of-prey rescue and rehabilitation, puts the "Do I, Don't I Intervene?" conundrum in context: "If a bird dies in your hands, it was probably at the point of no return anyway," he believes.

WAIT AND WATCH

If you're the owner, or neighbour, of one of the UK's nine million cats, you might not want to wait and watch too long. On average, the Mammal Society estimates, each cat kills around 33 small creatures, including birds and amphibians, every year. Wait and watch a while, if this is practical – then rescue the bird. Where you find it may give some clue as to what has happened to it.

If it's lying near a road, still alive, it may have been caught a glancing blow by a vehicle as it skimmed across the road, or been buffetted by backdraught. If it's lying by your back door, perhaps a cat dropped it there. If it's beneath a window, it's likely that the bird flew into it and has been concussed. Injuries may be as obvious as a drooping wing, oddly-angled leg or the bird may simply be lingering where it shouldn't. Any bird that lets you approach right up close – within touching distance – has something wrong with it.

DON'T APPROACH HEAD-ON

Move towards the bird at an angle. Try to get between the casualty and any escape route and any nearby road. Go slowly, keep low and don't stare directly at the bird – that's what predators do when targeting a meal.

Don't try to make a grab if the bird is excreting or flexing its legs. This isn't good manners, but common sense: such activities mean the bird is getting ready for takeoff. Pause for a moment if you spot these preparations. You must move carefully within arm's reach (and birds seem to know exactly how long human arms are) before you will stand any chance of capture and restraint.

Restrain it gently, but firmly, as you would handle a piece of delicate porcelain you didn't wish to drop. Use a flexible, "soft" hand that won't make the bird feel squashed. Covering the head with a very light cloth (don't suffocate it) will help calm the bird. Then get expert help without delay. If you can't transport the bird yourself, ask someone else to take the casualty to the vet's, wildlife hospital or bird rehabilitator. The faster the bird can be seen, and if necessary treated, the greater its chances of survival.

WARNING SIGNALS

◆ Bird is slow to move or evade your approach. It's either very immature, or stunned, in shock, sick or damaged.

◆ It can't fly

◆ It has one leg or wing hanging limply or held at odd angle

◆ It can't stand or perch

◆ It has noxious substance (e.g. sticky anti-pigeon gel) on feet and feathers

◆ It has broken or twisted beak

◆ It holds its head in an abnormal position

◆ It has no feathers and is out of its nest

◆ It is a fledgling that's been caught in a heavy downpour

◆ It is struggling to survive in extreme weather conditions

◆ It has a constricting ligature caught around legs or wings

TRANSPORTING

A bird casualty must be contained when carried in a moving vehicle.

Bolstered in an upright position, wings safely restrained, the bird will be more comfortable if it travels in a car's passenger footwell where the carrier cannot roll around. If the bird is placed facing to the front of the vehicle, it will be better able to handle braking and acceleration movements than if it were positioned side-on.

ORPHANS AND DISPLACED BABY BIRDS

Very young displaced or "orphaned" birds used not to feature much among great Wildlife Rescue success stories. It was popularly thought that the very immature, featherless ones (known unflatteringly as "plastics" in some circles) were beyond hope. They were considered not worth resuscitating, almost impossible to feed adequately and bound to fail upon release in the wild. Bigger babies, those that were fully feathered but unable to fly, were invariably best left alone so that the parent could continue to feed them. Hand-rearing was likely to result in having a "pet" for life, a wild bird which didn't realise that it was not a person.

Times have changed. The hidden role of bacteria from cats' teeth and claws in the "inevitable" deaths of rescued young birds is now better appreciated and care techniques have improved accordingly. These days, a youngster is usually presumed to have been "catted", even when there are no obvious signs of damage, and veterinary medicines and therapies are applied prophylactically, i.e. as a precautionary measure.

Even very young and unfledged nestlings are being successfully hand-reared and released, with very good success rates. Older fledglings are being supported for short periods in specialist units. They are kept with others of the same species, in naturalistically designed aviaries, and released when they are ready (i.e. have the necessary strength and plumage to evade predators), again with excellent results. This kind of care regime avoids the two biggest pitfalls of hand-rearing – **imprinting** (a natural process that makes a baby bird view the human who feeds it as its parent and role model for life) and inhalation pneumonia caused by allowing feed to trickle back down birds' airways (all too easy when **force-feeding**).

Very young birds, whose only health challenge is having to grow up away from their natural environment, thrive in the company of their own kind. They keep each other warm, comfort each other, copy one another and learn useful survival techniques from their peers. Even sick, injured or slow-learner fledglings that refuse to gape for food when kept in solitary confinement, are usually tempted to eat when there is some feathered competition about.

A specialist bird-care centre will identify a baby bird casualty quickly and provide the correct diet, expertly delivered at the right times. Many adult bird species in the wild will only eat live food, for instance.

Staff and regular volunteers at such centres are geared to demand-feeding their patients, every 10 or 15 minutes during daylight hours. They understand that baby birds, like all young creatures, can't regulate their own body temperatures and so provide exactly the right kind of housing.

Demand-feeding baby birds must be done every 10–15 minutes during daylight hours

Baby birds being hand-raised in captivity – with the important exception of members of the pigeon family – are fed on a sloppy mixture (see *Baby Bird Food* box below).

BABY BIRD FOOD

◆ 1 cupful of meaty (not fishy) dog- or catfood

◆ 1 cupful of dried insect mix

◆ 1 cupful of cooled, boiled water

◆ half-teaspoon of veterinary vitamin powder

◆ quarter-teaspoon of bonemeal feed

◆ quarter-teaspoon of enzyme additive
(from vet's)

The mix is mashed or liquidised until it is the consistency of soft icecream. It must be discarded after 24 hours and re-made afresh.

Tiny, pea-sized blobs are picked up on the end of small plastic tweezers, or smooth-ended wooden manicuring sticks, or paintbrushes, and introduced into the back of the bird's throat. Unless a baby bird is cold or unwell, it will gape and call for food. A light tap on the beak may stimulate the response. But a very young nestling, one of the practically transparent pink variety, won't be able to regulate its appetite. Carers must watch to see when the crop is full and judge, on the bird's behalf, when it has had enough.

The weaning of garden birds usually takes place quickly, before they have all their adult feathers. They are then offered the natural foods they would eat in their normal environment.

PIGEONS

These young need a different diet. They would probably be given a liquid parrot feed in captivity. This would be jetted directly into their crop through a large, needleless syringe, in carefully measured amounts at regular times. Such youngsters are used to getting their entire meal, in one go, as pigeon "milk" from their parents.

GAMEBIRDS

They are able to peck, unaided, at a mix of chickcrumb, seeds and some insects, from the start.

Young birds can be fed a special mix, or clean soft-skinned waxworms, using blunt tweezers.

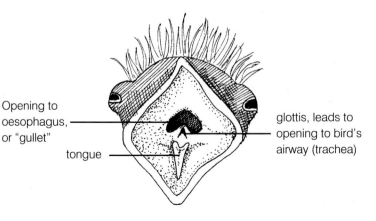

Opening to oesophagus, or "gullet"

tongue

glottis, leads to opening to bird's airway (trachea)

CORVIDS (JAYS, CROWS, MAGPIES, ETC.)

They will take a meaty petfood mixed with dried insects, plus a variety of occasional fruits, biscuits and ground nuts. Great care has to be taken not to make them tame.

BIRDS OF PREY

Night-feeders, like owls, need specialised care and daylight hunters, such as kestrels and hawks, must be passed over to a licensed Rehabilitation Keeper if they are to be hand-reared. They must be fed dead, *complete* birds and mammals in order to survive and are given, in captivity, frozen day-old chicks and "farmed" mice. Without this feathers-and-all diet, the birds won't develop properly. What isn't digested is regurgitated in the form of pellets.

TIME FOR RELEASE? WHEN AND WHERE

No bird is allowed out in the world until it has proved that it can feed itself and fly well. Release sites are chosen very carefully and, before they go "back to the wild", birds are kept in pre-release aviaries to get acclimatised. They are housed with others of similar age or species and monitored for a period. When they're thought to be strong and capable enough, they may be taken to the release site and **soft-released**. Several youngsters may be taken in a shared cage to a site and the door left open, so that the birds can go out together, when they choose. Soft-releasing enables the birds to get used to the surrounding sights, sounds and smells of the place they are going to be released into. Some birds would have to wait for the right time to get

released, if they were migrants. Others would require special licences for release.

Local birdwatchers, wildlife officers, park and commons rangers, rehabilitators and animal welfare charities tend to pool valuable information on suitable local release sites.

USEFUL ORGANISATIONS:

British Trust for Ornithology (BTO)
The Nunnery, Thetford, Norfolk, IP24 2PU
01842 750050; www.bto.org

The Hawk and Owl Trust P.O. Box 100, Taunton, TA4 2WX;
0870 990 3889; www.hawkandowl.org

Natural England 1, East Parade, Sheffield, S1 2ET
0114 241 8920; www.naturalengland.org.

The Royal Society for the Protection of Birds (RSPB)
HQ: The Lodge, Potton Rd, Sandy, Beds, SG19 2DL
01767 680 551 Wildlife enquiries 01767 693 690
www.rspb.org.

The Royal Society of Wildlife Trusts (RSWT)
The Kiln, Waterside, Mather Rd, Newark, NG24 1WT
01636 677711; www.wildlifetrusts.org

Scottish Natural Heritage (SNH)
HQ: Gt. Glen House, Leachkin Rd, Inverness IV3 8NW
01463 725000; www.snh.org.

◆►10 WAYS TO GET INVOLVED ›››››››››››››››››››››››››››

Get Wild

Leave at least part of your garden as natural as possible. Weeds such as nettles and teasels encourage butterflies and other insects – their larvae are a source of food for hungry nestlings. Dead, decaying wood (bury some below ground) is a **mollusc** and larva larder of free-range birdfood. Don't dead-head flowering plants, but let birds eat the seeds when winter makes such standbys invaluable.

Get the Buzz

Avoid garden chemicals that blitz insect-life – a future generation of garden birds will be grateful. Let the nasturtiums get infested with **blackfly**, plant areas that positively attract insects, give them bundles of hollow canes to overwinter in.

Start Climbing the Walls

Encourage climbers and thick or prickly plants (ivies, pyracantha, honeysuckle, clematis montana) over fences, walls and tree stumps to give birds safe **nursery** sites away from harsh weather conditions and predators. Ivy is a nest-heaven to sparrows, blackbirds, thrushes, starlings, flycatchers, wrens, robins, blackcaps, wagtails, wood pigeons, doves, and chaffinches. Left to flower, it will produce early summer berries.

Shy ground-feeders like wrens enjoy cheese crumbs

Make a Living Fence

Use hedges as boundaries instead of wood and wire. Don't clear clumps of dry leaves that have blown into lower branches.

Plant Berry Shrubs for Birds

Buckthorn, barberry, cherries, climbing roses, cotoneaster, crab apples, dogwood, elder, firethorn, guelder rose, hawthorn, holly, ivy, rowan, wayfaring tree and yew are all suitable. A patio can host a climber or two, in tubs. Even a window box, sown with annuals, can provide seed for birds. (Note: berries above include some that are poisonous to people and animals if eaten.)

Hang onto your Mature Trees

They're not always the house foundation-wreckers that some estate agents and insurance companies would have us believe. Instead of pouring used bathwater, etc., away, recycle it around tree roots to keep subsidence problems at bay in these days of speeded-up soil movements linked to climate change.

Many bird species nest in holes in old trees. Others need a thick canopy to shelter in, plus a high network of twiggy escape routes, too fragile to hold a predator's weight. Dead trees are good homes for some birds. Prune out central branches to create platforms for possible future nests. If you are short of space, remember some birds like a low nesting site – so plant smaller shrubs like the evergreen mahonia japonica.

Put up Nestboxes

There's a custom-made new home for every species. Buy from specialist catalogues (e.g. via RSPB) or make your own. Check which birds like to raise their young where. Birds naturally nest in places that aren't caught by driving rain or beating sun, so don't put boxes in south-facing sites. Put up several, in a variety of places – and don't be disappointed if they're not all used straight away. Birds like to consider their options!

Nestboxes provide winter night-time shelter, too. 63 wrens were once found in one box.

‹‹‹

Support-feed All Year Round

Routinely observing scrupulous hygiene at bird feeding stations in the garden will help to prevent the spread of many garden bird diseases, especially trichomoniasis. Key crisis times are harsh winter weather, drought, and **breeding seasons** (which vary according to species). It doesn't have to be cold and frosty – a long, damp summer can put paid to many birds because they can't find their natural foods. Help them with a range of feeders and fillings – either purchased from specialist suppliers or furnished by your own kitchen left-overs. Grow your own sunflowers. Make your own bird table. Add a squirrel-proof upturned biscuit tin beneath the platform. Avoid salty items, anything that could swell (rice, desiccated coconut) and kill birds, whole peanuts or dry lumps of bread that will choke them or spoiled, mouldy foods. Only give nuts that have been tested for dangerous levels of aflatoxin.

Do the Big Garden Birdwatch

This is easy and only happens once a year – one hour over one winter weekend – and is run by the RSPB to build up a nationwide picture of how our garden birds are faring. (See also *Useful Organisations*, p. 57).

Keep the Cat in at Night

This will cut the risk of your pet being killed on the roads (when cats are distracted by hunting instincts and vehicles may be travelling faster, with longer gaps in between). Put a bell on a cat's collar, too, to reduce **predation**. (The collar must be correctly fitted and should have a quick release mechanism, or stretchy section, so that it comes off should it become snagged.)

From top: yew, ivy, elder, holly and bramble. Birds avoid toxic chemicals in some berries by discarding the coating, only eating the seed.

Casualty Kit

✔ Bird-ringer's bag or length of soft, sports stretchy bandage

✔ Small, clean, tough cardboard box with lid (e.g. shoebox), holes punched around sides at base of box

✔ Long-handled, soft-rimmed knitted catching net (from aviary suppliers)

✔ Pet carrier (washable, plastic) for larger birds

✔ Clean plain paper, old cotton T-shirts, to roll up and put round casualty in transit

✔ Mild antibacterial disinfectant for bathing wounds

✔ Small towels

✔ Blunt-ended scissors

✔ Plastic tweezers

✔ Sachets of rehydrating fluid in powder form

✔ Cooled boiled or bottled water to mix with above

✔ Gel pad or animal-use hot water bottle

✔ Small sections of bubblewrap

✔ **Styptic** (shaving) pencil or blood coagulating powder

✔ **Sterile** dressing pads

✔ Powerful, damp-proof torch for seeking casualties in low vegetation or thick undergrowth

BIRD FIRST AID

Follow the A,B,C (and D) guide. Don't do more than is necessary.

AIRWAYS. Check that beak and nostrils aren't blocked by mucus, oil, mud, etc. Check that the bird's head and neck are in a position that facilitates breathing. Wipe obstructions away carefully with a clean moistened cottonbud, soft cloth or baby wipe. If the bird is soaking wet, hold it upside-down for a few seconds to drain liquid from its windpipe. Don't allow anything to restrict a bird's abdomen or it will be unable to breathe. Birds use internal air sacs as well as lungs.

BREATHING. Make sure the bird isn't on its back, or it will have circulatory and breathing problems. Lowering stress levels will help avoid panting, open-beaked breathing. If this starts, stop handling the bird immediately or it will die. Put it inside a small, warm container in darkened conditions. A bird's **metabolism** naturally slows down when light levels are reduced. Leave it for at least half an hour before handling it again.

CIRCULATION. Heavy blood loss will have killed a small bird by the time you find it. But you can stem slower bleeds from broken feathers or torn talons. Use a clean fingertip or handkerchief, a dab of caustic pencil or diluted **potassium permanganate** or other blood-stopper (available from a chemist or pet shop) for slight bleeding. Major vessel damage will need to be controlled with surgical forceps later. Support an unconscious bird upright on its "keel". Use a cloth or small towel rolled into a doughnut shape to hold it in position.

DO hold the bird so that its shoulders can't move and it can't open its wings. This is important so that a "closed" fracture does not become an "open" one. A small bird may be temporarily slipped inside a cotton tubular bandage, old sock or half a pair of tights with toes-end cut open, leaving its head free. Bigger birds will need to have their wings strapped to their sides.

DO put the bird in a container that doesn't allow it to tumble, flap or otherwise move around.

DO keep quiet – low noise levels and a darkened environment will calm the casualty and increase its chances of survival.

DON'T try to give the bird anything to eat or drink.

DON'T waste a second – it may need **antibiotics** and other medical help without delay.

DON'T cut embedded string, wire, etc. off legs or wings yourself. Use plain paper or towelling to mop up worst of mud, oil, paint if bird is covered in these.

HOW SHOULD I HANDLE A BIRD CASUALTY?

1 A light garment or cloth may be your best method of capture – assuming that you don't have a soft-edged caged bird-catching net, made of non-snagging fabric.

2 If it's a small bird, the safest container may be your hands until it can be examined. Many a rescue has gone wrong at the point of transferring the casualty to a container. Otherwise, a small box with ventilation holes around its base, or a permeable bag (of the kind used by bird-ringers) can be used to restrain it. The correct way to hold a small garden bird is to put your cupped hand over its back, allowing its head to poke between your index and middle fingers. Circle your thumb and little finger around the front of the bird's body, without exerting any pressure, to stop it kicking its feet and struggling. A bird's instinct, if it can't feel terra firma beneath its feet, is to flap its wings, i.e. "If this isn't the runway, I must be flying". Hold a larger bird against your ribcage so that its feet have something to push against. You may need to wrap a small towel around its body to keep wings shut.

3 Remember to keep any bird, of any species, away from your face. If you think the casualty is likely to peck you (crows, jays, blackbirds, magpies may have a go, hoping to surprise you into dropping them), offer the bird something other than your finger or ear to latch onto, such as the finger of a gardening glove.

4 Ask staff at your local veterinary practice, wildlife treatment centre or someone who keeps caged birds if they will show you how to hold a bird so that it remains comfortable, but secured, for the short time that you may need to handle it.

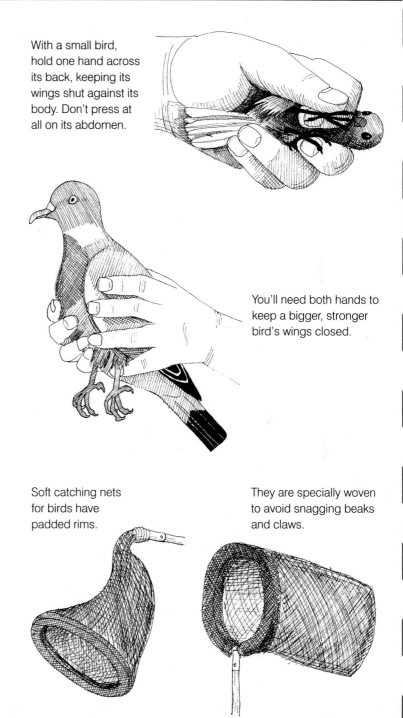

With a small bird, hold one hand across its back, keeping its wings shut against its body. Don't press at all on its abdomen.

You'll need both hands to keep a bigger, stronger bird's wings closed.

Soft catching nets for birds have padded rims.

They are specially woven to avoid snagging beaks and claws.

BIRD-FEEDING DOS AND DON'TS

DO provide clean water for drinking and bathing, winter and summer, in a rough-sided container plus stones in middle, so birds can climb out easily.

Do offer a variety of foods: wheat mix attracts doves and pigeons, black sunflower seeds are enjoyed by tits, finches and other small birds (black husks are thinner than striped variety). Sunflower seeds without shells save energy and are useful during the breeding season when birds spend hours **foraging** for their young. Fat smeared in tree bark cracks will be used by nuthatches, woodpeckers and treecreepers, dried fruit, raisins, leftover cooked meat scraps, dried dogfood or catfood and fruit, such as windfall apples, on ground or patio table will attract thrushes and blackbirds. Robins and dunnocks will go for crumbs and gratings of cheese. Live foods such as waxworms or mealworms will probably earn your birdtable Michelin stars, though you may prefer to offer these only in the breeding season and keep your garden naturally supplied with insects and larvae. Specialist birdfood mixes and feeders can be bought from catalogues, e.g. via RSPB and BTO (see websites) or blend home-made mixes from leftovers and scraps and make a simple platform feeding station yourself.

Do feed regularly, throughout the year. Each season can threaten different feeding and survival hazards (snow, drought, nesting stressors, etc). It's important to provide a dependable water source, too.

Do site feeders, tables etc. in an open space, so that birds can keep an eye open for predators, but close enough to shrubbery for quick, darting getaways. Put food in bushes if sparrowhawks use your garden. Make sure your feeding station is well away from cats' hunting hideouts.

Do move feeders and tables around, to avoid build-ups of droppings and other debris, otherwise you'll spread infection.

Do clean equipment regularly. Hot water and a little washing-up liquid will disinfect wooden items. Use dilute bleach for metal equipment and containers occasionally; rinse off thoroughly.

DON'T put out salty items such as crisps, salted peanuts and similar snacks. Soak dry bread, cake, cooked pastry scraps.

DON'T offer desiccated coconut, which can be fatal to birds unless well-soaked beforehand (it swells up inside the digestive tract if taken dry. So does uncooked rice).

DON'T put out mouldy or spoiled food.

DON'T put out whole peanuts – especially dangerous if parent birds feed them to their young because they will choke. Check that nuts come from suppliers who regularly test stock for poisonous aflatoxins.

DON'T leave food on ground overnight unless you want rats to visit.

DON'T add salt or antifreeze to any water container used by birds.

True or False?

1 Like some Swiss cheeses, birds' bones are full of airholes.

2 Young swifts stay in the air for a couple of years non-stop.

3 Owls' pointy, tufted ears are clearly visible.

4 All baby garden birds eat meat except for young pigeons, which drink "milk".

5 Birds can't roll their eyes.

6 A sick or injured bird may be calmed by music on the radio.

7 A bird of prey casualty will lash out with its hooked beak.

8 Most nesting attempts made by blackbirds don't succeed.

9 An owl has one ear higher than the other.

10 It's against the law to take any wild bird from the environment.

Answers

1 True. Many of their bones are hollow, others latticed with air spaces because birds' skeletons have evolved to be as aerodynamic and light as possible. But these wonderfully light bones are also very brittle and easily shattered.

2 True. Birds of the swallow family take to the skies after their first-ever launch and only land again to nest and breed when they're two or three years old. They need to take off from a high position (like a glider pilot) and catch a rising current of heated air to spiral them higher.

3 False. You can't see owls' ears – two big, smooth clean-looking holes normally concealed by interlocking feathers on either side of the bird's face. Any owl variety that appears to have upright ears on the top of its head is actually sporting a fine pair of feather tufts.

4 True. With the exception of pigeons, and whatever their adult diet will be, baby birds are all carnivores. They are fed live insects and grubs while in the nest. Corn-eating members of the pigeon family are fed a vegetarian diet, a regurgitated liquid (sometimes called pigeon milk) which parents of both sexes produce as a result of hormonal changes and then squirt down their young ones' throats.

5 True. Birds can't swivel their eyes within their sockets. They have to move their heads around if they want to take a close look or follow a movement.

6 Maybe. Select something peaceful! Battersea Dogs' and Cats' Home have reported the calming effects of music on dog and cat inmates. One wildlife ambulance driver used to play tapes of birdsong to apparently good effect. But until we have clearer evidence, it's best to keep bird casualties in surroundings that are as quiet as possible.

7 False. It's the feet you have to watch. They use their sharp, curving talons to kill and tear prey. Newly caught casualties sometimes roll on their backs and try to attack with these razor-sharp weapons, so rescuers and handlers of such birds wear thick leather gauntlets to protect their wrists and arms. Remember that even a small garden bird may peck at your eyes – so hold all species of bird casualty well away from your face.

8 True. Blackbirds aren't bad parents, nor are they alone in this low success rate. An amazing 90% of nesting attempts by all varieties of open-nest builders are estimated to end in failure, says the RSPB. Inexperienced pairs sometimes desert their nest or are forced to give up by cold weather, food shortages and predators.

9 True. One owl earhole is level with the bird's eyes, the other slightly lower. The slightly off-centre sound feedback helps owls pinpoint prey extremely accurately, sourcing the faintest rodent squeak under dense vegetation and in total darkness.

10 True. It's illegal to kill, injure or take any wild bird, its nest or eggs, or to have in your possession any wild bird, egg, or even a part of them. But you aren't breaking the law if you pick up a wild bird casualty so that it may receive medical attention. Nor is it illegal to keep a bird in confinement while it is being cared for, provided that it is intended for release back to the wild.

Red List Species

(Birds of highest conservation concern)

Bittern	Song Thrush
Common Scoter	(Common)Grasshopper Warbler
White-tailed Eagle	Savi's Warbler
Hen Harrier	Aquatic Warbler
Black Grouse	Marsh Warbler
Capercaillie	Spotted Flycatcher
Grey Partridge	Marsh Tit
Quail	Willow Tit
Corncrake	Red-backed Shrike
Stone Curlew	(Common) Starling
Black-tailed Godwit	House Sparrow
Red-necked Phalarope	Tree Sparrow
Roseate Tern	Linnet
Turtle Dove	Twite
Nightjar	Scottish Crossbill
Wryneck	Bullfinch
Lesser Spotted Woodpecker	Yellowhammer
Woodlark	Cirl Bunting
Skylark	Reed Bunting
Ring Ouzel	Corn Bunting

Some Bird Problems can be Hard to Stomach

The young pigeon was obviously "off-colour", hunched, greasy-looking and very quiet. He should have been screaming and jostling for attention, opening his beak and clumsily half-flapping, half-shrugging his wings, asking for a meal. He was easily old enough to feed himself, but pigeon teenagers, like human ones, see little harm in being "babied" when it suits. Yet this malnourished youngster looked as if he didn't care whether he lived or died. His breastbone edge was sharp to the touch and his inner eyelid was half-drawn across each eye. His crop, the muscular part of the bird's gullet where food begins its journey down the digestive highway, was visibly hard and distended.

The young man who'd found the displaced, lone fledgling under a railway arch, had been doing his best, feeding the bird and giving it drinks for a few days. But as the pigeon's condition began to deteriorate, he had decided that the job was getting to be beyond him, for some mysterious reason, and he had driven to the wildlife hospital on his way to work, to see if they could help.

"What's wrong with this baby bird?" he'd asked, clearly concerned. "He's just stopped feeding and I don't understand why. He looked fine when I picked him up, not injured or anything". Staff speedily lifted the skinny little pigeon from the cardboard box and took it into the treatment room for examination. They looked at the bird's chest and throat, covered with a mix of adult feathers and yellow-tinged nestling fluff, and noted the crop, as lumpy and bulging as an old sock stuffed with pebbles. "What have you been giving the pigeon to eat?" asked a member of staff when she returned to Reception. "Peanuts from the petshop," came the prompt reply. "I've been pushing them gently down his throat, so he can't be hungry." "And what about fluids, has the bird been drinking?" "Only a little milk from a teaspoon...." So now, at least, there was a diagnosis.

The ensuing procedure, tweezering out every last scrap of the pigeon's now fermented, stuck-fast meals and flushing out the crop with fluids that would disinfect the area and help it heal, must have been very uncomfortable for the bird. Its would-be saviour felt hot under the collar, too, when he realised what he'd done wrong.

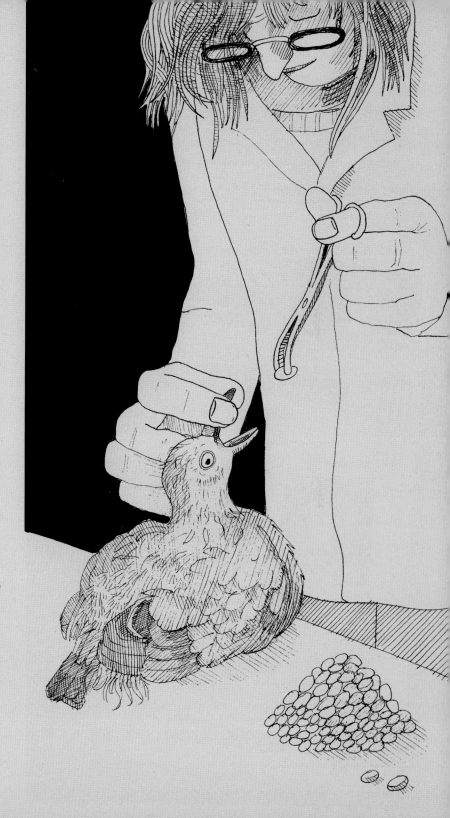

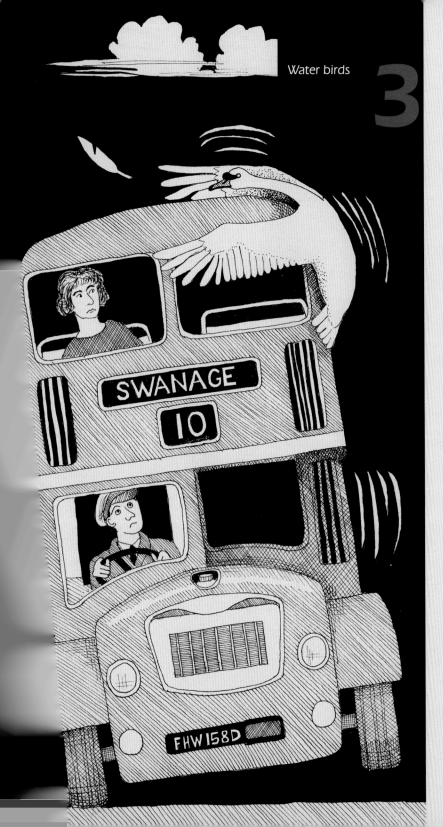

3

GEORGE THE BIONIC SWAN

*T*he driver didn't stop, but a passenger noticed the injured swan lying at the side of the road and reported it. George was a big male mute swan and he must have made quite a thump when he flew into a London bus that misty morning. His navigational error cost him dearly. One leg was so smashed that amputation would have been his only treatment option – if he hadn't been a swan. Swans are very heavy birds, one of the largest flying creatures on earth. Their chocks-away take-off – Stick neck out horizontally, Run like crazy, Flap like hell – requires speed, balance, powerful wings; and the pumping action of two strong legs. Just to get up from a sitting position or walk, slowly and swayingly, on land, swans need *to push hard with powerful leg muscles. There was no way a one-legged George would be a viable "release". He wouldn't even be able to stand up, let alone feed. The vet decided he'd have to be put to sleep. It was the kindest thing to do. Unless that shattered leg could somehow be repaired…*

The surgeon got to work, piecing together the jigsaw puzzle of bone sections and holding them in place with metal pins and plates. It was the kind of operation only performed on mammals, not on birds, whose inner bone structure is different, and certainly not on a swan. Luckily, there was still enough undamaged bone and healthy tissue at the very top of George's leg for the vet to anchor his repairs. The ground-breaking operation cost the wildcare charity over £600. Technically, it had been a success, a veterinary medical triumph, but would it work long-term? Would the swan be able to trust his whole weight onto that leg? Would the foot be flexible enough to paddle with? Would infection set in? At the wildlife hospital, where he was sent to recuperate, they could only wait and see.

Meanwhile, George was given antibiotics and steroids to help his body heal and gentle daily physiotherapy to keep his leg flexible and stop the muscles deteriorating. His female mate was traced and brought in to keep his spirits up. Visitors named him the Bionic Swan and, seeing him strutting about his pen, no one would have believed what a terrible state he'd been in weeks earlier. After a few hiccups – his "wife" went off with another, he refused to go back onto the water, then got beaten up by another male in a territorial dispute – George's release finally proved successful. A few years later, he was briefly back at the wildlife hospital, with a new family. The breeding pair had chosen a less-than-perfect nesting site and one cygnet had already been swept to its death over a weir, so the whole group came temporarily into care. All were released when the youngsters were strong enough to avoid fast water hazards. Overall, things worked out well for the swan who hadn't missed the bus.

Water birds

3

WATER BIRD FACTS

POPULATION AND DISTRIBUTION

In Britain we have a long history of enticing, then "looking after", birds that have become dependent on our waterways. Big nesting sites have been established for them, to conserve our waterfowl carefully – for the pot. Thanks to centuries-long encouragement of the wild birds that came here to breed, there are probably more mute swans in Great Britain today than in the Iron Age. Our hospitality was hard to refuse: in the Middle Ages, visiting birds were pinioned by having a section of bone amputated from the end of one wing, which made it impossible for them to fly any distance ever again. The monks who founded the mediaeval precursor of today's swan sanctuary at Abbotsbury in Dorset were super-efficient **poultry** farmers rather than wildlife conservationists. Swan was a popular item at rich banquets of the day: Henry III and his court ate 125 during one Christmas dinner.

Wild ducks were similiarly encouraged to stay, via traditional "decoy" tunnels. Today's booming mallard population owes as much to the post-1960s wholesale release of birds for shooting, as it does to the public's overfeeding with (wholly unsuitable) dry, white sliced bread. Today, Britain has many species of bird that rely on water, or whose lifestyles are associated with it. We're home to several varieties of duck, goose, swan and gull. There is a great range of shoreline

Kicking up a fuss: coots use their big feet to fight off rivals and predators – even on water.

waders and other specialist waterway feeders here, too. But these are unlikely candidates for "rescue".

Moreover, the waterbird population isn't static. Some birds are seasonal visitors and the numbers that arrive here in any particular year depends on mutable factors such as weather conditions. Mostly, the milder-weather seekers go away again. But some may stay behind permanently and interbreed with native birds. Canada geese clearly took a shine to UK hospitality. In the bird world, countries and frontiers are meaningless concepts. Surveys show fluctuating population trends for many reasons. Some water birds, for example, may thrive and increase while others may be in decline, affected by worldwide climate changes, disease patterns, persecution, water pollution, **habitat** destruction, fishing industry practices and adaptive changes in bird behaviour. No one has definitive answers. It is by no means clear why tufted ducks, oyster catchers and sanderlings should be seen to be steadily increasing in numbers, while similar types, like pochards and dunlins, now appear to be gradually declining.

A Breeding Bird Survey in 2005 by the RSPB, BTO and Joint Nature Conservation Committee gave these estimates for breeding population size and distribution of the most common water birds in the UK:

Moorhens 270,000 breeding pairs (more common in the South). Secretive, but tamer in urban areas

Mallard ducks up to 150,000 pairs

Herring gulls 144,000 pairs, decreasing, perhaps through **botulism poisoning**

Black-headed gulls 138,000 pairs – the most abundant gull in Britain in winter

Coots 50,000 pairs, needing open water for breeding, hence less common than moorhens

Canada geese about 100,000 adult individuals

Greylag geese 30,000 adult individuals, which now have large feral populations

Mute swans 25,000 adult individuals, which may live up to 30 years.

As a rescuer, you may come across a rarity like the migrating eider duck picked up cold, tired and miles off course, in London's West End. But you're far more likely to encounter one of the above-listed species because "rescues" tend to involve birds that are most used to living alongside people.

IDENTIFYING WATER BIRDS

Most casualties will fall into one of the following groups, graded here according to sizes and beaks. (All must be held away from your face, regardless of beak type.) More specific identification will come later, when it is vital that the casualty gets the correct diet, accommodation and social conditions for its species.

SMALL TO MEDIUM SIZED WITH BLUNT BEAK: DUCKS
Most types encountered in areas of human population are not unduly stressed by human contact. You are most likely to encounter the mallard, wild ancestor of our farmyard and pond ducks. A duck's beak has slight serrations along its inner edges, but a peck/bite won't hurt.

LARGER BIRD, WITH BLUNT BEAK: GEESE AND SWANS
Mute swans. The pure white mute swan is the most common swan in Britain, and is mostly resident. It's not mute at all, of course, but makes grunting, snorting and hissing noises, especially when disturbed or angry.

Polish swans. Named by poulterers when they imported similar birds from the Baltic. They are actually paler genetic mutations of the mute.

Whooper swans. Winter visitors whose black and yellow bills look as if they're painted in bright enamel. They have a bugle cry.

Bewicks. Slightly smaller and stockier, also visitors. They honk like geese.

Black swans. With red beaks, these are exotic introductions sometimes seen on ornamental lakes.

Pink-footed geese. Come to Britain in winter.

Other "grey" geese include: Greylag, White-fronted and Bean. Winter visitors.

"Black" geese: Brent, Barnacle. Found in our coastal regions, but breed in the Arctic.

Canada geese. Introduced from North America, also belong to the "black" geese category.

SMALL TO MEDIUM-SIZED WITH SHARP BEAKS: GULLS, GREBES, COOTS, MOORHENS
Many of these intensely dislike human contact.

LARGE WATER BIRDS WITH SPEARING BEAKS: e.g. HERONS AND CORMORANTS
Cormorants are not confined to our rocky shores – colonies have penetrated up-river, too, and may be seen inland: on the Thames in central London, for example. Herons and diving birds become highly stressed at attempts to capture them. Handlers must wear eye protection and keep contact to a minimum.

Lofty loners when fishing, grey heron can nest in colonies of up to 350 birds in the tops of tall trees.

Fishing tackle injuries are the biggest single cause of swan rescues

JUVENILES

Water birds that haven't yet grown their adult plumage can be hard to identify, but it's important to differentiate between species to avoid unnecessary intervention. While a duckling or gosling with no parent in sight can signal imminent disaster, parent birds of other species (e.g. gulls) routinely leave their young "home alone" for long periods while adults search for food. You should not remove a young water bird from the nest area, or handle it, unless you believe it is in immediate danger: for example, a young herring gull in the path of traffic, or a moorhen chick being attacked by predators or vandals, or if you have good reason to believe that its parent(s) is/are dead. Mallard ducklings, born on urban rooftops or washed down drains or weirs, for instance, would certainly need help. Contact a bird welfare organisation or wildcare centre for advice first.

COMMON HAZARDS FOR WATER BIRDS

ACCIDENTS CAUSED BY LITTER

"Fishing tackle injuries are the biggest single cause of swan rescues" (Environment Agency). In 2001, there were 3,000 such cases across England and Wales. Almost half were treated by the RSPCA, who now handle double the litter casualties among water birds that they did ten years ago. Careless fishing practices and inexperienced, unsupervised anglers are contributing significantly to the annual summer accident peak. Dabbling ducks also swallow hooks buried in silt; heron, coot and moorhen drown when discarded tackle gets entwined around them.

HOOK, LINE AND SINKER

Big black and white x-ray images are clipped to back-lit frames all around the walls. Each radiograph shows a pale grey tube snaking from top to bottom, a small white hook sharply outlined inside it.

This is the main hospital operating area of the Egham Swan Sanctuary. The patients whose neck x-rays line the walls are mute swans. The banks and beds of our rivers and water bodies, littered with lethal man-made flotsam and jetsam, are a dangerous front line for feeding birds. Egham, alongside the Thames in Surrey, is a key "field hospital" for the casualties of our carelessness.

Ducks in cardboard boxes and metal-mesh pet carriers, swans and geese trussed up in what look like postal sacks, necks sticking out one end, feet protruding from the other, are driven here for emergency medical treatment. That treatment can be drastic.

"We often have to cut the throats of swans to save them," says sanctuary secretary and rescuer Linda Grundy. "In the worst cases, a swan will have swallowed a barbed fish hook, along with the attached nylon line and tackle, and the fisherman will have tried to yank it back out again. That causes the hook to rip open the inside of the swan's gullet. Unless an injured swan is brought in to us very quickly, it will bleed to death."

The sanctuary also has to deal with accidental harm caused by rowers' oars and the propellers of powered pleasure craft, as well as deliberate damage inflicted by vandals armed with stones, airguns or crossbows. Swans continue to be **poisoned** by old, discarded lead fishing weights. Some birds recover to be released. Others must be **euthanased**, or stay as invalid, permanent residents.

PLASTIC LITTER causes many fatalities: plastic ringhold packaging from beer cans gets stuck around birds' necks or bodies, preventing normal feeding and flight. Plastic litter kills garden birds and small mammals that come to the water's edge to drink or feed, too.

SIGNS: Bodies of victims that got trapped, or entangled, and died from starvation, **blood poisoning**, drowning, etc. Survivors may have nylon fishing line so tightly wound around feet, legs, wings or tongues, that blood supply has been cut off, and flesh has become necrotic. The victim may be trailing litter, or have tangled debris around its neck and beak. The bird is likely to look thin, weak and **dehydrated** (it can't forage, because swallowed fishing line clumps inside the digestive tract and blocks it). It may have lost part of a foot or leg, or show damage to a beak or wing.

TREATMENT: If a swallowed hook, with no line attached, passes through the gullet without snagging, it may eventually be broken down naturally by the pieces of gravel in the **gizzard** and slowly dissolved by the bird's digestive juices. But not many water birds are this lucky. No attempt must be made to pull a hook and line free. Sometimes, a swallowed hook can be manipulated free by veterinary surgery staff using a rubber feeding tube to dislodge and safely cover the hook, so that it can be removed via the beak. But, more often, removal means surgery. Clumping swallowed line requires urgent surgery, too. ➤

➤ If a fish hook has caused injury elsewhere on the body, the bird must still be treated and given antibiotic cover. **Blood poisoning** can occur very fast in birds. **Toxins** released by harmful **bacteria** don't become isolated in **abscess** form, as they do in mammals, but circulate in the bloodstream. Litter that has tightly restricted a foot or leg may have caused tissue death, so the bird must be treated in hospital, not cut free and released immediately.

The casualty will need **rehydration** therapy and **antibacterial** drugs; possible **amputation** of necrotic tissue, depending on its site; otherwise, euthanasia. Post-surgery, some water birds may only be releasable on a sheltered or captive site.

OLD LEAD WEIGHTS

Although subject to sales restrictions since 1987, lead weights are still causing problems. Blood tests on swans at RSPCA wildlife hospitals between 1994 and 2000 revealed that 43–75% had raised lead levels in their bloodstreams. Swans churn up riverbeds, picking up tiny stones and pieces of grit which enable them to break up swallowed food in their gizzards. Old, discarded weights often lurk in deep mud. Inside the bird's gut, digestive juices gradually break the

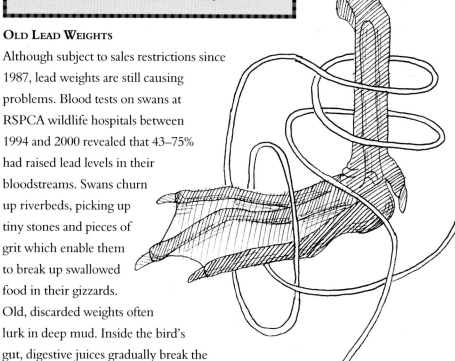

Lost or discarded anglers' line is often a death sentence to water birds.

Never try to yank a fish hook free yourself.

lead down, so that it becomes absorbed into the blood, and circulated. Ingested lead is a powerful **neurotoxin** (nerve poison).

SIGNS: Include weakness, weight loss and dehydration, loss of appetite and eventually starvation, as the muscular gizzard becomes paralysed and ceases to work. There is **nervous system** damage: **signs** can include a flaccid, floppy, kinked neck and bright green, foul-smelling **faeces** (although this last may also indicate **viral** infection).

TREATMENT: Unless treated promptly, lead poisoning is a killer. Initial treatment includes **rehydration** fluids, given by **drip** into a **vein**, plus **injections** of vitamin B12. B12 is important for red cell production, and is involved in maintaining a healthy nervous system and in energy production. Additional grit in food and increased water intake would be encouraged, to help to eliminate heavy metals from the bird's system.

Even when recovered, a lead-poisoned bird must be rehabilitated where it can continue to receive a good diet in order to stay well. Under stress from starvation, or extreme cold, lead "locked in" the bones may be released and there may well be a repetition of poisoning **symptoms**.

COLLISIONS WITH MAN-MADE OBJECTS

National Surveys show that 65% of British mute swan deaths are the result of the birds flying into man-made objects, such as power lines, bridges and transmission towers. The mute swan is probably the world's heaviest flying creature. Males have been recorded at 22.5kg (over 49lb). Their vision is relatively poor in the dim light of dawn or dusk. Unlike geese, which fly in flocks with a lookout posted at the front of a V-formation, swans tend to fly singly or in twos or threes, following the line of a river. But geese and herons often suffer flying accidents, too. An estimate of the numbers of *all* birds killed worldwide by collisions with overhead cables and transmission towers (and their guy-wires) is 4–5 million annually.

ROAD VEHICLES

Ducks are frequently run over, especially in the **breeding season** when females are escorting their young to the water. A courting couple may also be run over together, as they cross roads in search of a nest site away from the predator hazards of riverbanks.

BOATS

Water birds suffer propeller damage from motorised river craft, and accidental strikes from oars. During the Henley regatta, local waterfowl are temporarily corralled into a safe area, following past accidents in which ducks were beheaded during rowing races.

WIND FARMS

Birds may fly into the towers or blades of wind turbines, particularly when visibility is poor, or during storms. Thousands of all species have been killed in the US and continental Europe (more than half were raptors) and arguments continue over the potential harm to wildlife posed by wind farms. The RSPB, although in favour of renewable energy sources like wind farms, urges their siting away from migratory routes and wants to see environmental impact studies done before new ones are built.

SIGNS: Collisions are most likely to kill outright, but some birds may survive major injuries: severed or broken legs and wings, split beaks, electrical burns, widespread **abrasions**, and head **trauma** or concussion. The bird may be unconscious. Severe blood loss is likely to have ceased by the time you find the survivor. Heavy bleeding can occur after damage to the large feathers.

TREATMENT: Euthanasia (by a vet on site) may be the only humane option. Otherwise, treatment is given to counteract **shock**, replace and rebalance lost body fluids and reduce brain swelling. Cleaning and surgical repair work to wounds and **lacerations** is carried out once the bird's condition is stable. Bandages and dressings are not generally used for wounds on birds, as they would get dirty, damage feathers, hinder movements, and eventually be shredded by the casualty. Instead, wounds are **irrigated** (surrounding feathers often plucked beforehand), **anti-bacterial** spray is used and the area left open for speedier healing.

Fracture repairs are strapped, with the bird confined to a small hospital cage. Physiotherapy keeps wings and legs mobile, as wing readjustment must often be perfect for release (e.g. for seabirds). Damaged beaks are sometimes surgically re-attached, or a missing upper beak is replaced by a transparent, removable **prosthesis** that can be checked for **infection**. Most collision survivors are unlikely to be released back to the wild, as head trauma often results in loss of sight, for example.

ATTACKS BY PREDATORS

A sleeping water bird attacked by a mammal predator is usually instantly killed, but some birds may get away with limited damage. Young waterfowl are at great risk of **predation** – including by adult water birds of other species – before they gain their flight feathers. On land, lives depend on staying silent and well-hidden. On water, young are a potential mouthful for rats, which are excellent swimmers, fish (large pike can easily manage ducklings, moorhen and coot chicks), bigger species of water bird, or even terrapins – lakes and ponds are full of dumped Ninja Turtle-craze pets.

SIGNS: May include bloodied feathers, beak damage, missing toes and bone fractures. A broken leg will usually be hanging powerlessly below the point of the bone break. A broken wing will droop or hang open beyond the fracture area. Puncture wounds are deep and narrow and hard to spot: look for disturbed or bloodied feathers.

TREATMENT: **Antibiotics** (injected under skin or into muscle). Although water birds have good natural resistance to bacterial infection in their normal environment and a circulation system that enables fast **coagulation** at wound sites, delay between the injury being inflicted and the casualty's capture is likely to prove fatal unless treated promptly. Bacteria from a predator's teeth will soon spread through the blood, causing **septicaemia**.

Between July and October, ducks moult all their wing feathers and are unable to fly…

FIGHTING AND MATING INJURIES

Territorial fights are serious. A male swan may try to kill a rival by drowning it and even small water birds, such as coots and moorhens, can be very aggressive in their attempts to see an intruder off. In duck groups where the sex ratio is very uneven, mating frenzies can leave females injured and – not uncommonly – dead in the water. Even if she isn't drowned by over-zealous and too-numerous suitors, many a female has a bald, sore patch at the back of her neck where males have plucked away all her feathers.

> **SIGNS**: Mangled, wet, discoloured feathers, visible bloodstains (depending on coloration), poor condition; a single bird getting "mobbed" or noisily and aggressively chased and pecked.
> **TREATMENT**: This problem is often only resolved by re-locating the victim. The bird is kept in care while its injuries heal.

POLLUTION

Water pollution comes from many sources, from petroleum products to farming chemicals. Oil is a particularly troublesome menace – and not just the thick, black stuff you see congealed around dead cormorants washed up on soiled beaches. Even domestic cooking oil can kill when a bird's feathers become so coated that it becomes waterlogged, cold and unable to feed. It takes only a tiny dab of oil to cause mischief, because the bird will spread it all over its body while **preening**, and swallow it, too.

DEATH BY A THOUSAND DROPS: According to bird rescue charities, small car-oil spillages and leakages pouring in from road run-offs, as well as dumped car engine oil, produce a greater volume of oil damage each year than all the more-publicised major spills at sea.

Externally, oil damages feather structure, so feathers are no longer waterproof. It burns delicate **tissue**, like skin and eye **membranes**. Ingested, it causes corrosive damage to the throat and intestinal lining, so the bird cannot digest its food and becomes dehydrated. It causes potentially fatal damage to kidneys, **pancreas** and liver, making the bird anaemic by destroying red blood cells and weakening the **immune system**. This lays the bird open to secondary infections by bacteria and fungi.

Polluted water also harms in less obvious ways. Water birds that eat small aquatic animals, fish or shellfish absorb toxins from their tainted food chain, storing the chemicals in concentrated form in their livers. When this fat store is unlocked to provide energy (when the bird is short of food and needs to fight the cold during winter), its system will be flooded by the release of these harmful substances. They are toxic chemical cocktails to which the bird will have developed no natural resistance.

> **SIGNS**: Weak, listless, hypothermic, very thin birds, often with visibly contaminated, greasy, or discoloured feathers, unable to fly or feed. The bird may be half its normal weight – the breastbone ("keel") looks and feels sharp. **Pneumonia** develops from inhaling oily water – the bird is no longer able to swim or float adequately.

TREATMENT: A few hours of quiet recuperation; warmed rehydration fluids tube-fed or injected into its bone cavities or veins; the bird is given medicines designed to absorb toxins in the gut, e.g. **activated charcoal**, or Kaobiotic tablets to counter **enteritis**, plus drugs to counter fungal lung infection. Stress and shock suffered by casualties can cause them to succumb to fungal **spores** which have been carried in the lungs for a long time with no ill effects. Later, more fluids and some liquid nutrition might be tube-fed.

Only then would cleaning begin. Light oils, such as petroleum, are more of a removal problem than thick crude oil. Birds are usually washed – often by machines that can deliver several warmed water sprays at once. Handling is kept to a minimum. All soap or detergent is then completely removed from feathers. Often, birds are left to dry (and preen) naturally in warm, sheltered conditions. Weekly iron injections may be given. Sea birds and some water birds in captivity would receive salt tablets to prevent their salt **glands** from shrinking. Birds are carefully tested for buoyancy and water-resistance before being released.

POND NETTING

Netting, usually aimed at protecting fish and other pondlife from predation, can cause severe bloodflow restriction if it gets caught around a bird's foot or leg. Part of the affected limb may die off. A solid-frame, removable grille, dense marginal and floating plant cover, a rim of wobbly stones (amphibians and insects can pass through low gaps) and spiky twigs, tall grasses, etc., can all achieve the same effect without posing a hazard to visiting birds or mammals.

CRUELTY

Many geese, x-rayed for other unrelated conditions, turn out to have old, embedded shot pellets in their bodies. A record 88 swans were shot in one three-month period in Britain in 2002. Most died. Swans, geese and ducks are also injured by stones, bottles, airguns and crossbows. Call the police or the RSPCA emergency cruelty helpline (0870 55 55 999) if you see an attack or suspect that waterfowl are about to be harmed. Animal cruelty laws are designed to protect birds, as well as mammals.

SIGNS: Severe wounds; pellets may have both entry and exit wounds and fracture bones en route through the body. Look for blood on feathers, beak damage; weapon protruding, or the bird may be unable to walk or fly, **flystrike** if weather is warm.
TREATMENT: Embedded pellets not threatening a major blood vessel or organ are usually left in place. Injuries would be treated and, if necessary, repaired surgically after the bird had received emergency aid (for shock, dehydration, etc).

HABITAT LOSS

Wetlands are being lost through global warming and development (e.g. for sport and leisure). The effects are felt far beyond our shores. The UK is internationally important for water birds because of our climate and, up until now, our large areas of wetlands. More than five million water birds stop over on UK estuaries each year, in winter or during **migration**. They are totally reliant on this type of environment for their food.

ADVERSE WEATHER CONDITIONS

Ocean-going birds are sent off course by storms. On inland waterways and lakes, herons often find it hard to survive a severe winter, particularly when ice prevents them feeding. High temperatures and drought bring problems, too, drying out muddy areas where many water birds forage for food and creating the ideal conditions for fatal botulism outbreaks.

'Flu epidemics in people generally have their roots among farmed, not wild, birds and animals

> **SIGNS**: The bird is thin and debilitated, too weak to look for food. It may be panting, trembling (over-heated) or hunched and apathetic (too cold).
> **TREATMENT**: A malnourished bird may need to be brought in to warm, dry surroundings over winter; it may be coaxed to feed on its own, or have to be tube- or hand-fed. Supplementary food supplies may have to be continued at the release site.

SHOOTING

All wild birds are protected under the Wildlife and Countryside Act, 1981, but some may fall victim to the licensed gun. The law allows the landowner or manager of a site in which fisheries, or a wildlife conservation area, are being seriously damaged by wild birds to apply to Defra (Department for Environment, Food and Rural Affairs) for a licence to shoot a limited number of some species of water birds "as an aid to scaring". But the effectiveness of this varies, and numerous non-lethal tactics may be used instead to protect fish stocks effectively.

COMMON WATER BIRD ILLNESSES AND HUMAN HEALTH

You are unlikely to come into contact with the majority of very sick water birds because they will die in inaccessible places – far out to sea or along remote riverbanks and mudflats. But be aware that there are illnesses that can be transmitted from birds to people – viruses are always seeking new **hosts**. Ducks (and pigs) originally began sharing the influenza **virus** with humans, for instance. But it is among farmed birds kept in artificially dense, confined populations, that modern 'flu epidemics begin, not wild-living ones.

Zoonotic illnesses that can cross from birds (and animals) to people include:

SALMONELLOSIS, COLIBACILLOSIS AND CAMPYLOBACTERIOSIS

These are caused by bacteria and peak in warm, damp weather. Although cross-species infection may follow contact with birds' faeces, transmission is usually the result of people eating an affected bird or contaminated eggs. These illnesses are dangerous for babies and young children, for the elderly and anyone whose immune system is compromised.

HUMAN SYMPTOMS: Include feeling sick, with headache, stomach cramps and diarrhoea.
TREATMENT: **Rehydration** therapy; occasionally antibiotics, if infection has spread to the bloodstream. Thoroughly familiarise yourself with your vet practice's or local wildlife hospital's methods for cleaning in-patient accommodation, and your own hands, if you are involved in a water bird rescue. Use soap and a nailbrush.
SIGNS IN BIRDS: Smelly diarrhoea, runny or green droppings. The bird is **dehydrated** and very weak.
TREATMENT: **Rehydration**; possible **force-feeding** by tube of liquids containing **kaolin** and activated charcoal; **broad-spectrum** antibiotics to counteract **toxins** released by **bacterial action**.

CHLAMYDIA

These are tiny invisible organisms akin to **viruses** and **bacteria**, which can affect the lungs. Infection can be passed on in the dust of dried droppings. Wear a cyclist's or decorator's face mask if you need to come into contact with suspect cage droppings.

ORNITHOSIS

This is caused by one particular type of **chlamydial** infection. It can be a serious, even fatal, illness in birds, but it is rarely seen in water bird casualties and is more usual in **poultry** and members of the pigeon family and is most commonly spread by pigeon droppings and also occasionally in bird abattoirs.

HUMAN SYMPTOMS: **Pneumonia**, which can be dangerous, but infection is rare.
TREATMENT: Antibiotic drugs.
SIGNS IN BIRDS: May include **fever**, shortness of breath, runny nostrils (**nares**), diarrhoea. The **chronic** form may just make the bird lethargic. Diagnosis is by laboratory testing of blood and **faeces** to find antibodies.
TREATMENT: May include antibiotics.

H5N1 BIRD 'FLU

H5N1 is spread via nasal or **oral** secretions and faeces, but it's very rare in wild birds and, almost without exception, human H5N1 deaths have occurred in people who have been in very close contact with high-density, infected poultry. It first infected people in Hong Kong in 1997, causing a viral pneumonia which did not respond to medication.

In Asia, domesticated birds mingle freely with wild ones, especially water birds, making transmission easier, and the virus has spread from Asia to Africa, Europe and the UK. But, say British bird charities including the RSPB, Birdlife International, WWT and BTO, the risk to human health in the UK (e.g. via migratory water birds) is remote. It can be minimised by practising normal hygiene (e.g. washing hands with soap and water). The British Trust for Ornithology website has regular up-dates: www.bto.org.uk. Since the start of the outbreak in 2003, over half of those humans affected with H5N1 have died of lung damage. Treatment is with anti-viral drugs.

DISEASES THAT AFFECT WATER BIRDS

If a bird looks distinctly off-colour and you cannot see any injury or hazard that could have harmed it, you may assume that it is ill. A sick bird will look listless and miserable and be reluctant to budge. Its posture may be hunched and its eyes half-closed, with an inner membrane partially drawn across the eyeballs. It may be on its own, although you would normally expect to see it in a family group or flock. It may not be able to summon the energy to move away if you approach (but don't bank on it being easy to catch!)

RESPIRATORY TRACT INFECTIONS

Some, like the bronchial form of **avian diphtheria**, are caused by bacteria. The illness becomes life-threatening if toxins from the bacteria compromise heart, liver, etc. Other respiratory diseases attack in viral form.

Water birds with contaminated, feathers can get **inhalation pneumonia** from breathing water into their lungs while weak and hypothermic. Bacterial infection then sets in. Inexpert force-feeding can also result in inhalation pneumonia, if liquid is allowed to trickle down the airway. Internal **worm parasites** and fungal infections damage birds' **airways**, blocking the throat and interfering with the action of the **epiglottis**, the small flap of flesh that normally seals off the windpipe when food or liquid is swallowed. A sick bird, or one that is being artificially fed too fast, may lack this reflex. Fungal overgrowths (also see *Aspergillosis*, p. 81) will also interfere with breathing.

SIGNS: Some respiratory diseases cause slow, laboured breathing, others result in too-fast gasps for air. Look out for noisy breathing through an open beak, but don't confuse this with stress-panting in a newly-caught casualty. (If latter occurs, stop handling the bird immediately. Let it recover quietly before any attempt is made to examine it.)

TREATMENT: May include antibiotics to counter **secondary bacterial** infection of lungs or nebulised drugs to relax **airways**. Birds' breathing mechanism differs from that of mammals. They have relatively small lungs, but these are backed up by a network of airsacs and hollow spaces within bones. (This honeycomb structure also makes the bones as light as possible, without forfeiting strength.)

Clogged nostrils in oiled birds would be carefully bathed in weak **saline solution**, to remove debris; the casualty is then rehydrated and hand-fed, then barrier-nursed to prevent cross-infection with other bird patients (bacteria are easily spread in sneezed droplets).

BIRD POX

This viral infection is highly contagious (to birds), and is characterised by blistery skin eruptions.

SIGNS: Sores inside throat, or scaly scabs on skin (most easily seen around base of beak and on feet). Most often seen in sea birds.

TREATMENT: None. Supportive nursing only.

AVIAN CHOLERA AND VIRAL ENTERITIS

Avian **cholera**, an infection caused by bacteria, and **viral enteritis** both affect birds' lower intestines, causing **inflammation** and severe dehydration.

> **SIGNS**: Sudden onset of diarrhoea and subsequent dehydration; the bird is thin, listless, its eyes dull, feet and wingtips cold, inside of mouth dry, skin over breastbone tight; **clinical shock** follows if bird loses more than 10% of normal body fluid.
>
> **TREATMENT**: Rehydration fluids, and perhaps antitoxins to offset poisonous substances released by invading bacteria in lower intestine. Possibly antibiotics, depending on the type of infection.

OTHER SERIOUS CONDITIONS THAT AFFECT WATER BIRDS

MALNUTRITION DEFORMITIES

Birds tend to be more susceptible than mammals to vitamin deficiencies. Water birds such as ducks and swans are particularly prone to problems in captivity, or on sites where their natural diet is supplanted by the wrong foods, such as in public parks where a surfeit of white bread from well-meaning toddlers does not provide the right range of nutrients but fills the birds up so that they forage less. Vitamin B-complex deficiency, for example, may cause weakness in legs, wings and muscles and result in poor quality feathers which don't interlock and are not water-proof.

"ANGEL" OR "AIRPLANE" WING

A skeletal defect fairly common in geese and ducks. Underdeveloped, misshapen wings can be the result of lack of calcium and phosphate during the early growing period, or the deformity may be an inherited genetic fault. Lack of vitamin D in the diet (and lack of sunlight which would enable the body to manufacture it) will also stop calcium in the diet being properly absorbed into the bones.

LACK OF CORRECT DIET SUPPLEMENTS

Fish-eating birds in captivity can become ill, even though fed on the correct fish diet, unless they receive the correct vitamin supplement. An enzyme in fish breaks down the **thiamine** (vitamin B1) in the bird's body, and this must be replaced while the bird is in care, or it will die.

> **SIGNS OF MALNUTRITION PROBLEMS**:
> These may include skeletal abnormalities, (e.g. goose with too-short wings sticking out at an angle from its body); the bird cannot fly, is noticeably smaller than broodmates, and its feathers are in worse condition. Weakened, greasy-looking or very dry feathers, poor muscle co-ordination, loss of balance, deformed legs, **depression**, convulsions, are further signs.
>
> **TREATMENT**: None for birds affected by wing deformity; they're best released to join a group on "safe" sites, such as private lakes, where they can still swim and breed. Other malnutrition problems may be lessened by feeding a natural and complete diet to strengthen the immune system and build muscle.

Oiled sea birds are at high risk of lung fungal infection

BOTULISM POISONING

This kills birds by progressively paralysing their muscles and interfering with their nervous system until they cannot breathe. It is triggered by a bacterium, normally found in soil and untreated water, which only becomes life-threatening under certain conditions when there is no oxygen. Rotting vegetation sealed into warm, crusting mud by strong sunlight provides ideal conditions for these bacteria to multiply and release their toxins. Water birds can swallow the toxins if they feed or drink at the water's edge on a very hot day. (For people, the danger of **botulism** poisoning lies in eating food that has not been properly preserved or canned.)

Some water birds (waders, some types of duck) can also be accidentally poisoned by eating molluscs which have absorbed chemicals, such as solvents used to disperse spilt oil.

SIGNS: Dead or dying birds, including **corvids** that came to scavenge corpses and garden birds that came to the water's edge to drink. Botulism toxins remain potent for a long time. Survivors may have **paralysis**, floppy legs, or explosive diarrhoea (but not foul-smelling, like that of salmonellosis).
TREATMENT: Includes flushing out bird's digestive system with tube-fed, toxin-absorbent liquids, and rehydration therapy. Speed of treatment is vital. Supportive nursing and liquid food for those that survive; appetite-stimulating B12 injections, antibacterial drugs. Recovery, in a cool, quiet environment, may take weeks.

FOOT AND "KEEL" (breastbone) PROBLEMS

These affect heavy water birds in captivity on a hard surface, such as concrete, particularly if it is not clean. "Bumble foot" starts as a large corn. The bird's bodyweight squashes it flat and walking constantly irritates the tissues. Harmful bacteria may enter via small wounds and scratches on the sole. The infection can become intractable, resulting in a very swollen, distorted, painful foot and ankle joint. Many water birds get cracked, dry feet, too, if they don't have access to water (although very young ones in captivity can become waterlogged and hypothermic if they do!). Grebes, their bodies designed for mobility in water, not on land, automatically slump down onto their "keel" in a hospital cage and abrasions and infection can be problems in captivity.

Heavy water birds can suffer foot damage on dirty, hard surfaces in captivity

SIGNS: Bumble foot – bird limping, holding up a clenched, swollen foot; a **tumour**-like mass build-up on horny skin under its foot.
Other conditions produce raw, cracked skin and hot, painful, infected areas.

TREATMENT: **Granulation** tissue is removed, avoiding excess bleeding. The wound is cleaned out and treated with antibiotic powder; the bird is kept in clean, dry conditions until the sole heals. Physiotherapy. Cracked, dry skin on soles can be soothed by a small amount of olive oil. A bird not allowed access to water may be given a foam rubber mat to cushion its breastbone.

FUNGAL INFECTIONS AND PARASITES

FUNGAL INFECTIONS

The Aspergillus group of fungi are widespread in the environment. So is **Candida**, the type that produces green, fluffy mould on damp, stale bread and causes varieties of thrush in humans. Fungal spores can cause fatal infection in birds if they gain access to any part of the body. Under normal circumstances, a water bird may already be carrying and tolerating fungal spores in its lungs. But if the bird is subjected to stresses such as cold and starvation, the spores multiply rapidly. The fungus will form clumps that fill up and block the airways. Many produce toxins that will damage tissues. Infection finally overwhelms the victim. Nestlings and old, debilitated and oiled birds are most at risk. Ocean-going birds are especially vulnerable to lung fungal attack because of the way their bodies hold and re-use air while underwater. Warmer seas caused by climate change are also spreading **parasites** in sea birds.

These types of fungal spores flourish in damp, decaying vegetation, but dry, dusty conditions help spread them. Dirty cages and pen floors covered in food debris, mouldy straw or hay, chaff, seeds and other dusty materials are notorious trouble-makers. Harmful spores may also be coughed up or excreted by infected birds, contaminating shared food. Spores remain viable for a long time, so the problem can spread fast where large numbers of sick, weakened birds are cared for together. Progressive weight loss, despite treatment for obvious clinical conditions, can signal **aspergillosis**. But its symptoms may go undiagnosed, only revealed in **post-mortem** examination. Because of the risk of human fungal infection, strict nursing hygiene protocol has to be maintained (e.g. at centres treating oiled seabirds).

SIGNS: Fast, laboured, open-beak breathing when disease is advanced; rattling noise (as air vibrates over fungal overgrowth in airways.) Weight loss, deteriorating condition, depression, convulsions, **coma**. Birds may also die suddenly without showing obvious symptoms.

TREATMENT: **Systemic antifungal** drugs (**orally**, or misted into airways via a **nebuliser**), but the infection can be very slow to respond. **Bronchodilators** and **oxygen therapy** ease breathing. New admissions may be treated **prophylactically**. Housing and feeding equipment are cleaned daily with a non-**phenol** type of disinfectant that is not toxic or corrosive to birds. Supplies of shredded newspaper bedding must be renewed daily, but bedding is never given to seabirds.

INTERNAL PARASITES

These include **worms** and their larvae. They may infect the windpipe, lungs, gizzard, intestines, liver and other organs, or be present in microscopic form in blood. Birds that feed under water may also pick up **leeches**, which latch on inside their mouths or block their nostrils. Parasites cause no symptoms, but they can weaken through sheer numbers and potentially lead to fatal illness. A water bird that is injured, or already sick, is likely to have an undue number of internal and external parasites.

> **SIGNS**: Loss of condition, failure to gain weight; worms in faeces.
> **TREATMENT**: Leeches are carefully tweezered off, without leaving the mouth parts behind. Wormer is powdered on food, injected under skin, or administered as a tablet by mouth; anti-protozoal drug; antibiotics if there is any secondary infection; anti-inflammatories, given orally or injected.

EXTERNAL PARASITES

These include **mites**, **lice** and **biting flies**. It might be expected that a bird that spends much of its life swimming on, or diving through, water would be free of such tormentors. But a swimming bird's feathers stay dry underneath, thanks to the efficient meshing of the feather edges. This results in an airlock layer next to an invitingly warm body. Parasites are well-adapted to their hosts and their lifestyles: one kind of swan parasite is well camouflaged by its creamy-white colour.

Some mites (tiny creatures with eight legs, like spiders) attack airways. Some feed relatively harmlessly on feather dander. Others suck blood and harm the bird's general health. Lice and biting flies (also called **louse** flies) suck blood. None of the above can fly.

> **SIGNS**: May include excessive scratching; there are moving specks on feathers.
> **TREATMENT**: Bird-safe **insecticide** on neck skin (e.g. a light dusting of **pyrethrum**-based powder) or the **parasites** are removed and drowned in a dish of mild disinfectant or salted water. No treatment at all if the bird is stressed.

FLYING INSECTS

Common flying insects such as blackflies and **bluebottles** can transmit disease or cause fatal blood poisoning. Blackflies can spread a malaria-like parasitic disease among wild ducks. Bluebottles (blowflies) lay eggs on wounds, then their hatching larvae eat into their host. Bacteria in bloodstream release toxins that will rapidly kill. A bird will be affected more quickly than a mammal and is very susceptible to the toxic side-effects of organophosphate insecticides, too.

> **SIGNS**: Fly eggs and maggots around a wound; bird severely weakened.
> **TREATMENT**: **Wound management**, antibiotics; treatment of underlying disease.

WHEN WATER BIRDS NEED HELP – AND WHEN THEY DON'T

The plight of many waterfowl accident victims is often only too easy to spot: bloodied feathers, trailing tangles of line, torn webbing on feet, missing toes, damaged beaks, dragging wings. Everyone can recognise feathers that have been discoloured and damaged by pollutants. It's not hard, either, to single out a bird that is lethargic and unable to support its head and neck, or one that has a plastic food or drink container stuck on its body.

Sometimes, though, a congenital deformity is mistaken for a recent bone break, or a bird's choice of a grassy inland landing spot may be thought to mean it is stranded and cannot fly. If in doubt, take a closer look. Ideally, use binoculars. A brief watch is usually enough to distinguish the casualties from the curiosities. If you think a bird is unable to fly, walk slowly behind it and see if it takes off. But if you see signs of stumbling, a drooping wing tip or an awkwardly angled or held leg, treat the bird as a potential casualty. If you think it's stuck on ice, try briefly waving your arms and shouting once, to see if it can move off. If you still think there's a problem, then:

DON'T RUSH IN. If the water bird is not in imminent danger, there is no advantage in moving fast and startling it. You're most likely to secure it on land.

BE QUIET AND CALM. People-shy species such as heron, grebes and moorhen, will panic, injuring themselves further, if you flap about noisily. Plan your moves.

Enlist any help and seek equipment you may need. **TRUST YOUR INSTINCTS** and those of regular bird-watchers. Water birds, like other kinds of wildlife, are good at covering up illnesses and injuries and trying to get on with the business of living. But a person who watches, or feeds, those birds daily will soon notice when something isn't right.

In poor light, birds can mistake wet roads for rivers.

Some mother ducks lay their eggs in very dangerous places.

Do not put yourself, or other people, in danger. This is very important when attempting a rescue near water. You may be so focused on preventing a land-bound casualty from making a getaway on water that you lose your balance and fall in. Never let your enthusiasm blind you to the perils of hidden currents, deep mud and thin ice.

Try to make sure the casualty doesn't get back into the water, though. If it does, the rescue will require specialist helpers and equipment, including an inflatable boat. You will stand little chance of catching the bird yourself (unless the water is very shallow).

Young Birds

Unlike garden bird species, many young water birds are physically mature enough to leave the nest almost immediately after they've hatched and follow their parent, who leads them to a watercourse. They can also feed themselves, or take food from a parent's beak, without having to be force-fed. But they will not stay in the water for prolonged periods, because their downy feathers are insufficient to prevent them getting waterlogged and cold.

Apart from natural dangers, such as predation and the hazards of motor and boating traffic, things can go very wrong for a newly-hatched chick, gosling, duckling or cygnet. The most common problem is a poor original choice of nesting site. Some female ducks lay their eggs in very dangerous places. It is normal for them to pick a spot away from the riverbank. But one female chose the flat roof of a high-rise office block in Croydon (perhaps it was a rainy night when she landed and she thought she was beside a lake!). Came the moment for the ducklings to follow their mother on their first journey, there was a very long drop to ground level. Miraculously, so light and fluffy were the youngsters, that all but one made it alive. But they had to be collected, en masse, from the car park below and raised in captivity.

Heron chicks that leave the nest too early also end up in trouble. Parents will ignore a premature leaver. Stragglers and strayers that don't keep up with their siblings in a floating procession are also liable to get snapped up by a fish, bird or mammal predator. As a rule of thumb, a very young water bird that is clearly in the wrong place, at the wrong time, with no sign of a parent around will need to be taken into care if it is to survive.

Transporting

It is illegal to drive a vehicle with any unrestrained wildlife casualty loose inside, for obvious safety reasons. But do not waste time searching for the ideal carrier when a garment, rucksack or *space blanket* will do. Or a passenger could hold the bird (around its shoulders, its body and feet supported on their knees) while you drove. Make sure that the bird casualty, however secured, can still breathe freely. Keep its surroundings quiet and low-key.

Any well-ventilated container (disinfectable if you intend to re-use it) will do to carry most types of water bird. Provided that it is not left in a crouching position for very long, even a tall bird like a heron can temporarily sit inside a large cat-carrier. Any container must be big enough for the bird to sit in without buckling its feathers, but not so large that it can open its wings or roll about. If you use a cardboard box, put a generous amount of airholes low down along its sides: this is more effective than piercing the lid or cover. If you use a bag, or small garment wrapped around the water bird's body in transit, be sure to leave the bird's head and neck free, otherwise it may suffocate.

With wings held shut inside an open-top fabric bag, swans and geese should travel in vehicles in a sitting-down position. Swans' feet are usually folded gently behind them, across their lower back (they often swim with one leg up in this position). All large waterfowl should face front-to-back, so they can use their necks to help stabilise themselves when the vehicle brakes or corners. Otherwise, they may roll over on their sides, causing pain and exacerbating pre-existing injuries.

If you cannot take the casualty for medical attention yourself, stay with it until aid arrives and you can help a wildlife ambulance team locate it and keep onlookers, dogs, etc., away from it meanwhile. It's very important not to let a casualty become panicky and start moving about. This could make injuries beyond help.

FEEDING IN CAPTIVITY

Ducklings, goslings and cygnets can all feed themselves. But sick youngsters may initially need to be force-fed by hospital staff.

Mallard ducks, geese and swans, youngsters and adults alike, are fed corn and chickcrumb, plus grit. Inside their muscular **gizzard**, grit helps break down and digest their food. They also need to eat greens:

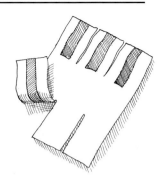

One swan wrap to go – with Velcro strips to secure a snug fit.

Custom-made wraps are quick and easy to use.

But a pillow-case or sack with one corner cut out, or a canvas open-top tool bag, will also work.

DID YOU KNOW?

◆ A swan's neck has more **vertebrae** (25) than that of any other bird or mammal.

◆ Many water birds can drink seawater; they have a special salt-filtering gland above each eye.

◆ Geese are thought to pair for life, but studies of marked Barnacle geese showed that two per cent of couples parted, even though both birds were still alive. Getting separated during migration from the Arctic Circle, plus the imperative of finding a new mate in time to catch the **breeding season**, is thought to be the cause of breakups.

◆ Gulls can live for 30 years, natural perils permitting – a good reason not to handle an orphaned chick more than necessary, if you don't want it to get imprinted and hang around!

◆ Ownership of Thames swans is decided each July at the Swan Upping ceremony. Leg rings are checked to show if a bird is owned by the Queen or by a City of London guild, e.g. Vintners' or Dyers' Company.

◆ Ducks don't start incubating their eggs until the whole clutch is laid. This way, ducklings hatch around the same time. Eggs that get cold before brooding begins are dormant and won't die if left uncovered for a while. This will only happen after the female has started sitting. So leave them alone.

◆ To wash one oiled marine duck by machine takes 15 minutes. By hand, it takes an hour.

◆ Britain's biggest gull, the Great Black-Backed, eats fish, rabbits, meat scraps – and other sea birds.

cut-up, **pesticide**-free fresh grass blades, chickweed, lettuce, green cabbage. Very young birds need a small chickcrumb pellet and greenery would be finely cut up. Egg-laying water birds have ground oyster-shell supplement sprinkled on food. Ducks like meaty snacks – such as slugs – and enjoy finding their own earthworms. They must have a water supply placed directly beside their food. They need to dabble their beaks in water between mouthfuls, otherwise they will have difficulty swallowing dry food.

OTHER DUCK SPECIES: Some eat chiefly shellfish and crustaceans, some hunt fish and frogs. Others feed largely on water plants, seeds, small water insects, larvae and **worms** from the rich mud on river or lake beds. Beak shape is usually a clue to diet, although ducks are highly adaptable and all will manage on a vegetarian diet for a short while. An adult will be identifiable from its shape and plumage, but most ducklings look alike before they get their final feathers. So a wide range of foods is offered to them all.

Fish-eating birds, such as gulls, herons, grebes and kingfishers, are fed small, oily fish (whitebait, sprats) in clean, shallow water. A gannet might be offered bigger fish such as mackerel. Fish is served cold and whole, or the bird usually won't take it. Some birds (gulls, herons, shags, cormorants) are given meat in the form of dead day-old chicks. All water birds in care are given daily vitamin and **mineral supplements** and cod-liver oil capsules. Some species receive a salt supplement, too; others are given daily thiamine.

If a bird is unable to feed itself, it will be artificially fed. Usually, one carer will hold the bird's beak open, gently extending the neck, while another slides a small, complete fish down its throat. A very young sea- or ocean-going bird will be fed a liquified fish diet, syringed via a flexible lubricated rubber tube introduced into its throat. (The tube should be lubricated and kept clean with dilute antibacterial fluid to prevent **pathogens** from being transmitted from bird to bird.) This method of feeding – known as "**gavaging**" from the French word for cram or fill up with food – would only be done by experienced handlers. Artificial feeding ceases as soon as the bird can feed itself.

TIME FOR RELEASE? WHEN AND WHERE

By law, only native species should be released back to the wild (Also see *Is it a Migrant?* p. 87). Ducks and geese are normally released back onto their original sites as soon as they are judged fit enough to fend for themselves. Swans are released on stretches of water where they will not come into conflict with other swans (e.g. a resident male guarding his **territory**). Divers and grebes need highly specific release sites. Local birdwatching groups and wildlife recorders can advise on site suitability. Moorhen and coots need fresh water with thick marginal plant cover and good privacy.

LONG-TERM OR NON-RELEASABLE PATIENTS. Birds that aren't physically A1 (perhaps having undergone an amputation or been admitted with pre-existing deformities or old injuries) are usually found protected release sites, such as among a flock on a private lake, with a low risk of predation. They are continually observed to check that they are coping and staying healthy and are given support-feeding when required. Even with a missing upper beak, a swan may feed from a deep hand-held bucket, for example.

Is it a Migrant?

Many birds travel vast distances each year to mate and produce young in milder climates than their own. Winter-visiting geese from Greenland and Iceland usually do the trip in one "hop", flying at 2,000 to 5,000 feet (the height of Ben Nevis) at about 40 miles an hour. Others come from Arctic Russia, with European stopovers. Some migrants get driven off course by bad autumn weather and are forced to "ditch" (maybe in a garden or shopping mall). They're kept in care long enough to recover from exhaustion, but released as

Storms at sea can throw migrating birds miles off course.

Casualty Kit

✔ Fish landing net, for a casualty in water: bring up under the bird.

✔ Thick gardening gloves

✔ Mild disinfectant, e.g. dilute antibacterial handwash, for bathing wounds

✔ **Styptic** pencil (from chemist) or anticoagulating powder for minor bleeds, including feather stubs

✔ Small, clean lightweight towels, for bolstering the casualty, covering the container. These may also be used to secure wings

✔ Large towels (for drying, containing and warming bigger birds)

✔ Bubblewrap, or **space blanket**, for insulating – leave head free

✔ Blunt-ended scissors

✔ Cat carrier or large box for medium-to-large-sized water bird

✔ Small cardboard box with lid – well ventilated with airholes

✔ Pillowcase or hessian sack with one corner cut out (for carrying swans or geese). Or use a canvas, open-top tool bag with handles

✔ Newspaper or a couple of old blankets to cover the back of your vehicle

✔ Wellington boots or waders (for marshy ground, shallow water)

✔ Latex gloves: a good idea if you have cuts or grazes

soon as possible, to avoid risk of fungal infection. They may be shipped, or flown out, to a release point further along their migration path, to make up for lost journey time. Some gulls that used to live chiefly along our coastline are now moving inland for richer pickings and better shelter. Reuniting them with their fellows, on suitable sites, is no problem. Convalescents may release themselves when they feel ready to go, if kept in open-air accommodation. But a juvenile gull would have to wait until its flight feathers were fully grown before it could join companions in the wild.

YOUNG WATER BIRDS IN TROUBLE

Young birds, such as the late-hatching duckling that failed to catch up with its siblings when they left the nest, will need to be taken for attention very quickly. They will be very cold (hypothermic) and won't survive long if left. They require emergency regulation of their core body temperature, rehydration and feeding, little and often. They need to be reared with others of the same, or similar, species. Some youngsters won't eat or preen unless they can watch others doing so. Being in an artificial brood prevents them **imprinting** on their rescuer, too. An adult water bird

that believes itself to be a feathered person is doomed to a life in captivity. They are prone to trampling their feed, faeces and water supply into a slurry you could fix and grout tiles with. Many are loudly vocal. Animal sanctuaries are full of geese whose owners were forced to part with them by their neighbours' complaints.

The very young and fragile are nursed in intensive care, under a heat source they can move away from at will. They are given a comforting mother-substitute – which may be a real live hen, an alarm clock in a fluffy towel or a feather duster. One young cygnet's comforter was a large toy polar bear. Baby water birds need to be able to hide. In the wild, many remain, for long periods, virtually invisible beneath their mother's wings or chest feathers.

Introducing young water birds to swimming must also be carefully stage-managed. Although, in the wild, very young ducklings may be seen bobbing around on the water's surface without saturating their thick, but soft, first feathers, in captivity it's a different story. Given a miniature pool in their cage, they soon become waterlogged and hypothermic and can easily drown. So young ducks in captivity are not introduced to water until they are at least 16 weeks old. Other species, such as cygnets and goslings, are also introduced gradually, under supervision, for limited periods only.

WATER BIRD FIRST AID

Members of the public are allowed by law to carry out first aid on an animal or bird to keep it alive, alleviate suffering and keep it in a stable condition until medical help is found.

Follow the A,B,C (and D) guide. Don't do more than is necessary.

AIRWAYS. Check they are clear of oil, mud, mucus and water. If the bird is soaked, it may be worth holding it upside-down for a few seconds to allow any excess liquid to drain from its airways.

Wipe away any chemical pollutants from the beak area (and eyes) using a clean damp cloth or wipe.

BREATHING. Check that the bird is able to breathe. Make sure that it is not on its back and has not rolled onto its side. Keep its body supported in an upright position (e.g. on a coiled fabric "doughnut"). Watch for signs of extreme stress (gasping, open-beaked breathing) and keep handling to a minimum. If panting, put the bird in a warm, darkened, well-ventilated container and leave it alone until it has calmed down.

CIRCULATION. Immobilise wings. If the casualty has a fracture and flaps, the bone could cut a major blood vessel and it might bleed to death. If in shock, the bird will need **fluid therapy** later. Stem minor bleeds with a caustic shaving pencil, diluted **potassium permanganate** or a light dusting of antibiotic powder (from pet shop or your vet). A bird's thin, inelastic skin makes it difficult to halt stronger blood loss with a pressure bandage: blood will continue to seep under skin.

DO give the bird a quiet, darkened environment at a comfortable temperature. If it's very cold, wet or oil-damaged, use bubble-wrap or space blanket to conserve body heat. Be careful not to interfere with breathing. In an emergency, in very hot weather, over-heating may be countered by a light misting from a houseplant spray.

DO transport the bird in a container that will prevent it moving around, falling on its side or opening its wings.

DO take note of the situation in which you found the casualty, plus details of injuries and its state of health (e.g. **nasal discharge**, eyelids half-shut). These will assist diagnosis.

DON'T give a bird anything by mouth – you could choke it to death and will certainly stress it.

DON'T try to remove any fishing tackle, hooks, glass, embedded constriction or other foreign object from its body. Instead, protect the area with a thick pad so no further damage can occur.

DON'T throw away any soiled paper used in transporting bird until the vet or wildlife rehabilitator has seen it. It can be an invaluable aid to diagnosis.

HOW SHOULD I HANDLE A WATERBIRD CASUALTY?

A waterbird casualty should be treated in the same way as a rescued garden bird, its wings restrained by being held in the natural shut position against its body, to prevent it injuring itself further. But, especially with larger species, beak and legs must be reckoned with, too, and a long neck may need to be supported. All these things have to be taken care of at the same time. Some water birds are more than a handful and need at least two, preferably long, arms to contain them securely.

All casualties will do their best to get away from you, unless they are partially paralysed or trapped, e.g. in fishing line or weed. Unlike garden birds, which can rise up into the air or dash along the ground, these birds will usually have a third escape route to call upon – the water – making rescues more complicated.

Your prime aim should be to minimise any frantic flapping and struggling. Wing movements are bound to exacerbate injuries and increase the dangerous shock effects that go with trauma or serious illness. Even if the bird has an obvious wing injury, you will have to hold, or wrap up, its body so it can't move that wing around. A broken beak has to be held still, or stabilised with a temporary **splint** or bandage. You may feel hesitant about doing this, but the alternative may be to watch a casualty bleed to death from fresh injuries it has caused itself through panic.

If you don't have a clue how to hold a water bird, and are nervous about the prospect should you come across one that needs help, ask someone who keeps wildfowl, a vet or an animal charity like the RSPCA that takes in injured or misplaced water birds to give you some practical advice. Picking up an uninjured duck or goose, under the watchful eye of an experienced wildlife handler, farmer or conservationist, when there is no time pressure, is invaluable training for the moment when you may need to rescue one as an emergency.

A Mobile Casualty: If it is a small wildfowl, such as a duck, it may be possible to "round it up" gradually. Stretch out your arms and manoeuvre it into a restricted space, such as a wall corner or clump of bushes. Don't look directly into the bird's eyes. Always keep yourself between it and any nearby stretch of water (or road).

It may be tempting, if the water bird is relatively big and you think it has the potential to give you a nasty nip, to secure its beak by tying something around it. Don't. Binding up the beak could interfere with the bird's breathing if its nostrils are blocked, or condemn it to death if it escapes from you with its beak clamped. Secondly, many water birds, like herons, rely on a lightning-fast stabbing action when defending themselves, so tying up their beak will do you no good whatsoever. A hand placed, without undue pressure, across and around the beak is often all that is needed while handling this type of water bird. If the rescuer has a helper, looking after the casualty's sharp end could be his/her responsibility. Otherwise, hold the beak first, then quickly secure the wings. Keep any bird, whatever its species, well away from your face.

Throwing a lightweight garment, cloth or towel over a small to medium-sized bird may be your best option if it is beyond arm's reach (wildlife casualties are very good at judging the length of rescuers' arms). A soft-rimmed net is one of the least traumatic methods for catching a swimming bird. You need to bring it up underneath the bird if it is on the water. On land, an up-ended cardboard box or light waterproof kagoul may be all that is on hand to confine it. Either will suffice. If you're in a remote place and need to collect a seabird casualty, you can always pull down a sleeve to protect your hand as you pick the bird up. A gull can grasp a finger in a bruising pinch, but it's the sudden, screaming racket that often makes an inexperienced handler drop it!

Moving slowly and calmly produces better results than acting in a hasty, ill-thought-out manner. The fewer attempts at capture, the better for the bird and the greater your chances of success.

Approach from an Angle. Stoop to make your silhouette look low and less threatening and don't stare into the casualty's eyes directly. That is the look of a hungry predator.

Don't let onlookers crowd the bird. Involve them, instead, asking them to quietly form a barrier, hold a box ready, block off the casualty's exit to a dangerous road. Someone whose hands are freer than yours could use their mobile to arrange transport or fix up veterinary attention for the casualty.

Ducks are relatively easy to handle: compact, blunt-beaked and unaggressive (pecks are unlikely to break skin). Some types of duck live closer to humans than others, so their levels of stress at being touched will vary. Ducks can take off in a very small area, i.e. almost vertically. Hold their wings shut, carry them against your torso, so that their feet have something to press against.

Geese are heavier than ducks and have big strong, webbed feet to help them struggle free. But they, too, have blunt beaks and aren't difficult to pick up, once cornered. Noisy protest is mainly bravado. Hold the goose's neck, carefully but resolutely, to stop it moving away. Then you can set about restraining its wings. The goose should be encircled supportively with one arm around the middle of its body and held against your side. At the same time, gently support its neck with your free hand. If you don't think you have a secure, comfortable hold on the bird, put it down on the ground, gently push it into a sitting position, and start again. The goose will not struggle if it feels secure.

Swans can inflict bruising blows with their wings, but these aren't usually enough to seriously harm a human. Like geese, swans should be calmly and systematically approached, restrained and carried underarm, with their neck supported. It may be helpful to stand over the swan, with one foot on either side of it, with its head facing away from you. Once it is still, you can take hold of its neck. Gently use your flexed knees to nudge the swan into a sitting position. Then lift it, keeping its wings closed against its sides. You may find it more comfortable, for both of you, if you support the bird's weight on your hipbone. Swans tend not to struggle when being carried in this way. In fact, many seem to be doing everything in their power to look dignified, as if the whole thing was their idea in the first place. But if you feel the bird is slipping, stop and start again, so that you're holding the swan more securely. If there is any line, litter or foreign object entangling or attached to the swan's body, be careful not to move it or put pressure on the area.

Moorhens and coots move fast and usually need more than one person to catch them. They should be handled as little as possible and not stressed by a long chase.

Fishing and diving birds, like herons and grebes, and some gull species, are not at all keen on human company. They panic easily and need to be stressed as little as possible by capture and containment. You must protect your eyes when attempting to rescue any bird in this category. They are custom-built to spear small, sparkling lumps of flesh that present themselves within lunging distance of their rapier-like beaks. Don't underestimate neck reach or speed of movement and use sunglasses, borrowed reading specs, DIY goggles, or a peaked hat worn very low to safeguard your sight.

Offer a gull a distracting sleeve, or glove, to "bite" while you get hold of its body, fold its wings shut and then lightly grasp its beak.

Large fishing birds are best held just behind the head, being careful not to twist the neck, so the beak faces away from you.

Useful Organisations:

British Trust for Ornithology (BTO)
The Nunnery, Thetford, Norfolk, IP24 2PU; 01842 750050; www.bto.org

The Royal Society for the Protection of Birds (RSPB)
HQ: The Lodge, Potton Rd, Sandy, Beds, SG19 2DL
01767 680 551 Wildlife enquiries 01767 693 690; www.rspb.org.

The Swan Sanctuary Felix Lane, Shepperton, Middx, TW17 8NN;
01932 240790; www.swanuk.org.uk

The Wildfowl and Wetlands Trust (WWT) Slimbridge, Glos, GL2 7BT;
01453 891900; www.wwt.org.uk

>10 Ways to Get Involved >>>>>>>>>>>>>>>>>>>>>>>>>>

◆ Tackle an angler: suggest barbless hooks.

◆ Pick up all lost or discarded fishing litter you find, taking it home for disposal.

◆ Campaign for more warning disks on overhead power lines, luminous flashes on the sides of rail and road bridges that cross rivers, and on their lamp-posts, to help flying birds.

◆ Get in deep water. Help clear waterways, create new wetlands, revitalise urban rivers. We need wetlands, green areas, "porous" cities, to soak up water in an era of climate change and floods. Ask British Trust for Conservation Volunteers, wildlife trusts, Wildfowl and Wetlands Trust, for details.

◆ Give a winter warmer. Supplementing birds' food helps them survive harsh weather conditions and fight off disease. Kitchen scraps you'd normally throw away or compost – outer cabbage leaves, fatty meat offcuts – make a feast for geese and gulls. No stale food, bones, or white bread, though.

◆ Don't "mess about" in boats, dumping litter and fuel, disrupting water birds' habitats with harmful, noisy machinery.

Jet-skis aren't fun if you're in their path or in their oily wake. Cleaner motors are available, but why not sail or row instead?

◆ Be a nosy parker, if you suspect water birds are in danger. Hang around ostentatiously, use your mobile, digital camera, dictaphone, etc.) One young boy watched while feeding swans was found, on closer inspection, to be handing out pellets of bread containing hidden fishhooks.

◆ Maintain your road vehicle so that it doesn't leak fuel.

◆ Boycott any oil company whose practices lead to oil spills at sea (ageing, poorly maintained vessels, inexpert crews and other corner-cutting "economies").

◆ Blow the whistle on any individual or company you know to be illegally dumping pollutants into water. Report environmental pollution: Environment Agency 24-hour emergency line 0800 807060. Take your own oil (e.g. drained from car) to an oil recycling bank. Don't mix it with other substances like paints and solvents: it makes recycling difficult. Make sure any oil at your place of work doesn't leak into water courses.

TRUE OR FALSE?

1 Bewick swans, winter visitors from Russia and Scandinavia, look so alike that the only way to identify them is to put coded rings on their legs.

2 Nestling ducks need to eat special baby duck food, fed to them by their parents.

3 Very young gulls need to be force-fed by their parents, too.

4 All ducks eat the same kind of food, in the same kind of places.

5 Ducks can't drown - they're so buoyant, they always bob up again when submerged.

6 Geese, swans and ducks need a long "runway" in order to be able to take off, and swans can only take off from water.

7 Male ducks only look bright and colourful in spring.

8 Cormorants are seabirds only seen at the coast.

9 Bitterns, which live in reed beds and have a strange, deep booming call, are almost extinct in Britain.

10 Ducks can't fly in late summer and early autumn.

ANSWERS

1 False. All Bewick swans may look alike to us. But variations in pattern and distribution of colour on their yellow and black beaks are as unique as sets of human fingerprints.

2 False. From the moment they hatch, ducklings can feed themselves.

3 True. Gulls have perfected the art of fast-food delivery to their chicks, jetting an oily, soupy mixture (chiefly regurgitated, partially digested fish) directly down the youngsters' throats.

4 False. Duck diets vary from tiny water plants and molluscs and invertebrates (snails, slugs and worms), to fish, crustaceans and shellfish. Some ducks dabble in water for their food, heads down, bottoms up. others dive deep; some live in freshwater, others are seagoing; some ducks spend most of their time foraging on dry land, and some (though not in Britain) even perch in trees.

5 False. Ducks drown if they're entangled with underwater weed or submerged litter. If feathers get damaged, or they're too sick or injured to preen, they become waterlogged, hypothermic and weak and will eventually drown if they can't climb out of the water. Ducklings in captivity can drown if introduced to water too early.

6 False. Ducks take off from an almost vertical position within a very confined space. Geese and swans need a bit more of a run to achieve lift-off, but not as much as most people think. Swans, although famous for their spectacular footslapping walking-on-water routine, can make do with a dry runway, if necessary.

7 True. Most males are sartorial show-offs in spring and shed their vibrant breeding season colours for more muted tones in the rest of the year.

8 False. In recent years, cormorants have established a number of inland breeding colonies. They are regularly seen fishing near Waterloo and Westminster bridges on the Thames, in central London.

9 True. Destruction of the birds' natural habitat, plus changing coastline problems caused by global warming, have squeezed this shy bird to the brink of disappearance. Good news is that the RSPB recently reported the re-emergence of breeding pairs (the first seen since the 1940s, in one case) at new sites near the east coast. Better management of deliberately created fresh sites holds out hope.

10 True. During this period – called the eclipse – ducks moult their wing feathers and can't fly again until these have regrown.

Don't Try This at Home – or at School!

PUDDLES

The boy put the huge egg in a quiet, dark, warm place. It was his secret project. How exciting, to see what big chick came out of it! What if it hatched while he was at school? He'd just have to hurry home each day as soon as he could, to check…

His mother paused. She could hear a funny tapping noise. It seemed to be coming from the airing cupboard. She opened the door cautiously, and saw in the gloom a large goose egg from which a young bird was trying to emerge. It had only partially succeeded and one leg was jutting awkwardly from the cracked shell. The leg was sticklike and useless, having dried out and lost all flexibility in the desiccated atmosphere of the airing cupboard…

Staff at the wildfowl centre quickly put the egg into an atmosphere-controlled incubator. Piece by piece, they gently prised off the remaining portions of shell, keeping pace with the gosling's exhausted pushes.

Gradually, Puddles – as staff named him after he'd knocked over his water dish for the umpteenth time – gained vitality. But he needed plenty of care. Sandra, a volunteer, was happy to let him nestle under her shirt collar. He'd poke his head out whenever she spoke and preen the hair around her neck, as if it were feathers, making quiet gosling chitchat all the while. One leg was still useless, though. It got in the way constantly and tripped him up. That's why he kept upsetting his water.

Puddles became a favourite with staff and visitors. His photo appeared in the local paper. He underwent a delicate half-hour operation to correct his leg's misalignment. There was panic when he suddenly "died" under the anaesthetic, relief when the vet managed to bring him round again. He tolerated his leg splint well, and got to like his twice-daily bath in lukewarm water. In fact, he began to look rather beautiful. His feathers grew strong and shiny, his eyes were button-bright. He devoured his food, snaffling up fresh grass clippings as soon as they were sprinkled on top. When the weather was fine, he enjoyed soaking up the warm sunshine.

Staff were hoping that their prize patient was over the worse. It began to look as if imprinting on people might be Puddles' only future problem. Then he had a severe epileptic fit. Within three weeks of struggling out of his egg in the airing cupboard, he was dead. Staff at the wildfowl sanctuary believe that if he had been allowed to hatch naturally, where the egg was laid, he would still be around today, a healthy grown adult. Each year, the centre is called by teachers, concerned about the sudden deaths of birds they've hatched on site as an educational aid. They continue to urge people to leave the eggs of waterfowl and any other birds alone. Or learn a very sad lesson.

Foxes

4

GONE TO EARTH

"*I was jammed, head first, in a low, narrow space, going after a fox with a broken front leg. It was cold and dark and I didn't fit in very well. There was only room to crouch. But I knew the fox was down there and didn't want to lose it. So I squeezed myself along as far and as fast as I could, and in my enthusiasm, I'd got both arms squashed by my sides. Then the tunnel took a bend and, as I turned the corner, we came face to face. The vixen's ears were down, her eyes wide, her teeth bared. I shut my eyes, expecting my nose to take some damage. But all I felt was a blow like a punch, as she leapt forward and headbutted me with her muzzle. I was so startled that I backed away. Then I wriggled free and went back for her again. Hands first, this time!*"

Eddie Williams is an experienced wildlife rescuer who cheerfully admits that going head-to-head with a panicky cornered fox down a trench was probably his least sensible rescue approach ever.

"Normally, if a fox is within arm's reach – down a drain, or in the corner of two walls, for instance – I'd look at it and move a hand slowly over the top of it. Then I'd see if I could put my hand down smoothly on its head. I'd tickle it, and it might move a bit, but many seem to realise that you're not going to hurt them and stay perfectly still. I'd do this a couple of times, until I could scruff it – you have to twist the loose skin at the back of their neck a little and lift at the same time – and put it in the carrier. Most fox casualties come along quietly. As a former postman, I've come across many a domestic dog that would love to cross the road to bite you. But a fox – even one that was injured and in pain – would never do that."

The fox was badly hurt – probably hit by a car during the night. But she was still mobile, and she could have got away if Eddie had not "collared" her quickly. Disappearing would have been very bad news for her. True, many foxes in the wild do suffer a broken leg and recover, without complications and without any help from people. Foxes brought into care for other problems, such as severe mange or shotgun pellet or snare injuries, sometimes show signs of old, healed leg fractures, during examination or X-ray. The limb might have become slightly twisted and thickened and the fox might have ended up with a permanent limp, yet the animal had obviously been able to cope and recover. But in almost every instance, the once-broken leg will have been a back one.

This vixen had broken her front leg and it was a complicated fracture, too. The injury would have prevented her from climbing, pouncing on prey or digging. She would have been unable to run fast from danger. Trying to put weight on the damaged leg – apart from being painful – could have caused fatal blood poisoning if bacteria had got into the wounds, kept open by being scraped along the ground. Or the fox could have bled to death if a sharp, broken bone edge had cut through a blood vessel. It was important, therefore, if a vet was to save the leg, for the fox to receive treatment promptly.

Fox Facts

Population Distribution

There is a variety of fox types throughout the world. The fox you'd see in Canada, for example, looks slightly different from the one you might watch in Britain, and those from both sides of the Atlantic vary in shape and coloration from the African variety. Foxes in very cold winter climates (e.g. Arctic foxes) develop white coats seasonally (historically making them prime targets for the fur trapper) while some that live and hunt in hot desert areas have enormous ears and small bodies, to help them lose excess heat efficiently.

In this country, you're likely to encounter a member of the European Red Fox family, a lightly built **canid** with distinctive "mask" facial markings and – in a healthy animal – a long, very bushy tail. But you would be amazed at some of the descriptions given when people report seeing a fox that's injured, or complain about one that's been digging up their plants. Male red foxes "as big as German Shepherds" have allegedly been sighted. This must be a case of (sub)urban myth in the making, as foxes of either sex rarely exceed the height of a medium terrier and are of far lighter build than most domestic dogs.

The Mammal Society puts the estimated pre-**breeding season** fox population in Britain at a quarter of a million. London is thought to have around 10,000 foxes. Although fox numbers almost treble in early summer every year, with the appearance of the new

80% of householders surveyed in Greater London were pleased to see foxes in their gardens. Only 4% positively disliked them.

cubs, by the time the next pre-breeding season has come round again, the population will have returned to its previous size. Fox numbers in this country remain stable from one year to the next, with cubs only surviving in sufficient numbers to replace adults that have died. The suspension of hunting during the **foot-and-mouth** crisis – at its height in 2001 – did not affect this self-regulatory rise-and-fall pattern – i.e. there was no population boom.

Habitat: Town and Country

Foxes are highly adaptable small wild dogs and are consequently found in an astonishingly wide range of **habitats**. They both hunt and scavenge, eating practically anything – one reason why they do so well in our towns, where a great choice of food is available.

But like all wild-living predators, foxes can only live where they can find enough food and hospitable shelter to support them. Mammalogists calculate that the maximum number of fox families a town can support is five families per square kilometre. Where overcrowding starts to occur, excess numbers are "culled" by Nature through the effects of starvation, disease and accidents (many foxes are killed on roads when moving across unfamiliar areas, trying to establish new territories). The Wildlife Trusts say that a third of urban foxes are killed by motor accidents.

Some people don't believe that foxes should be in towns at all. They think that this is "unnatural" and that the animal's normal **habitat** is the countryside. But this world view ignores two facts of vulpine family history: foxes, like other wild-living canids, learned thousands of years ago how to exploit the advantages of living near human settlements. They reaped the benefit of easier meals. Why waste precious energy hunting, with its high failure rate, when there were the rich pickings of penned-in **poultry** and waterfowl, stored and left-over food – and the **rodents** attracted to it?

Secondly, the barriers between countryside and township have long been blurred on these overcrowded islands. Buffer zones between wild and domesticated landscape have disappeared, hedgerows and orchards have been dug up, patchwork fields given over to crop monocultures. Many a new-build conurbation and creeping town-edge sprawl is fringed with the remains of the ancient woodland it has eaten into and segmented.

Wildlife habitats have had to become more varied and opportunistic in response. Gardens have become oases for displaced wildlife – suburbia is the new wilderness as far as many mammals, birds and invertebrates are concerned. Foxes began to move deeper into built-up areas around the time of the First World War, taking advantage of the new rail networks that were being constructed to link suburbanites to their jobs in town and city centres. Urban foxes became yet more common sights after the last war, colonising even the heart of London.

Home for a fox may be anything from dry vegetation below a bramble patch to a corner of a noisy factory or timber yard. A fox with procreation in mind may choose the self-build option. It might dig holes at the edge of an overgrown garden, or beneath a shed (which provides a readymade dry roof). Left to its own devices, it will construct a series of tunnels, leading to one or more "earths" and bolt-holes with alternative exits. Or it may take over another animal's existing dugout, such as an old rabbit warren or disused badger sett. It may move into a human building, empty or occupied. Often, the first a householder may know about the cubs below their floorboards is hearing them playing noisily at night.

IDENTIFYING FOXES

A healthy, full-grown male fox stands about 35cms at the shoulder and weighs around 6.5kg. For comparison, an average household cat might tip the scales at around 4kg.

Some male foxes might be heavier than average. Many will look bulkier than they really are, if they have a thick, winter coat. But they won't be much taller (certainly not German Shepherd height!). It's worth noting that a fox can squeeze through a gap only 10cm square. But they do not, as one national paper reported, have collapsible rib cages that enable them to hide under cattle grids. Vixens tend to be smaller and slighter than males, and may have narrower muzzles – but not always.

From a distance, you might be able to tell which is which, if the fox is scent-marking with **urine**: both sexes can leave hundreds of scent marks on both new and familiar landmarks around their territories during the course of a single night. Dog foxes tend to cock a leg, while vixens may squat. But, as with domestic dogs, some dominant females go in for the raised leg position, while some males lower their rears to the ground, when scent-marking with urine.

There is considerable colour variation in fox coats, both inherent and seasonal, from honey gold, through silver-tipped ginger to darker chestnut, with plenty

Bin there, done that! Foxes take advantage of our wasteful habits.

Urban foxes became a common sight after the war, colonising the heart of London

of charcoal grey at the darker end of the range. Some foxes look more like jackals, their coats a blend of black, white, grey and gold, with little russet red on view. Some have large areas of pure white on their underbellies, while others reveal only the smallest patches of oatmeal coloured fur. The amount of jet black tipping (of ears, paws and tail-ends) varies, too, and this is a great help when trying to identify individuals, if you're out fox-watching.

Foxes can sometimes be visually mistaken for dogs – especially if they have a congenitally short, or damaged tail. Viewed in profile, however, a fox's hindquarters are usually much higher off the ground than those of a domestic dog. Casual observers sometimes take them for ginger cats, too – until they move off in characteristically fast, loose-limbed trot.

BREEDING AND CUBS

Although dogs and foxes occasionally fraternise and both are members of the same species, they cannot breed together.

A vixen is only receptive to the dog fox for a very short fertile period – about three days in the year. Around this time, the dominant female in a group will scent-mark her **territory**, to advertise for a mate. He will tag around with her for days, waiting for that brief window of breeding opportunity. Dog foxes are themselves only fertile for a while, from November to March.

A fox pair – unless road accidents and persecution intervene – may stay together for life. March is the peak birth period, after a (circa) 53-day pregnancy, but cubs may be born as early as January. Blind and deaf at birth, cubs initially have pale blue eyes which turn brown,

Very young fox cubs are candidates for the oddest instances of mistaken identity

or golden, later. Their first coat is soft, fluffy and brown. The dog fox (and sometimes another related individual) brings food to the den and the young won't emerge from the earth until some time in April.

They will be eating solid food (hunted for them by the adults) in May and abandoning the breeding earth altogether in June, when the vixen stops producing milk. By August, cubs should be foraging for themselves and they are fully grown by September. The family then tends to break up, although some cubs (often the females) may stay. Most of the cubs will perish before the age of 10 months, the age of sexual maturity. Possible causes include the vixen being killed before the cubs are weaned, cold, flooding, road or other accidents, starvation after weaning, canine diseases, parasites and attacks by dogs or by people.

CUBS (also see *Cubs in Peril?*, pp. 115, 116)

Very young fox cubs are candidates for the oddest instances of mistaken identity. People who bring "orphaned" or injured cubs to wildlife rescue centres often think they have found exotic kittens, young rabbits, pedigree puppies or even little otters. Animal charity ambulance drivers, too, may be unsure what they have in their van, especially if they're new to the job. This is not entirely surprising because, with their fluffy, mushroom-brown fur, tiny flattened ears, short bearcub faces and stumpy tails clamped to their stocky bottoms, newborn cubs don't look anything like adult foxes. Even if the young cubs' eyes have opened, their pale blue colour won't be much of a pointer, either. That characteristically foxy gold or chestnut brown pigment doesn't appear until much later.

Tiny cubs may appear to be out alone for a whole range of reasons. Their mother out hunting for supper is just one. Often, a cub may simply be exploring, playing or just waiting quietly for the vixen to return. If the cub is extremely young – it may even have its placenta still attached – it may have been accidentally dropped, or deliberately set down, while the mother was switching hidey-holes for her litter (perhaps because of disturbance or flooding). If this is the case, she should normally return when all is quiet and pick up the cub.

TERRITORIAL MARKING AND PACK-LIVING

Foxes use urine or **faeces** to mark their territory. A strategically placed dropping is a visible, and smellable, warning to potential intruders, such as wandering young males looking for new territories to call their own. Foxes get their No Trespassing message across via a strongly scented oily liquid secreted in small sacs inside the anus. This may be sprayed onto an object directly, often the remains of a kill, or passed via droppings.

Fox language includes a vocal mixture of barks, howls, screams, growls and chunters, as well as a range of facial expressions, ear positions and whole body postures. A submissive fox will crouch low in front of a more dominant animal, ears flattened, tail held low. A family member will greet another with a wide open, "smiling" expression, tongue lolling, tail wagging. A play-bow is an invitation to join in some fun, a tail between the legs is a sign of extreme submission or fear. Tail movements give other visual signals, too, as well as wafting glandular scent messages to other foxes. Many signals will be familiar to owners of pet dogs.

Sparring foxes often "dance" around each other (remember that ballroom competition favourite, the foxtrot?) paws on each other's shoulders, jaws agape. It seems that the winner is the one who makes their opponent lose their balance. Some fox rows are very noisy – plenty of scolding chattering or loud, high-pitched screaming. Or they may take place in total silence. Confrontations between same-group members are usually resolved without bloodshed. There is a strict hierarchy among family members, and each fox conforms to the established pecking order. But occasionally, fox fights with outsiders can be vicious and may lead to an animal's death.

FEEDING HABITS

Foxes are pretty omnivorous. Stomach content analyses of what road-killed town foxes had consumed for their last-ever meal revealed a huge list of ingredients. One study of more than 500 urban fox corpses showed that scavenged meat, bones and fat made up about a quarter of what had been recently eaten. Wild mammals and birds, and earthworms (accounting for more than 12% of the overall diet), insects and various other kinds of scavenged food made up a further two-thirds of the meals. The remainder (about a twelfth) consisted of fruit and vegetables, plus a small proportion of pet mammals such as rabbits and guineapigs, and domestic birds.

The eyes have it, but often it's the ears that give away what a fox is thinking or feeling.

Foxes, it seems, will eat whatever's on offer, at that time of year, in that particular place. It might be ripe, soft fruits one season, a glut of rats, pigeons or **worms** the next. If a human being has made the job of hunting and scavenging easier by confining the prey for them, they will seize the chance of a meal. Foxes are not fussy (their strong stomach acids make short work of items that are, to our noses, distinctly "off") and they are highly adventurous feeders. One group of young animals developed a (probably lethal) taste for brake fluid, a toxic viscous alcohol which apparently tastes rather sweet, sucked from tubing beneath vehicles left in a car park overnight.

Rehabilitators prefer to err on the side of feeding caution – after all, they don't want to add a bout of colic or diarrhoea to the convalescent's problems. The fox in captivity will usually be fed meaty dog food, dead day-old chicks, sprinkled with vitamin and minerals supplements, plus a little fresh or dried fruit, and some fresh meat or liver, depending on the animal's digestive condition. Clean drinking water is supplied at least twice a day (some foxes in captivity "mark" the water bowl with urine or faeces to keep other foxes away, or vigorously up-end it, as soon as it appears).

Like other wild dogs, foxes like to store food "for a rainy day". They bury – or "cache" – it, from the French word *cacher*, to hide. Hens' eggs, cached in cool soil, can be preserved for a long time. But any one fox's supply may be dug up by another hungry fox, lured by the smell. Cached food may serve as the fox family larder. Incidentally, foxes on a so-called "killing spree" are taking advantage of a glut of prey. They are naturally hard-wired to take away, and bury, as much of their kill as they can carry. This is normal behaviour for mammal predators.

Foxes also dig much shallower holes – "scrapes" – when foraging for invertebrates like beetles, grubs and earthworms. In a garden, young "learner" foxes are liable to leave numerous mini-digs on lawns and in flowerbeds in summer, while trying to master the key skills of prey location.

FOXES AND THE LAW

Under the Veterinary Surgeons Act (1966), no person is allowed to make a diagnosis for an animal casualty, or "practise as a veterinary surgeon", unless they are included on the veterinary surgeons' register. However, in an emergency, if no vet is immediately available, a lay person is permitted to perform first aid, in order to preserve the life of an animal, or relieve pain, until professional veterinary help can be sought.

Foxes are sometimes perceived as "pests" – i.e. a nuisance – and it is legal to hire pest controllers who will arrange to trap a fox and have it removed. Most firms then destroy the fox off-site, usually by shooting it while in a cage trap. Most local authorities stopped fox "control" in the 1980s.

> ### HUNTING
> Fox hunting with dogs became illegal in England and Wales in February 2005. It was already banned in Scotland. Hunting foxes within the law is now confined to drag hunting or "flushing out" foxes, then shooting them.

Foxes are highly adventurous consumers.

BRAKE FLUID

There are no specific legal restrictions on night-shooting of foxes, but it is against the law to use an automatic or semi-automatic weapon or dazzling device while doing so. It is, however, legal to "lamp" them, i.e. use a light to attract foxes, then shoot them.

DEALING WITH FOX PROBLEMS

If you have a problem with foxes, don't call in pest controllers. They will either destroy the fox, or relocate it on the quiet (with little thought for the animal's territorial needs and survival chances) and they will charge you for the privilege. There will then be an invisible "To Let" sign in the neighbourhood and a new incomer fox will soon move into the vacant territory.

If you've a fox visitor that you would rather moved on, you can solve the "problem" in the following humane, environmentally friendly ways:

◆ Discourage unwanted digging by eliminating fish/blood/bonemeal fertilizers from the garden (the fox will think there's a tasty kill cached underground in that spot and try to raid the larder).

◆ Use a harmless, but evil-smelling deterrent at key sites on a fox route, to fool the fox into thinking there's a threatening territorial rival around, its system awash with aggressive hormones. Human urine can act as a deterrent – but it has to be a man's!

◆ Discourage fouling by removing petfood and other edible leftovers, and compostable vegetation etc., which will also attract rodents (themselves another lure for fox visitors). Odour from droppings may be mitigated by scooping them in scented (ideally biodegradable) sacs. Dispose of them in dog litter bins.

◆ If drinking from your garden pond is the chief lure, leave a clean water alternative elsewhere in your garden and ring your pond with wobbly logs and stones (it discourages cats, too, from taking fish and hunting amphibians).

◆ Don't try and get rid of musky urine smells by using water – this will only spread the oily secretions passed from the fox's scent **glands**. Try masking scents with a citrus oil spray instead.

◆ Fox-proof equipment for housing mammal pets and **poultry** has to be seriously sturdy. Chicken wire won't do. Foxes can easily dig under hutches or runs, bite through wire, undo latches and lift the edges of cages. Make housing heavy. Make sure that the floor is also made of the same tough, galvanised impenetrable metal mesh as the sides and top, or bury the under-wired base under soil.

◆ Don't make the mistake of thinking that a fox won't seize a pet or poultry from your garden in daylight or if you are around. Look at your pet through the fox's eyes and don't tempt fate. Don't leave small kittens or frail, elderly or sick cats at risk of possible **predation**, either. (Adult, fit cats will co-exist with the local foxes.)

◆ If all else fails, why not rig up a heat-sensitive outdoor light (the foxes will soon learn to ignore it) and enjoy watching your after-dark garden and pond visitors from the comfort of your armchair? Maybe try your hand at wildlife photography? Much more fun than shooing foxes away.

If you've a problem with foxes, don't call in pest controllers

COMMON HAZARDS FOR FOXES

Studies of urban foxes reveal an average life expectancy of 18 months – only 14 months in London, where 60% of the fox population dies each year. (This won't necessarily result in a declining population, though, because local birth shortfalls are made up by itinerant young foxes seeking new territories.)

In the country as a whole, it is estimated that roughly half a million foxes die each year, from all causes. Major causes of harm – many of which are man-made – include:

ROAD TRAFFIC ACCIDENTS (RTAs)

Drivers nationally account for the deaths of at least 100,000 foxes a year, according to the Mammal Society. Even that total is probably a considerable underestimate, as researchers only count visible corpses. Fatally injured foxes often manage to drag themselves back to a garden, or **nursery** den, before dying; other corpses are scavenged overnight.

Cars are certainly the most common cause of death for city foxes. The Wildlife Trusts estimate that a third of all urban foxes die in road traffic accidents. Young male foxes, ignorant of the dangers of traffic but impelled by instinct (and the off-putting territoriality of other, older males) to look for a home ground of their own, are especially vulnerable. Accidents peak during the October-November cub dispersal.

Road accident survivors' injuries commonly include fractures (e.g. smashed back legs and **pelvis** from mistiming a crossing at night, when vehicles may be travelling faster and lights can confuse), severe head **trauma** and internal organ damage.

SIGNS: Fox, probably unconscious, on the road or in bordering undergrowth, or **collapsed** in a nearby garden. Heavy external bleeding – which may have stopped by the time you find the fox – is signalled by bright red arterial blood that flows with some force. Flesh wounds such as severe **lacerations** and fractures may be evident, but internal damage like brain swelling, organ rupture and internal bleeding won't be obvious although they will have caused life-threatening **clinical shock**. *Signs of shock include loss of consciousness, shallow, fast breathing, feeble pulse, enlarged pupils, paws and feet cold to the touch, pale gums.*

TREATMENT: First aid; stemming obvious bleeding by applying finger, bandage or pad pressure to source of spurt. Care must be taken not to cause further injury when handling an unconscious fox (disturbing blood clots, causing bone splinters to puncture a blood vessel or organ). The fox should be wrapped in a blanket or contained in a cat-carrier and taken for veterinary treatment immediately. Pain-relief should be given as soon as possible, shock treated as a priority. The fox will be stabilised, and immediate surgery carried out only if there is continued internal bleeding. Injuries should be assessed by a vet before any decision taken to continue treatment, or to put to sleep humanely by injected anaesthetic overdose. ➤

→ This is important because severe spinal bruising initially produces the same **signs** as a broken back; diagnosis should include an X-ray.

Initial treatment would give the fox isotonic fluids by **drip** into a **vein**, to counteract effects of shock, rebalance blood chemicals and replace lost blood volume. There is no emergency donor blood bank for wildlife, so a commercial plasma volume expander, derived from gelatin, would be given instead. Brain swelling would be targeted by a specific diuretic and painkillers given, plus **antibiotics** to counteract bacterial **infection**.

Later, bone fractures would be stabilized by **splinting** or **pinning**, under **anaesthetic**, or a supportive bandage applied. A back leg, or the tail, might need to be amputated. Foxes can manage in the wild with only one hind leg. 10% of urban foxes are believed to have lost all, or part, of their tail. The fox may need dentistry, using special veterinary dental equipment (mammals' teeth are harder to drill than human teeth) to deal with broken canines, exposed pulp cavities or jaw problems, all common results of road traffic accidents.

Fox RTA casualties would be treated in the same way as an injured dog or cat but nursing care is complicated by the fact that they don't always make such co-operative patients. They are prone to bite through their drip lines, which can have fatal results if not spotted immediately (because this could lead to their bleeding to death).

HUNTING

Hunting with hounds was causing the deaths of an estimated 20–30,000 foxes a year (Burns Inquiry Appendix 1). At the time of the inquiry, up to 25,000 were being killed by registered packs and about 40% of foxes killed died in the autumn cub-hunting season. Statistics would not take into account the numbers of foxes that might have died later as a result of stress or injuries incurred during a chase.

SIGNS: You would be unlikely to encounter a hunt survivor even though, now, the hounds are not legally supposed to be the cause of a fox's demise. But occasionally, one may seek refuge in an outhouse or under sheds and buildings, and should be left quietly alone.

TREATMENT: Traumatic injuries should be referred to a vet. They would be treated as above for road accident trauma victims. Monitor your local earths for interference (badger setts, too – foxes sometimes take over disused ones). If you find entrances blocked, unblock them and report your findings to appropriate organisations.

SHOOTING

The Game Conservancy Council carries out a "gamebag census" of all "pests and predators" killed by gunfire. Their best estimate of numbers of foxes shot by gamekeepers (directly, or while held in traps or snares) is 70–80,000. The British Association for Shooting and Conservation issues a code of conduct which recommends the use of a centre-fire rifle for clean-kill destruction. Snared foxes should be dispatched "quickly and humanely by a shot from a rifle, shotgun or pistol".

Many foxes are killed by pest control firms, usually shot offsite, and by private individuals (no figures available). There's no legal restriction on firearm type, although by law, a gun user must possess a firearms licence from the police. There are also 4 million air rifles in this country. While they are not subject to all the same restrictions as guns, they frequently blind and maim animals, or allow them to die slowly, of **infection**. Wildcare centres often have to treat, or put to sleep, victims of botched shootings.

There are no specific legal restraints on night-shooting. Automatic or semi-automatic weapons and dazzling devices are not allowed, but lamping (attracting animals with a bright light in order to shoot them in the darkness) is legal. So is night-vision technology.

> **SIGNS**: Complicated damage, including bone fractures, severed blood vessels, with **tissue** destruction at both entry and exit points of missile. An exit wound will be bigger than a point of entry. Shot may be embedded in muscle or bone, but external signs can be obscured by fur. Look for **symptoms** of **shock**, bloodied fur, a limb at an odd angle or the fox being unwilling to put weight on it. Survivors are likely to have severe **secondary bacterial infection**.
> **TREATMENT**: Injury outcome is unpredictable: one fox survived a rifle shot, the bullet having ➤

> ➤ passed clean through its flank, while another had to be put to sleep because a single airgun pellet had lodged in its spinal cord. Treatment would aim to counteract shock, stabilise and rehydrate the casualty first. Surgery may follow (some shot or pellets would be left in place if not interfering with blood vessels or organs). Reintroduction would normally be to the fox's original territory via an interim **soft-release** pen (even if there were a risk of the fox getting shot again).

TRAPPING AND SNARING

Foxes are sometimes deliberately entombed in an earth, along with their cubs, often because someone wants a building development to begin without delay. Or they get shut into sheds or cellars by people who consider them frightening, or a health-hazard. Knowingly imprisoning foxes is an offence, liable to a prison sentence or fine. Foxes get themselves stuck in places accidentally, too – for example, a factory that's closed down.

> **SIGNS**: A shut-in fox will probably be very **dehydrated**, although some survive for miraculously long periods on tap leaks, or rainwater seepage.
> **TREATMENT**: A conscious fox may need emergency **oral rehydration** on site (e.g. with made-up powder-form solution) before being captured and taken for medical care.

Wildcare centres often have to treat, or put to sleep, victims of botched shootings

Foxes also fall victim to a variety of legal and illegal gadgets designed to hold them fast. Walk-in cages – which rescuers and rehabilitators use to catch mobile casualties – are a legal form of trapping. They close behind an animal when it steps on a treadle. Free-running snares are legal, too (though many charities are fighting to see them banned). Self-locking snares and traps that catch limbs in serrated steel teeth, are illegal but gin traps, banned for more than 50 years, still occasionally turn up. But even small, snap-shut traps designed to kill rodents cause considerable pain and tissue damage and can lead to **necrosis** (flesh dying off).

Although a legal, free-running, tethered wire noose with a stop on it (to prevent a struggling animal strangling itself while waiting to be killed) sounds humane, it is not. It can cut into the flesh because the captive is tempted, again and again, to try to break free. The BASC (British Association for Shooting and Conservation) code stipulates that such snares should be checked at least once every 24 hours and their occupants dispatched as speedily and humanely as possible. In practice, a snared animal may be at the mercy of the elements, passing predators and carrion-eating birds, for hours. The RSPCA believes free-running snares are "among the most cruel and indiscriminate killers of wild and domestic animals".

Foxes can get caught or impaled upon fencing. The result is usually either deep puncture wounds, if from barbed wire that they've failed to clear, or other serious traumatic tissue injuries, including pressure wounds, if they have fallen and become wedged or speared by wood or metal.

SIGNS: The fox may be collapsed; showing signs of clinical shock.

Hypo- or **hyperthermia** (core body temperature too low or too high) and **flystrike** (infestation with maggots), according to weather conditions and time of year. Limbs may be stripped of skin and muscle; there may be deep lacerations, eye injury or loss (from attack by birds).

TREATMENT: A fox caught in a trap or snare should never be cut free and immediately let go. If it runs off, and the device is still attached, it won't be able to hunt or forage. It's likely, too, that a deep line of (invisible) dead and infected skin cells will kill the animal within days. The same applies to a fox snagged on fencing – tissue damage, though not always evident, will go very deep and must be treated. The fox should be scruffed (grabbed by the loose skin at the back of the neck) and secured, and any attached wire or other restriction must be removed and taken, along with the casualty, for emergency care. Embedded foreign material will need to be removed under anaesthetic – don't tug anything off the fox yourself unless it is interfering with breathing.

Treatment will include surgical cleaning-up of wounds, removing dead tissue, antibiotic and **anti-inflammatory** drug cover, painkillers – then observation for at least a week to monitor changes around the wound site prior to release.

An illegal self-locking snare.

A legal free-running snare.

An old-fashioned (now-illegal) steel trap.

POISONING

This is against the law, and may have disastrous knock-on consequences for inquisitive humans and pets – but people still try to deliberately **poison** foxes. Some foxes get poisoned accidentally, too. Infectious diseases, like canine hepatitis, can also produce signs that mimic those of deliberate poisoning.

SIGNS: Include loss of coordination, low energy, fast breathing, vomiting, explosive diarrhoea, **collapse**. Some **rodent**-killers work by preventing blood clotting, so victims may show signs of internal bleeding, such as pale mucous **membranes** (e.g. gums), and possible nosebleed. Other **poisons** affect the digestive system. Caustic substances may cause visible chemical burns around mouth (when the animal has tried to clean its fur).

TREATMENT: You are unlikely to discover what harmful substance has been swallowed. But if you can identify it, your vet could contact the Poisons Information Unit, which will advise on possible **antidotes**. Generally, treatment is likely to centre on flushing out the system with fluids and dosing the casualty with **activated charcoal**, or another poison-binding agent, to stop further gut absorption. The fox would be nursed in quiet, darkened surroundings and kept still, to avoid knocks.

BROKEN BONES

There's plenty of evidence that foxes, especially dog foxes, often break bones and recover – although the legacy is often limb shortening, odd bends and arthritis. Sprains and strains are frequent, too. Ligaments and joint capsules get stretched or torn and muscles injured, when a fox jumps, or falls, from a considerable height.

SIGNS: A limb being dragged, or looking awkward if there is a fracture (e.g. bends where it shouldn't). A fox in obvious pain won't put weight on its leg. There may be skin damage, bleeding, bone exposure, grating noise, **paralysis** due to nerve damage.

TREATMENT: Observation and support-feeding on site if a sprain or strain is suspected. The benefits of hospitalisation (pain relief, cold applications, bandaging, etc.) may be outweighed by the stress of capture. Support feeding for a recuperating fox, on site, would include good quality dogfood, dead day-old chicks, whole sardines, raw eggs in their shell, raw chicken wings (bones small, not too sharp), fresh drinking water daily. This will relieve the fox's need to hunt or forage for food, allowing it to rest. Veterinary treatment is necessary for a bone break. A fox charity may be able to loan you a walk-in trap. During warm weather, it's particularly important to take an incapacitated fox casualty into care to avoid the fatal risk of **blood poisoning** from maggots. Fracture management might include initial immobilisation (a rolled magazine or newspaper, taped around the limb, can be a first aid splint). Customised bandaging may follow, or surgical **plating** and pinning, possible **amputation** of a single hind leg if the bone is beyond repair. The fox will need antibacterial drugs.

The "Robert Jones" bandage – a stiff cotton wool-filled bandage used to stabilise a broken leg.

Fox Diseases and Human Health

Foxes, being members of the dog family, can catch and transmit a number of canine diseases. One or two are shared by other mammals and can affect humans, too. Most notorious of these zoonotic diseases are **rabies** and the also potentially fatal **leptospirosis** (the human form is called **Weil's Disease**). Rabies is unlikely to affect wildlife rescuers and rehabilitators in this country, but you should be aware of all potential health risks. The fox's role in the transmission of leptospirosis is thought to be small, but it is vital to practise good hygiene at all times when handling wildlife casualties.

Rabies

Widespread throughout the world, the **virus** can affect all warm-blooded animals. Reservoirs usually exist in wildlife – red foxes in mainland Europe, coyotes, raccoons and skunks in the US. But the virus's transmission route to humans is commonly from wildlife to domestic animals, thence to people. The virus is passed by contact with infective saliva, usually through a bite that breaks the skin, or via a cut being licked. The virus can then move from muscle and enter the **nervous system**, at which point it is almost invariably fatal.

Britain has strict restrictions on movement of animals in and out of the country, including the use of vaccinations for travelling domestic animals. **Rabies** does exist on the other side of the Channel and isolated cases have been reported in the UK, too,

from time to time. However, the vast bulk of cases are the result of a bite from a rabid dog and most occur in Asia, Africa and Latin America, where dogs often run wild. Only about one person in four who has been bitten by a rabid dog will contract the disease. Even today, though, rabies is usually fatal once it reaches the nervous system.

Rabies Signs in Animals: May include behaviour changes, e.g. a normally people-shy one becomes aggressive; sometimes hyper-irritability, glazed eyes, hanging lower jaw, dripping saliva, progressing to paralysis. Alternatively there may be only raised temperature, **malaise**, appetite loss.

Treatment in Animals: Infected animals usually collapse within 14 days of infection, go into a **coma** and die.

Human Symptoms: These include brain **inflammation**, delirium, muscle **spasms**, headache, **fever**, possible paralysis, **seizures**.

Treatment for Humans: For someone whose nervous system has been affected by rabies virus, treatment consists of intensive care aimed at maintaining breathing and heartbeat, but has seldom been successful.

In an Emergency: Passive-immunisation **injections** (lasting weeks and using ready-made human antibodies) after exposure to an infected (or suspected infected) bite is usually entirely successful, if given within two days. It may also work if given later provided the virus has not moved out of muscle into the nerves. ➤

Wash any bite wound thoroughly with soap and water. Rabies virus is very sensitive to detergents, including ordinary soap, and to heat and light, and can't survive long outside the body. Seek medical help if there is a chance the animal may have been infected. If you work routinely with animals in a country where there is rabies, or deal with wildlife that may have come in from abroad, or handle bats under licence (bats can transmit one variety of rabies), talk to your GP about getting passive immunisation.

WEIL'S DISEASE & CANINE LEPTOSPIROSIS

Various strains of canine **leptospirosis** bacterial infection have been found in foxes (and dogs), including one that can cause the potentially fatal human illness **Weil's Disease**. But the fox's role in human transmission is thought to be small. Rats are commonly carriers.

SYMPTOMS IN HUMANS: These are flu-like: fever, severe headache, chills, muscle pains, eye inflammation. Possible skin rash, meningitis, liver disease. Do not ignore early symptoms.
TREATMENT: Hospitalisation; large doses of antibiotics **intravenously**, supportive therapy to counter liver and kidney damage.

SALMONELLA, E-COLI AND CAMPYLOBACTER

These organisms cause illness in both animals and people, usually via inadvertent contamination from **faeces**. The gastro-intestinal symptoms can be severe and very dangerous to the elderly, the very young and to those whose immunity is compromised.

Diligent hygiene precautions are necessary when handling all wildlife casualties and remember not to eat or drink with possibly soiled hands.

CANINE DISEASES THAT CAN AFFECT FOXES

Foxes are vulnerable to a range of dog diseases, but natural selection has generally kept even the most urbanised fox an efficient survival machine compared to many a pedigree pooch. Canine viruses are ever-present in the environment, though, and large numbers of roaming, un-vaccinated dogs, particularly in towns, are a constant reservoir of infections. Young foxes are highly vulnerable. Secondary bacterial infections are common in animals whose resistance has already been lowered by viral attack.

INFECTIOUS CANINE HEPATITIS (ICH)

Foxes are considered to be vulnerable to this dog-family infection, picked up via infective urine, other bodily secretions and faeces. Foxes, like other members of the dog species, tend to explore their world through sniffing, licking and mouthing which makes disease spread highly likely. ICH damages linings of small blood vessels first, then spreads to the liver. Severe infection can kill within a week and the virus can survive off a **host** for up to ten days. An animal that has itself recovered can continue to shed the virus from its kidneys, via urine, for up to nine months.

SIGNS: An **acute** fast-onset illness with high fever, tonsillitis and a swollen liver that causes great pain. Restlessness, thirst, vomiting, blood-tinged diarrhoea, shock symptoms, **jaundice** (yellow gums, whites of eyes). Cubs may die suddenly. "Blue-eye" clouding (an immune-response) may signal recovery but can lead to permanent sight loss.
TREATMENT: Supportive intensive care; intravenous fluids, **steroids**, strict **barrier-nursing** and disinfection (ICH is resistant to some disinfectants). Some wildcare centres now immunise all cubs in their care.

CANINE DISTEMPER

Foxes are susceptible and a canine distemper-related virus has spread to other wildlife species in this country, too (most recently in epidemics that devastated our grey and common seal populations). Distemper is caused by a virus related to the one that causes measles in people. It damages the **immune system** first, then destroys cells in the breathing and digestive systems, skin, eyes, brain and spinal cord. It is spread by inhalation or contact with body secretions. But it does not survive long in the environment and it is destroyed by heat and light.

SIGNS: Depression, fever, swollen tonsils, cough, thick discharge from eyes and nose, restlessness, dehydration, scurfy skin; later on paralysis, muscle spasms, fits. Nervous signs can occur years after infection. It is thought that distemper-like symptoms in foxes may sometimes be the result of an infestation of a microscopic blood parasite in the brain.
TREATMENT: No treatment can destroy this virus in the body. Euthanasia is used if symptoms are severe. Otherwise, antibiotics are given to prevent or treat secondary bacterial infections, drugs to control vomiting, fits, muscle spasms and diarrhoea. Intravenous fluids. Intensive care. Quarantine.

CANINE PARVOVIRUS

This virus came from a similar virus in cats, mutated and spread to dogs worldwide in the 1970s and has been recorded in foxes. (Its clinical signs have been observed in badgers in captivity, too.) Picked up via the throat or intestines, it travels around the bloodstream but can only grow in those of its host's cells that are themselves multiplying (e.g. gut lining, which is constantly renewing itself, or the still-developing heart muscle of very young animals). It can survive for months in contaminated faeces on the ground and can be carried on animals' coats (and on people's shoes).

SIGNS: May be masked in young cubs. Depression, reluctance to eat, sudden-onset vomiting, profuse foul-smelling liquid diarrhoea; ➜

➤ shock, dehydration; rapid death. Damage may provoke heart failure much later.

TREATMENT: Supportive care (as above for ICH). A fox that survives may have immunity for life. Newly admitted cub patients are quarantined.

LEPTOSPIROSIS

Caused by bacteria. Different strains affect different mammals. One type that affects foxes, dogs and humans can get into the fox's bloodstream by penetrating its mouth lining, or enter via cuts and grazes on its feet. **Infection** can also be the result of coming into close contact with – or eating – an infected animal. Rats are commonly **asymptomatic** carriers of **leptospirosis** organisms, shedding them in **urine**.

SIGNS: These may be none, if the infected animal is recovering. Depending on the bacteria type, signs may include **fever**, appetite loss, scanty black diarrhoea, small bleeds under skin and in eyes, severe liver swelling and pain, **jaundice**; **shock**, dehydration, excessive **urine** production, vomiting (with a smell of ammonia on the breath). Diagnosis by blood samples.

TREATMENT: Aggressive antibiotic treatment may be successful if started early enough; **rehydration** (though kidney damage will be irreversible); intensive care, **barrier-nursing**.

PARASITES – INTERNAL

Foxes can carry heavy worm burdens without significant symptoms, but they can cause fatal blockages in very young cubs. Temporary hosts in the developing internal parasites' lifecycles may include mice, rats, rabbits, chicken, sheep, pigs – and humans.

CANINE ROUNDWORM (TOXOCARA CANIS)

One of a number of threadlike internal parasitic worms that can affect dogs and foxes, this is the most prevalent canine gut **roundworm** in the UK. Its larvae can cross the placenta from an infected vixen to her unborn cubs or be passed on in her milk. Fox cubs are thought to develop a degree of immunity to roundworm infestation by the age of four months.

Roundworm eggs are too small to be seen with the naked eye, but are ever-present in the environment. Humans, especially young children, can be vulnerable if they inadvertently swallow viable eggs from contaminated faeces. The eggs are highly resistant to physical or chemical damage (and several thousand a day may be shed by one animal). But they must stay moist in soil for up to two weeks for the larva to mature inside the egg. Getting dried out kills them.

Although they cannot grow into mature **worms** inside people, canine roundworm larvae can migrate within the body and if they go to the muscle at the back of an eye, can cause damage leading to sight loss. An infestation in humans may be symptomless, but once identified, it is easily treated by anti-helminitic drugs (wormers). 2% of Londoners are thought to have been infected by toxocara canis larvae.

Young children should be discouraged from sucking grass stems, etc. in areas where dogs or foxes are likely to have defecated, told why and be encouraged to wash hands, especially under their nails, before eating.

> **SIGNS**: In cubs, swollen abdomen, poor condition, coughing, diarrhoea, retarded growth. Immature **worms** are sometimes sicked up or passed in **faeces**. A heavy worm tangle can block the gut.
> **TREATMENT**: Drug that paralyses or kills worms, which are then passed. Heavy infestation may need surgery.

LUNGWORM

This type lives in the windpipe or lungs, producing larvae that are coughed up and swallowed. A vixen can pass them on to her cubs while washing them.

> **SIGNS**: Breathlessness, persistent cough, poor condition, weakness.
> **TREATMENT**: The fox is checked for underlying disease that could have triggered heavy parasitic load. Toxic drugs are given to kill worms at various stages of development. Treatment may be possible on site under veterinary supervision, if the fox is in reasonably good overall health.

HEART WORM

Once only seen in the UK among pet dogs that had lived abroad in tropical and sub-tropical climates, they are now being diagnosed in dogs in southwest England and south Wales. Foxes are thought to be a wildlife reservoir. Hookworms are also seen in foxes.

> **SIGNS**: Anorexia, cough, breathing difficulties, eventual heart failure.
> **TREATMENT**: Heart worms are unlikely to be diagnosed in time, but could be treated by a proprietary wormer drug in early stages.

TAPEWORM

Tapeworm live by attaching hooked and suckered mouths to their host's gut lining and "mugging" them for meals. Eggs mature in the last of the long, paper-thin body's segments and are passed out when the host defecates. Foxes pick up **tapeworm** by swallowing eggs from the environment, by eating a go-between host harbouring an egg-filled cyst (a flea or **louse** they have swallowed while grooming), by eating a rodent, rabbit or hare host they have caught or by scavenging an infected sheep's corpse.

> **SIGNS**: The fox looks thin, in poor condition and may have diarrhoea. (Signs of anal irritation, such as dragging the anus on the ground, can also indicate blocked or infected anal glands.)
> There may be no visible signs, apart from ripe egg-segments being shed. They look like small grains of cooked white rice that move slightly when fresh. (Canine tapeworm eggs will only grow into adult worms inside a member of the dog species.)
> **TREATMENT**: Wormer, by mouth or injection.

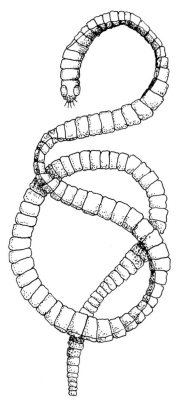

Tapeworm that are specific to members of the dog family cannot develop fully in humans. Very rarely, they can cause cysts.

PROTOZOA

Some of these single-cell micro-organisms live harmlessly in the gut. Others are health threats that cause disease.

Some can pass to people from animals, although most cases are the result of people eating undercooked, infected meats. Foxes can carry dog-family-specific parasitic **protozoa** that are passed directly from animal to animal, being inadvertently ingested via eggs shed in faeces.

There have been no reported cases of significant diseases caused by protozoa in foxes, but one type (*toxoplasma gondii*) found in the brains of **post-mortemed** dogs has been linked to previous distemper-like symptoms.

PARASITES – EXTERNAL

Foxes may play host to fleas, fur **mites**, ear mites and **ticks**. They may be treated **topically** for the above, any ticks being removed and destroyed (taking care not to leave embedded mouth parts behind in the skin to cause infection). But one kind of mite causes more misery than all the other external parasites put together, leading to many a fatality…

Sarcoptic mange passes between dogs and foxes, and is often fatal to foxes.

CANINE SARCOPTIC MANGE

Highly contagious, it is caused by a tiny, spider-like mite that lives under the skin surface. **Mange** mites can pass to and from foxes and domestic dogs (though the latter are far easier to treat using standard prescribed veterinary drugs). The mites may be easily passed by direct animal-to-animal skin contact or via a fence, or hedge, harbouring infectious skin flakes rubbed from the back of an infected animal. Sleeping hollows or breeding earths can harbour large numbers of sloughed-off mites, larvae and eggs, so nursing vixens and their cubs are particularly vulnerable.

Female mites dig burrows in the skin and lay their eggs in them. When these hatch, larvae make their way up to the skin surface. A new generation is produced every three weeks. An acute infestation causes intense itching, worst in warm weather, and an affected fox bites and scratches its body until it is covered with raw, open wounds. The fox becomes increasingly bald (unluckily, the mites like hairless skin best) and dehydrated, its body covered with thick crusts of dried lymph and dead skin, its eyes gummed shut by conjunctivitis. Bacterial infections run riot because the skin, the body's biggest organ and its first-line defence against infection, has been so broken down. The liver and kidneys are damaged, the latter organs irreversibly so. A severely affected fox will be dead within four months, unless treated early enough.

Wear disposable gloves while handling foxes with mange – the mites can cause a mild, self-limiting itchy rash, or an allergic reaction, in human skin.

Help a garden-visitor fox suffering from mange by regularly providing clean water or freshly made-up rehydration fluid. Add vitamin and mineral powdered supplements to any food, plus a handful of raisins or sultanas. Add a teaspoon of good quality vegetable oil; put out a little oily fish (sardines, mackerel).

> **SIGNS**: Self-inflicted bite and scratch wounds, hair loss, **abscesses** (especially around tail root), dehydration, eye infections, thickened, crusty, bad-cheese-smelling skin that flakes, shock, starvation, **collapse**; maggot infestation.
>
> **TREATMENT**: This may be possible on site with drugs prescribed by vet, hand-fed to the targeted fox only, at repeated intervals. Great care must be taken not to give one fox an overdose, or to allow another species to swallow drugged food (both would be lethal). Otherwise the fox must be cage-trapped and treated in care.
>
> A severely affected animal with advanced liver and kidney damage would be **euthanased**. Others would be rehydrated, medically treated and released once they had reached normal bodyweight and fitness levels.

FLIES AND MAGGOTS

In warm weather, flystrike leads to bacterial poisoning and death in a fox that has been immobilised in a road accident, or one that is suffering from debilitating diarrhoea or carrying the open sores of severe mange. In warm-weather, blue/green/blackbottle flies settle on warm, damp skin and lay eggs, if they are not driven off. Next day, hatching maggots start to feed, eating healthy as well as necrotic flesh because there are so many clustered at one site.

> **SIGNS**: Tiny white eggs, maggots (if deeply embedded, you will only see their tail-tips). Open flesh wounds, which may smell foul.
>
> **TREATMENT**: Wounds are thoroughly washed out with **saline solution**; all maggots and eggs are removed with surgical forceps, followed by a surgical clean-up of the site to remove all dead flesh. Antibacterial drugs and non-steroidal anti-inflammatories are given against possible endotoxic shock. Rehydration.

CUBS IN PERIL?

"Orphaned" or apparently lost or abandoned cubs form the bulk of rescues that need not have been. Unless a cub or litter is in immediate danger or exposed to extremely cold or wet weather, it is best to wait and watch a while and see what happens. Hopefully the parent will return and move its offspring to another den.

WHAT YOU CAN DO

If this does not happen, or you do not believe conditions are safe enough (e.g. work on a building site is continuing, it is snowing, etc.), call a fox welfare charity immediately. They will ask you for details of the cub's whereabouts, age and condition. There is a chance that the cub was dropped by a predator, or removed from its den by people and "relocated". Or perhaps it was deliberately dumped by a vixen because

"Orphaned" or apparently lost or abandoned cubs form the bulk of rescues that need not have been

she instinctively suspected there was something the matter with it and she did not want to jeopardise the rest of her litter. A bigger, more active cub may have wandered into a potentially lethal situation because it is over-adventurous – or because its mother is dead and it has become very hungry.

There is no easy fix. Even when an adult fox does return and pick up a cub, the scenario is not always a rosy one. If it is an adult male from another territory, he may want to kill the cub. If the vixen is an inexperienced mother, or feels threatened, she may do the same.

WHAT YOU CAN DO: Very young cubs can go physically downhill very fast. Their coats and **metabolisms** are not mature enough to cope with temperature drops and they need feeding little and often. They must be helped with toileting. Distressed, dehydrated, starving or hypothermic cubs must receive care as soon as possible or they will die. Do not delay. Take a cub to a wildcare centre or veterinary practice yourself, to save time, if advised to do so.

If the vixen does not return, and attempts to reunite the cub with its mother the following evening do not succeed, the cub will be hand-reared in care. Once weaned, it will be fed on a diet that's as similar as possible to its natural one in the wild. Cubs are housed in pens in artificial "litters" of four to six, probably vaccinated against deadly canine infectious diseases and "soft-released" together as a group as adolescents, when they would normally be seeking territories of their own. An ideal group mix might be four vixens and two dog foxes.

Cub rescuers should always return to the place where a cub was found. It is possible that the rest of a litter will also be in trouble (e.g. if the vixen has been killed in a road accident).

WHEN TO INTERVENE (AND WHEN NOT TO!)

THINK FIRST how you are going to tackle a fox problem you have seen. Try to get someone else to help you. Don't put yourself, or others, in danger: there are no medals for rescuers who cause road accidents, or break limbs falling off walls.

INVESTIGATE OPTIONS. Ring an animal welfare organisation with particular knowledge of foxes. No one will mind if your query turns out to be a false alarm. Many unwell, injured or in-danger foxes are first noticed by members of the public.

BE AS QUIET AND STILL AS POSSIBLE. Take a good look. Foxes often won't register your presence unless you move (if the wind isn't blowing your scent towards them). Even an injured fox won't want to waste precious energy trying to move off unless you make a noise, or movement, that it will interpret as threatening.

PLAN YOUR RESCUE: You will probably only get one chance. Once you go in to pick up an ill or injured fox, it's likely that it will do its utmost to get away from you even if it has a broken back. A panicking fox will move far quicker than you can give chase.

GET THE EQUIPMENT YOU'LL NEED – a towel or gardening gloves are better than nothing. Make sure you have an escape-proof container beside you. If you're unable to collect a casualty yourself, try to get it into a confined space so that someone else can take it for help.

Cubs look cute, but the rescuer's main aim is to "wild them up".

TRANSPORTING

It is illegal to carry a fox casualty loose inside your car. Although most accident victims are usually too unwell to explore the dashboard wiring, it has been known. Extricating a frightened fox from beneath a seat won't help its recovery, either.

A metal-mesh cat carrier, big enough for a fox to be placed on its side without disturbing its legs or back, is a means of transporting an injured fox. Galvanised metal open-mesh ones, without plastic coating, are less chewable and easier to keep clean (less chance of spreading mange, etc.) Wedge the carrier in place in the vehicle to produce the minimum movement when you brake and accelerate – perhaps facing front-to-back lengthways, so the fox is facing the direction in which you are travelling. The fox must not be able to roll around inside the carrier, or the container tip off a seat.

The fox will feel safer if the carrier is covered by a cloth, or towel – but make sure there is enough air circulating, too.

TIME FOR RELEASE? WHEN AND WHERE

Once it is judged fit and strong enough, a fox patient is normally put back into its former territory. This does not rule out the possibility of bust-ups with "incomers" if the fox has been off the scene, recovering from an injury, for a while. But a new territory in unfamiliar terrain can be a recipe for disaster. An adult fox may try to return to its original stamping ground, often becoming a road accident victim in the process. But if the original site is considered too dangerous, a new suitable one may have to be found.

Orphaned and displaced cubs are "soft-released" via support feeding and an initially closed pen in an area that has been carefully reconnoitred and which is considered to have sufficient resources for their survival. In nature, most of the litter leave the family group, to establish territories of their own, by autumn. Nursing vixens are hospitalised for as short a time as possible, or treated immediately on site, so that they can return quickly to their cubs.

WHAT YOU CAN DO: Rehabilitators require temporary pen placings in large gardens, with wild secluded areas, on the edges of potential fox territories. Wildcare charities pay for and arrange construction. These pens act as invaluable halfway houses for adolescent cubs, and sometimes also house "non-returnables", too.

LONG-TERM OR NON-RELEASABLE PATIENTS

Wildlife rescue aims to give animals a second chance at life in the wild. But some fox patients turn out to have disabilities, such as blindness or deafness, which would not allow them to survive in the wild. Very occasionally, a normal, healthy cub will reject all the efforts of a wildcare centre to "wild it up" (minimal human contact, new littermates) and insist on relating too trustingly to people. Then there is the head-injury case who, at first glance, appears to have made a full recovery, but whose insistent begging for snacks in the park on release is a sure sign that they are themselves "a sandwich short of the full picnic". Unfortunately, a fox that wants to have its stomach tickled, or lick people's chins, is liable to provoke fear and mistrust if left to live free in the average urban or suburban setting.

A cub in Camberwell, south London, that had been hand-fed in the grounds of a local hospital when it was small, menaced the neighbourhood when it grew larger. It nipped the ankles of one elderly man, stared meaningfully at women laden with shopping bags and so petrified a couple of teenaged girls returning from a night's clubbing that they asked officers from a nearby police patrol car to accompany them from their minicab to their front door when they saw it blocking the garden path. "It wouldn't move, just sat on the pavement eyeing us," they claimed. A wildlife organisation eventually stepped in to trap and relocate the young dog fox after locals began discussing extermination. Rehabilitators believed that the fox had become conditioned to expect food handouts from humans because of its early life experiences.

Permanent pen accommodation is often the only option for many such foxes, apart from euthanasia. Although under-wired pens located in natural settings may be satisfactorily provided by private individuals, running them can turn out to be an expensive, all-consuming long-term commitment.

DON'T TRY THIS AT HOME

Providing comfort, mental stimulation, clean surroundings and other quality-of-life requirements for a permanently confined fox is hard work. It requires other, permanent resident animal companions, for a start. It's usually best left to the resources (including volunteer workforce) of specialist centres and experienced rehabilitators.

Many an orphaned fox cub needs to be rescued, all over again, when its toilet/marking habits and destructive play become more than someone can cope with in their home. Problems usually begin at the "adolescence" stage. By that time, returning the youngsters to the wild will no longer be an option.

▶ 10 WAYS TO GET INVOLVED ▶▶▶▶▶▶▶▶▶▶▶▶▶▶▶▶▶▶

- ◆ Carry a First-Aid kit in your car, plus a **space blanket**.
- ◆ Bone up on trauma management and resuscitation skills – handy for human and wildlife emergencies alike.
- ◆ Attach a sonic warning gadget to the front of your car – every little helps.
- ◆ Put out clean drinking water for wildlife daily.
- ◆ Don't use chemicals in your garden – or bonemeal fertiliser.
- ◆ Leave garden ends untidy (so that foxes can hide or rest).
- ◆ Remove dangerous litter (glass, sharp cans, nylon twine, plastic containers that can trap cubs' heads) that you see when out walking.
- ◆ Snip up snares you find with wire-cutters, leave pieces on site.
- ◆ If your neighbours call in pest controllers, talk to them (and the firm) explaining why it's ineffective and a waste of money and time. Suggest more ecologically sound methods to move foxes on.
- ◆ Find a local vet who's interested in wildlife and see if they're prepared to give a fox initial emergency treatment. Vets are not legally, or professionally, obliged to offer subsequent treatment free to wildlife, apart from this. The fox would be referred on to an animal welfare or wildcare charity, who use regular or in-house vets specialising in this kind of work.

FOX FIRST AID

FOR AN UNCONSCIOUS OR IMMOBILE FOX

As an ordinary member of the public, if you have no medical or veterinary qualifications, you are allowed by law to carry out FIRST AID on an animal to keep it alive, alleviate suffering and keep it in a stable condition until expert help can be found.

Follow the ABC (and D) guide and don't do more than is necessary.

Stop obvious external bleeding by applying pressure with clean pad, finger and thumb. Cover wound with a doughnut-shaped ring pad (twisted, coiled T-shirt, towel, neck tie, scarf), tie in place and if blood still comes through, add another layer. Do not remove original pad – it could disturb clots. Stem minor bleeds with caustic shaving pencil, ice or other coagulator (from chemist).

Signs of internal bleeding (which will need surgical attention) include pale gums. Keep the body horizontal, or raise the fox's back legs higher than head, to help its heart concentrate on supplying blood to the major organs.

AIRWAYS. Check they are clear. A road casualty may have facial injuries, blood, grit and dirt blocking its mouth and nostrils. A gentle sweep with a damp cloth or baby wipe will help remove debris. Only remove what is obviously interfering with breathing. Pull the tongue forward – it may have fallen back to block the throat. If you do not suspect spinal injury, gently roll the fox on its side, head and neck extended.

BREATHING. Watch chest for movement, or pluck a tiny amount of fur from the coat and hold it in front of the casualty's nostrils. If you have access to an ambulance emergency bag, you might use an endotracheal tube and rubber bulb to get oxygen into the animal's lungs (one small "breathful" of air every two seconds, counting "one-and-two"). Open the mouth, each time, to let the breath out.

CIRCULATION. Check for a heartbeat, or pulse – in front left armpit. If none is detected, do chest compressions. Put one hand each side of the fox's chest, just behind the elbows, gently squeeze hands together at rate of two compressions per second. For every four chest compressions, you would have to give the fox two breaths. Stop when you can feel a consistent pulse.

Do note details of injuries, signs of illness, exact location where you found the casualty and the circumstances in which you found it. **DON'T** cut away embedded wires or other restriction yourself, don't prod or handle the casualty to keep checking if it's alive, don't give even a conscious fox anything by mouth and don't muzzle it. It might vomit and choke if it can't open its mouth fully, or escape with the muzzle tied on.

HOW TO HANDLE A CASUALTY

1 Approaching an active fox casualty is best done at an angle. Crouch down if you want to look less threatening. Make a quick mental note of escape routes and move or act to block them off. Only attempt to touch the back of the fox's neck and "scruff" it (pick it up) once you're less than an arm's length away. Move smoothly and calmly and don't look directly into the fox's eyes. This will appear aggressive. Between each of your moves or gestures, wait to see how the fox reacts.

2 If possible, shut a fox casualty in a safe, confined place such as a garage or shed, and call a local wildcare unit or animal rescue service (also see *Useful Organisations*, p. 121). Otherwise, stay nearby and show rescuers where the animal is when they arrive.

3 If you are unable to call in a rescue service, get yourself a cat carrier – preferably one that can be opened from the end, as well as the top. If you are lucky, you may be able to encourage the cornered or confined fox to walk into it. An injured or ill fox will be looking for a bolt-hole in which to escape, and if you cover your carrier so that it looks dark and invitingly safe, and position it in a corner, you may be able to steer the fox inside.

4 Get some thick, leather gardening gloves. Use one empty glove as a "distraction", giving the fox something to nip should it so desire, while you secure the skin at the back of its neck with your other hand. Some rescuers take along a medium-sized old towel with which to cover the animal's head before picking it up. But, bare-handed or gauntleted, one of the best accessories in the rescuer's armoury is confidence. Unfortunately, only experience handling wildlife can give you that, and until that is acquired with time, you will just have to fake it.

5 If the fox is a road accident victim, and you suspect a spinal injury, improvise a stretcher (a board, thick plastic bin bag, heavy duty carrier bag, clothing or travel rug). Position this behind the fox's back and ease the animal onto it, before dragging it to a safe place and transporting it for medical attention. Try to move the body around as little as possible. A thermal "space" blanket or roll of bubblewrap in your car would double as a stretcher and a bodyheat preserver for an animal in shock. Put it in a carrier in as smooth a movement as possible; an unconscious, or semi-conscious fox should not be carried loose in a vehicle in case it comes round – it is against the law, too. If you think, from the sound of its breathing (gurgly) that it may have fluid on its lungs, or it is bleeding inside its mouth, try to position its head slightly lower than its body to prevent blood or vomit trickling back down its airway.

6 A dog grasper – a lightweight hollow metal pole with a retractable, cushioned line and noose inside it – may be used for foxes in awkward places (trapped between two walls, under buildings etc.) But it must be positioned correctly around the animal's neck, without tying in any limbs, and the fox's weight taken at the rump end as soon as possible. Fishing landing nets are also used in some rescue circumstances.

PRECAUTIONS TO TAKE WHEN HANDLING A FOX CASUALTY

◆ Avoid direct contact with bodily fluids (urine, faeces, saliva).

◆ Wash any bite wound with disinfectant handwash at once.

◆ Keep up to date with your tetanus jabs.

◆ Do not eat, drink, rub eyes, etc. while handling casualties.

◆ Protect your inner wrists (where veins are close to the surface) with sweatbands or leather wristlets or use gauntlet-length gloves.

◆ Keep your face well away from the casualty.

True or False?

1 A male fox, if mated with a female domestic dog, will produce a hybrid animal, half-dog, half-fox.

2 Foxes will kill all the occupants of a chicken coop, just for fun.

3 Fox cubs tell their brothers and sisters to "butt out" when it comes to mealtimes.

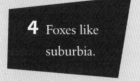

4 Foxes like suburbia.

Useful Organisations:

Royal Society for the Prevention of Cruelty to Animals (RSPCA)

Wilberforce Way, Southwater, Horsham, West Sussex, RH13 9RS

24-hour cruelty and advice line 0870 55 55 999;

enquiries 0300 1234 555 www.rspca.org.uk

The Fox Project (Operates in parts of Kent, Surrey, E. Sussex and S. E. London only) The Southborough Centre, Draper St, Southborough, Tunbridge Wells, Kent, TN4 0PG

advice line 01892 514 863 mobile ambulance 07778 909 092

head office 01892 545 468; www.foxproject.org.uk

National Fox Welfare 135, Higham Rd, Rushden, Northants, NN10 6DS; 01933 411991; www.nfws.org.uk

Answers

1 Never. It won't work the other way around, either, with a domestic dog and a vixen. Although both animals are members of the overall "dog" (Canidae) family, they have different numbers of chromosomes and are also fertile for differing periods – both female and male foxes are only fertile for brief times of the year, for example. (Dogs can, however, breed with other types of canid, such as wolves and coyotes.)

2 True – for the first part. A fox will kill every chicken in a coop once it gets in. But not for amusement – the fox is simply a predator obeying its hardwired hunting instincts to Seek, Target, Catch and Kill, and the sequence is re-triggered afresh every time one of the panicking birds makes a move to get away. In natural surroundings, a flock of birds could scatter once a fox had launched an attack, allowing all but the victim to get away. Having successfully snatched its meal, the fox would normally take away as much food as it can after a kill, caching any excess, because it has no means of knowing where its next meal is coming from. It would not expend more energy on a repeat hunt straight away. But in an artificially confined and crowded space there is no natural block to this pattern.

3 True. Cubs play with one another, but their interactions are also a serious preparation for adult survival methods, so cub play includes a lot of rough-and-tumble competition and play-fighting. Sibling rivalries abound – as in human families – and pretty quickly, a pecking order is established in the litter. Food, or a coveted play object, is jealously guarded and the holder will shield their portion by consistently swinging their bottom around, so that rival brothers and sisters can be shoved aside.

4 True, as long as the fair-sized gardens of suburban residential areas are not destroyed by being paved over. Shrubs and sheds provide foxes with shelter, including safe lying-up spots and breeding earths, grassy areas yield plenty of earthworms and other edibles, and there may be a pond or two, plus a good-sized bird population – perhaps with bird-feeders thrown in.

Casualty Kit

✔ Clean cotton towels - for immobilising, carrying, insulating, pressure bandaging, support

✔ Sterile pre-wrapped bandages plus blunt-ended scissors

✔ Animal-safe antiseptics - e.g. Hibiscrub, saline spray

✔ Space blanket or bubblewrap - to conserve heat in an unconscious casualty

✔ Metal-mesh (cat) carrier - ideally, both end and top-opening

✔ Retractable-noose dog grasper

✔ Large fish landing net (with extendable handle)

✔ Leather gardening gloves/gauntlets; wristbands; disposable latex gloves optional

✔ Wire-cutters (for snares, barbed wire)

✔ Powerful torch/emergency light that can be stood on ground

✔ Hazard warning triangle for parked car

✔ Fluorescent/reflective jacket or gilet
…and don't forget your list of local vets' and animal welfare 24-hour phone numbers

CASE HISTORY – BORIS

It was gone midnight, the streets were empty and the small fox cub, lying on its side in the middle of the road, looked dead anyway. But it was worth getting out of the car to have a closer look, before something came round the corner and flattened it. The cub's coat, yellow under the street lights, betrayed no motion, there was no sign of breathing. On the car's front passenger seat, the cub lay limp as a damp face flannel. Then, suddenly, a small, whimpering sound came from its throat and it half-opened its eyes for a second. If the cub was to stand a chance – and it looked like a very slim chance indeed – it would have to get medical attention straight away.

The drive across London to the wildlife hospital seemed to be all green lights and fast, tailgating lorries. There were few chances to glance down to check that signs of life continued to give the half-hour journey a point. Meanwhile, Lyn, the 24-hour duty staffer on call, waved a weary goodbye to her night's sleep and prepared to put her clinical care skills into practice. The young dog fox cub was quickly examined, admitted as an emergency and put into a warm, oxygenated incubator, to be resuscitated on a drip. As is routine, the new patient was named

Boris (for reasons no one can now recall) and his details entered on a record card. He had not been hit by a car, evidently, and apart from being deeply unconscious, he seemed to have nothing else wrong with him, apart from some small eye haemorrhages that reminded Lyn of "shaken baby syndrome". How he ended up in the road was a mystery. Perhaps he had been attacked by a dog, or adult male fox from outside his mother's territory. Whatever the cause, he was not expected to last the night.

It was to Boris's good fortune, and Lyn's eternal credit, that she did not cease working throughout the night to keep the cub alive, even though she would have to work a full shift next day. Her past experience as a highly-trained paediatric nurse, specialising in the care of premature babies, tipped the scales in the cub's favour. He survived. In fact, he thrived, going on to join a group of foster littermates and growing into a tough, boisterous little adolescent fox before being released back to the wild. And because he was such a fighter, and because Lyn had such a soft spot for him, he got five-star treatment when the time came to pick new territorial release sites for that year's cubs. Talk about a second chance.

In our case history, the cub was taken to the wildlife hospital on a front passenger seat in an emergency. Carrying an unrestrained wild animal in your car is, in fact, hazardous and illegal: try to keep a box for such an emergency!

5

MEDICINE TO BE TAKEN BY MOUTH – ONE SPECK EVERY TWO HOURS

I'd just been playing tennis out the back. I came back through the garden and saw one of the cats, his head low, running in a weird way. It looked like he had something in his mouth. I chased after him and stopped him, and managed to pick him up around the belly. He dropped something and I saw it was a tiny brown mouse (I later found out it was a wood mouse), lying on the ground. It had a bit of blood on its body, but nothing major. I thought it was dead at first, but then it started to move its legs.

I picked it up and called my mum and we put it in a shoebox with some hay and left it in the outhouse. Later, we checked and it was still alive, so we transferred it to a plastic lunchbox with some holes cut into the lid and left some food in there. Birdseed, muesli, sultanas, a bit of apple, stuff like that. We put some water in a bottle cap in case it wanted a drink, then shut the door so the cats couldn't get in, and left it to recover.

My mum went to the vet's and got some antibiotic powder. He told her just to put a very tiny amount in the water and sprinkle a pinch over the food, too. He said it was very hard to work out what kind of dose to give the mouse because it was so small and their bodies worked at a fast rate. The vet said they were used to treating bigger things, like people's pet dogs and cats, and they always weighed them first, but he told my mum not to try to weigh the mouse. It was looking perky and was eating OK, but we didn't mess about with it, or clean out droppings or anything, in case we upset it or let it out by mistake.

We kept the mouse for ages – about three weeks – then we let it go on the edge of allotments beside some woods near us because we were worried about it being caught again by one of our cats if we put it back in the garden. When it was gone, I did miss it a lot, but I felt, and still feel, extremely chuffed at having helped save its life.

Becky Nicholson-Lord, 9

Why Rescue Rodents?

It may seem strange to talk about **rodent** conservation, given mankind's millennia-long desire to keep rodent populations down through fear of disease, foodstore contamination, loss and damage to crops, grass and trees, and so on. But rodents are part of a wider picture, a vital component in a vast ecological house of cards. Take away one seemingly lowly element and the whole biodiverse edifice is in danger of **collapse**.

Nevertheless, many animals within this versatile and widespread "extended family" of small mammals draw the short straw when it comes to wildlife rescue. Some people might be inclined to label almost everything in this chapter "vermin". Even among those who admire rodents (and see little logic in making one variety a family "pet" and demonising another), a "fluffy" nestling squirrel orphan may attract more sympathy than a pink and hairless young mouse – and rats may be off the agenda altogether.

Apart from animal welfare and philosophical considerations, there is an important ecological reason why rodents might need helping. Some species' populations are now known to be declining. Some, like the water vole (*The Wind In The Willows'* Ratty) have done so very dramatically in the last decade.

The 1995 first-ever Mammal Society census of British mammals highlighted some surprising, sharp and accelerating declines – of harvest mice,

Red squirrels are lighter than greys, but without their ear tufts and with less red in their coats in summer, they look very similar.

yellow-necked mice, common dormice, red squirrels, lesser white-toothed shrews and field voles. Field voles are valued simply for being field voles, of course, but they also play an important role in the survival of other species. They constitute up to 80% of what an owl eats, for instance.

In 2005, publication of revised mammal population figures painted an even blacker picture. Earlier estimates for some rodents had evidently been far too generous and their numbers had been dropping during the intervening ten years, too. The 1995 estimate of half a million native common (or hazel) dormice was slashed to 40,000 in 2005 and the species is in decline. This current population size is itself a mere quarter of what it was a century ago, hence the emergency breeding and distribution recovery programme now being managed by the People's Trust for Endangered Species. It's incredible now to think that, not so many years ago, these tiny 3-inch (7.5cm) long rodents were often pocketed and taken to school (while in their **hibernation** torpor) by budding schoolboy naturalists. Today, who, apart from a conservationist, is ever likely to hold a "sleeping" hazel dormouse in the palm of their hand?

Rodent populations are known to undergo regular boom-and-bust fluctuations. Numbers occasionally peak to plague proportions. Then they crash and the cycle repeats itself until, once again, local food resources can no longer sustain the animals. Norwegian lemmings are a famous example. Millions pour through the countryside every 30 or 40 years, crossing rivers, even taking to the high seas, in a desperate bid to find new territories. But we cannot bank on populations always bouncing back in future. There comes a tipping point beyond which no species can recover and their losses will affect our planet, impoverishing it in ways which we cannot yet fully anticipate or appreciate.

IDENTIFYING RODENTS – AND THEIR RELATIVES

Rodents' ancestors evolved some 70 million years ago and although today's rodents come in various sizes worldwide, from beaver and coypu down to house and wood mice, they have not deviated much from their original design blueprint. In recent times, their labels have altered slightly. Zoologists now put rodents into three family groups (mouse-like, guineapig-like and squirrel-like). Rabbits and hares, originally banded in with rodents, are given a separate category (lagomorphs) because they have more teeth than rodents. But that's virtually all that has changed.

The name "rodent" comes from the Latin verb *rodere*, meaning "to gnaw". Indeed, a rodent *has* to gnaw and keep on gnawing, not only to fill its belly and fuel its fast **metabolism**, but to wear down its incisors. These grow constantly throughout the animal's life. Such is their toothy genius for extracting nutrition from every possible source, from toughest wood and nut shells to the fiddliest of minute seed cases, recycling their food by eating it twice, plus an ability to breed prolifically from a very early age, that rodents and their relatives have spread worldwide across a huge variety of habitats. In the UK, in settings close to human habitation in daylight, you may see rabbits munching grass shoots on railway embankments and roadside verges, or grey squirrels leaping from tree to tree, via bird table or litter bin. And that's not counting the rats and mice you don't normally see, scurrying along hidden networks of tunnels and caverns beneath the streets.

POPULATION FIGURES

Mammal Society estimates for (minimum) numbers at start of the **breeding season** in any year in the UK:

Rodents and Lagomorphs

Field Vole	75,000,000	(declining)
Rabbit	40,000,000	(*increasing*)
Wood Mouse	38,000,000	
Common Rat	7,000,000	
House Mouse	5,000,000	
Grey Squirrel	2,500,000	(*increasing*)
Water Vole	875,000	(declining dramatically)
Brown Hare	817,500	(declining)
Yellow-necked Mouse	750,000	
Mountain Hare	350,000	(declining)
Red Squirrel	160,000	(declining)
Hazel Dormouse	45,000	(declining dramatically)
Ship Rat or Black Rat	1,300	(declining)

Insectivores

Common Shrew	41,000,000
Moles	31,000
Pygmy Shrew	8,600,000
Water Shrew	1,243,000

Map shows the distribution of red squirrels throughout England, Scotland, Wales and Ireland.

IDENTIFYING RODENTS AND OTHER SMALL WILD MAMMAL CASUALTIES

In areas close to human habitation, the rescuer can expect to encounter grey squirrels, wood mice and the occasional rabbit. Those that survive mishap or starvation to present as viable "wildlife casualties" are likely to have been injured by cats, dogs or traffic, trapped inside buildings or by discarded litter, or displaced by home improvements or building developments. Wildlife hospitals are twice-yearly handed nestfuls of young squirrels accidentally removed during loft conversions or tree work or grounded by severe weather, for example. Throughout the year, cat and dog owners may be presented with a wide variety of small mammals of various species, including juvenile rats, voles and shrews, brought indoors alive. You may also come across the odd displaced young small **mustelid**, too, such as a weasel or stoat "kit".

SQUIRRELS (RODENTS)

IDENTIFICATION AND HABITAT

Red squirrels are native and are smaller than greys, which were introduced in Britain in the late 19th century. Reds measure about 24cms from end to end, half of which is feathery tail, brownish red above, white underneath. Reds also have ear tufts that grow longer in winter. In summer, their coats actually look more grey. Once heavily persecuted, red squirrels went extinct in many parts of Britain during the 20th century. There have been isolated attempts to reintroduce them. Today, they survive mainly in upland areas, chiefly in pockets of the once vast ancient Caledonian pine forests in Scotland, and in northern England. There is a small colony on Brownsea Island, near Poole Harbour, Dorset.

Grey squirrels are common throughout lowland regions. Introduced to Britain from eastern North America, their coats are speckled grey above, white underneath. In summer, their legs and flanks take on a chestnut hue (so people sometimes mistake them for reds). Greys are significantly bigger (head and body almost 30cm long, tail adding a further 20–24cm to total 50–54cms). Originally brought in as pets in the 19th century, greys escaped in various parts of the country. But they did not become widespread nationally until around the time of the First World War (when gamekeepers went off to fight). Greys' progress really took off then, with a major diffusion from Bedfordshire into neighbouring counties. It appears that their successful colonisation coincided with a sudden decimation of reds by a **viral** disease against which the North American squirrels had better immunity. In a current bid to contain the tide of "grey power", the Forestry Commission was given the go-ahead in January, 2006, to encourage "effective and humane control of grey squirrels" where it was considered necessary to protect the environment.

Squirrels have played an unconscious landscaping role – planting new trees. They don't always reclaim buried acorns. Located by scent, all buried tree fruits are shared by the rest of the local squirrel community on a "finder's keepers", averages-out basis. But by taking an acorn far away from the parent tree's shadow, where it would have fallen, the squirrel gives the acorn it has forgotten a better chance of establishing itself as a healthy seedling oak tree.

FEEDING AND BREEDING

WHAT THEY EAT: There is no major difference in the natural foods consumed by red and grey squirrels – both eat tree seeds (nuts, fir cones, beech mast, etc.) plus a seasonal range of green vegetation, some fungi, fruit, and occasionally birds' eggs and nestlings. Squirrels particularly like sweet, sappy bark and young shoots of growing trees, hence their deep unpopularity with foresters. If they nibble a complete ring of bark away from a trunk, it's the equivalent of **amputation** as far as a tree's circulatory system is concerned: everything above that ring-barked line will die. All squirrels spend a large part of their lives looking for, and storing, food (starvation is the most common form of death for squirrels). They cache (bury) as much food as possible in winter, sharing it with others in the neighbourhood and locating hundreds of hidden stores by scent.

YOUNG ONES: There are two breeding seasons, one around March, one in July. Young ones are born blind and furless, 3 or 4 at a time, usually high up in trees in a sheltered, domed drey. This ball-shaped nest made of sticks, leaves and moss is often in an angle between branches or in a trunk hole. Sometimes, squirrels build a nest in a house roof-space, causing problems to householders because their chewing attentions can turn to electrical cabling.

RABBITS (LAGOMORPHS)

IDENTIFICATION AND HABITAT

Rabbits are lagomorphs, classified in a different mammalian group ("order") to rodents, because their dentition is slightly different. Alongside the upper and lower paired sets of chisel-edged grass-chopping incisor teeth – a dental pattern shared with rodents – rabbits also have smaller teeth, one on either side of the big pair.

Our (European) rabbits were originally foreign imports, deliberately introduced to Britain (probably by the Normans) as food. Being considered valuable commodities, they were kept "under lock and key" within wealthy landowners' warrens. Being rabbits, some dug their way out and it didn't take long for their descendants to fan out throughout the British Isles, excavating burrows in any suitable soil. European rabbits grow to about 45cm and individuals' coat shades in the wild range from light greyish-brown to black. Rabbits are easily distinguishable from hares; the latter are significantly larger, with much longer back legs and longer, black-tipped ears. Rabbits can hop and run at a fair pace, but hares are faster and have a very powerful leap.

Rabbits have redesigned large parts of our landscape. Where their nibbling has kept grass perpetually short, and their droppings have fertilised the soil, a particular type of open downland has been created. Only certain types of wild flowering plants will grow

European rabbits were introduced to Britain for fur and food for the wealthy.

there. They, in turn, attract a particular range of insects to feed. So when disease wipes out rabbit populations in an area, the plants covering the ground in their former **territory** change – along with the rest of the ecology and the wildlife it supports, such as localised species of butterfly.

FEEDING AND BREEDING

Rabbits, as the Australians found to their cost when they imported them, eat grass and any other growing vegetation they can find. They particularly like dandelions, clover, coltsfoot, carrot and turnip tops, cabbage, grain, cereals and windfall apples. It is normal for rabbits (as well as **rodents**) to eat some of their own **faeces**, the type passed during the night in the burrow. Such recycling enables them to digest their food more fully, safely out of the way of predators.

Hares are bigger than rabbits, their powerful back legs much longer.

YOUNG ONES

Rabbits are born 2–8 at a time in a short, dead-end burrow just below ground. This is dug away from the main living quarters to avoid the young being attacked by an adult male rabbit (buck). They are initially without fur and their eyes and ears are closed. Female rabbits are able to produce litters one month apart from January to June and breed sporadically throughout the rest of the year.

Rabbits live in a group (called a "herd") and they congregate at favourite feeding sites. In this country, rabbit-foods such as grasses are plentiful, yet it's very unusual for a wild rabbit to live beyond a couple of years. Three-quarters of baby rabbits die within their first three months.

HARES (LAGOMORPHS)

IDENTIFICATION AND HABITAT

In the British Isles, there are two wild species, brown and blue (or mountain) hares. (The two types can produce fertile hybrids.) The brown hare evolved originally on the wild grasslands of central Asia. Here, it occurs in practically all **habitats**, but prefers to live on cultivated land and in open, broad-leaved woodland. Most of our blue/mountain hares are found only in Scotland (there are isolated populations in the Faeroes and in Ireland) and it has been introduced into England and Wales. Brown hares grow up to about 70cms, blue hares are a little smaller, with slightly shorter ears and a greyer coat. (The coats of blue hares turn white if they live at sufficiently high altitudes.) ü

Both types have long, black-tipped ears, but the brown hare has a more distinctive black upper side to its tail.

FEEDING AND BREEDING

Hares feed on grasses, roots, crops and tree shoots and bark. The brown hare population has slumped. It is thought that fewer leverets are being born in what used to be the peak **breeding season** (spring and early summer). Hares are assumed to have died out in part of the west and south-west of England – a tragic vanishing act, considering that it was originally the hare, not the rabbit, that was a folklore fertility symbol.

YOUNG ONES

Baby hares are called leverets. They are much more physically advanced than rabbits at birth. In litters of 2–4, they are born with eyes open and a short coating of soft fur. Their mother normally leaves them above ground between milk feeds, each leveret sheltering, motionless, in its own shallow dent ("form") in vegetation. Theoretically, hares can reproduce all year round, with breeding peaks in spring and summer. But modern farming practices, habitat interference and new viral diseases have resulted in a steady decline in European brown hare numbers over the last 40 years. Blue hare numbers are also believed to be declining.

RATS (RODENTS)

IDENTIFICATION AND HABITAT

Two types live wild in Britain and both came originally from abroad. The larger is the common rat (also called brown or Norway rat), which has brown fur and can

grow to 25cm, plus a long, fur-less tail. It lives both in town and on agricultural land, often near water, and is an efficient burrower and strong swimmer. The smaller, rarer ship (or black) rat, in decline since the common rat was introduced here in the early 18th century, can have a coat of dark brown as well as grey and true black. It's a good climber and also tends to live near water. Both rat types live in social groups, but ship rats tend to be more shy of people.

The ship rat's notoriety harks back to its role as carrier (via their fleas) of the bubonic plagues that wiped out large sections of Europe's populations in the Middle Ages. But by the nineteenth century, rats began to enjoy a new-found popularity as intelligent captive-bred companion animals. Most tame "fancy" rats nowadays are descended from wild-caught common rats, although, more recently, a few have been bred from ship rat stock.

One of the great pioneers behind the keeping of rats in captivity was Queen Victoria's Royal Ratcatcher, Jack Black. Jack used his spare time to breed rats from interesting colour mutations he had come across at work among the streets, docks and sewers of 1840s London. Even more amazingly, he sold these attractively marked baby rats to young ladies as delightful pets. (Tame, unusually coloured and patterned "fancy" mice also became popular in Britain, after a show in Oxford in the 1890s. It led to the

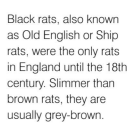

Black rats, also known as Old English or Ship rats, were the only rats in England until the 18th century. Slimmer than brown rats, they are usually grey-brown.

Baby rats are weaned at three weeks, able to reproduce at about three months old.

Found mainly in ancient woodland in Wales, central and southern England, the Yellow-necked mouse is becoming very rare.

foundation of the National – formerly British – Mouse Club soon afterwards.)

FEEDING AND BREEDING

Rats are omnivorous and, in the wild, their diet includes meat, all kinds of vegetable matter, grains, fruit, **carrion**, insects, amphibians and **invertebrates**. Ship rats are more vegetarian in their diet than common rats.

YOUNG ONES

Ship rats have a lifespan of about a year, compared to the common rats' one-to-two years. Common rats can breed all year round, if sufficient food is available, but the ship rat's breeding season is between March and November. Litters of up to five are produced, born naked and with eyes initially sealed shut in both varieties. Young are fully furred at 14 days.

MICE (RODENTS)

IDENTIFICATION AND HABITAT

Wood mice (sometimes called long-tailed field mice) live in woods, mature gardens and, if they can still find any still intact, hedgerows. In cold weather, they'll come indoors. Their bodies are 8–10cm long, tails the same length, and they have dark, yellow-brown fur that's white below. Wood mice have prominent eyes that look all-black (large eyes show they're out and about mainly by night), long back legs and long oval ears. They're very agile, able to zig-zag, leap high from all fours and even swim to evade predators. They need to be nimble; wood mice are eaten by owls, foxes, weasels, stoats, hedgehogs and cats.

Mice use ultrasonic squeaks to communicate with each other underground. Despite their slightly protruding "beady-eyed" look, their eyesight is poor.

If you find a similar-looking, but slightly larger mouse with yellow or orange markings on its chest, count yourself lucky. You will have encountered a yellow-necked mouse, a pretty, native species now in decline. Both wood and yellow-necked mice are chiefly nocturnal and most active at dawn and dusk. Neither, incidentally, produces the tangy smell associated with house mice (although all varieties of mice go in for constant territorial **urine**-marking).

House mice also live in woods and fields, although traditionally they've made their homes next to human habitation, especially buildings where food is stored. They are brownish-grey and similar in appearance to wood mice, but their eyes and ears are slightly smaller. They may grow a little heavier than their "country cousins", too. The fur under the body is usually not quite so pale, so there isn't quite the degree of colour contrast with the back, either. Colour variations occur naturally and white, black and piebald house mice are occasionally seen. Mainly nocturnal and very athletic, house mice climb walls and leap across big gaps in search of food. They can squeeze into the smallest of spaces, such as holes in walls or skirting boards no more than 9mm wide (narrower than the tips of most adults' little fingers).

Harvest mice, which have fur that is reddish above, white below, are the smallest European rodents at 75mm long, plus (partly) prehensile tail. Their habitat is very specialised: the "stalk zone" of cereal crops, reed stems, waste ground weeds and untrimmed hedgerows. Harvest mice have bright, black eyes and small, rounded ears and they are active both day and night-time. They are becoming very rare.

FEEDING AND BREEDING

The diet of wood mice includes grains, seeds, nuts, haws, acorns, fruit, bulbs, buds and seedlings, fungi, moss, snails, insects, spiders, slow worms, earthworms and occasional eggs. They store food in winter, apparently communally, and unclaimed hoards of fruits and seeds are responsible for much tree and shrub regeneration. House mice feed on grain for preference, but they will eat practically anything, including paper, and can make do with very little water. Harvest mice have a diet that includes seeds, shoots and buds, berries and insects. Grain is stored inside burrows for winter.

YOUNG ONES

Wood mice may produce several litters between March and November (sometimes nesting in bird-boxes) with up to nine young in each litter. High numbers are always offset by equally high levels of **predation**. Offspring are able to breed that same year.

Likewise, there may be several house mice families a year, numbers of young and frequency of litters varying according to **habitat**. Baby mice (average five per litter) are hairless when born, their eyes sealed shut. But they develop quickly, weaned at 18 days and able to breed at six weeks. Young harvest mice are born (up to six) inside a ball-shaped nest woven from grasses and anchored to stalks, or lodged in prickly bushes.

Harvest mice also used to tunnel into hayricks to give birth. Several litters a year could, theoretically, be produced, but nestfuls of young in cultivated fields are highly vulnerable to modern reaping machinery.

VOLES (RODENTS)

IDENTIFICATION AND HABITAT

Voles of the smaller kind may be mistaken for mice at first glance, but have rounder faces, chunkier bodies and much shorter, blunter ears and smaller-looking (deeper-set) eyes. The brown, short-tailed (field) vole is only 9–13cms. long, plus a short, stiff, furred tail. Its fur is greyish white on the underside of its body and its ears are covered in hair. The bank vole is of similar size, but is a much brighter, russet colour, and its hairy tail is black above. (As in other mammal species, however, albino and black varieties have been recorded.) Both voles are found in gardens, as well as in well-wooded and hedgerow habitats, although short-tailed voles spend more time **foraging** in open fields. While short-tailed voles construct burrows, bank voles use shallow runs in the earth and are more agile – they are good swimmers and divers, too. They may come into houses and farm buildings in winter. Numbers of both these voles are declining.

Our biggest type of vole is the water vole, which lives on well-vegetated banks of rivers, ponds and drainage ditches. It used to

Bank voles have red-brown fur and may be seen, in summer, both during the day and at night. They live in woods, grassland and mature gardens in mainland Britain.

be called the water rat, although it is not a rat, and it is often misidentified as such and killed. Water voles can grow to a surprising size: up to about 22cm long, weigh up to 180g (double in summer) and may live up to 18 months. They are active by day. But they are shy animals. You may hear one plop into the water, yet fail to catch a glimpse of it. They have very specific habitat requirements (constructing bankside burrows with both underwater and above-ground entrances and exits) and have undergone a dramatic decline in numbers since 1995.

FEEDING AND BREEDING

Short-tailed (or field) voles eat practically anything in the vegetable line, from grasses to bark, plus a range of insects and larvae, and some small animals. They store food for winter in burrows. Bank voles eat fruits, berries, seeds, nuts, plant stems, bulbs and roots, snails, and sometimes, small birds. Insects and larvae make up a third of its diet. This vole does not hibernate and generally does not lay up a food store for winter. In turn, voles are themselves eaten, in great numbers, by many mammals (e.g. weasels, foxes), and birds such as **corvids** and birds of prey. Water voles feed mainly on vegetables: reeds and other waterside plants such as flags, sedges, loosestrife and rhyzomes, plus some other vegetation (including crops) and a small amount of animal and insect food, snails and freshwater mussels. They store food, including nuts, acorns, beech mast and roots, in winter.

A "plague" of voles in southern Scotland in the 1890s was so devastating – whole fields of crops disappearing – that a government enquiry was set up. At the time, they thought that gamekeepers' mass destruction of owls and weasels was to blame. Nowadays, it is believed that such huge, rapid increases in numbers is a normal feature of many rodent species. When they happen, too, they attract great influxes of predators to the area – the incoming populations of short-eared owls often staying for a couple of years after the peak.

YOUNG ONES

Short-tailed voles are born (naked, eyes shut) in domed, woven grass nests near overground "runs", up to seven per litter, with several litters in a season. Nests are extremely hard to detect. Bank voles breed from April, with several litters (of 3–6) born during the year in nests of grass, moss, plus feathers or wool, constructed above ground. (Sometimes a bird's nest may be used.) Voles become sexually mature at six weeks.

Water voles, usually about five, are born in a thick-walled nest of reeds and grasses inside a chamber dug into a bank, or sometimes inside a tree hollow. The **breeding season** lasts from spring to mid-autumn.

OTHER SMALL WILD MAMMAL CASUALTIES MAY INCLUDE:

SHREWS (INSECTIVORES)

IDENTIFICATION AND HABITAT

They may look like skinny mice with domed foreheads and long noses, but they aren't actually rodents. Instead, shrews belong to the same ancient category of insect-eating mammals (insectivores) as moles. Tinier than mice, shrews have very long, sharply pointed, whiffling snouts. The common shrew, found in this country, measures only 7cm or less from mobile, whiskery nose to tail tip. Its brown fur is very short and velvety. Shrews living on land use regular pathways through vegetation. If the grass is tall, these runs become virtual tunnels. The water shrew is usually found near water, particularly slow-moving streams (but has been recorded miles from the nearest water body). Slightly bigger than the common shrew and with denser fur, it may be watched by a river bank or chasing beetles and other prey through the water. It builds a nest burrow in the bank and is active even in winter, hunting beneath ice on frozen rivers. The pygmy shrew is found across Europe and Asia (except for the south) and the red-toothed pygmy shrew is the only shrew found in Ireland. Pygmy shrews need plenty of vegetation cover and are found in forests and grassland areas. One variety of pygmy shrew, not found in Britain or Ireland, is the smallest of all living mammals, being only 50mm long. Shrews are solitary animals and don't interact with other shrew species.

Shrews excrete musky-smelling liquid from **glands** on their sides which may be why, although domestic cats sometimes catch them, they rarely, if ever, eat them. Perhaps they taste very bitter. Owls, however, don't mind the flavour. Neither do kestrels, magpies, jackdaws, stoats or snakes.

FEEDING AND BREEDING

Shrews really live life in the fast lane. Their hearts beat about 1,000 times a minute. Not surprisingly, they have to eat at regular intervals to fuel this pace, consuming at least three-quarters of their own bodyweight each

day. If they don't find any food for a few hours, they die. Insects and invertebrates, like earthworms, are the basis of their shrewish diet, but they also eat some plant matter. Although they're on the lookout for food most of the time, their activity peaks at around ten in the morning and ten at night. Shrews often search the underground burrows of neighbouring mice and voles, looking for a bite to eat.

YOUNG ONES

Breeding is from May to September. A female shrew can produce at least two litters a year, average six young in each. Although naked at birth, they grow up very speedily, and are able to leave the nest at three weeks.

All shrews, like this common shrew, can swim but only the water shrew hunts its prey underwater.

MOLES (INSECTIVORES)

IDENTIFICATION AND HABITAT

MOLES: These fellow-insectivores have a cylindrical-shaped body (11.5 to 13cms, plus tail), covered in very short dark fur that looks like black velvet, but which is actually dark grey. Albino, golden, mottled brown and pinky-orange coats have also been recorded. A mole's powerful front limbs have very big, paddle-shaped paws, which point palms to the fore, making it look unmistakable. The hairs of its coat can lie in any direction, a handy attribute for an animal that spends its life tunnelling underground. A mole's deep-set eyes appear very small, and although fully functioning, their vision is not thought to be very good. Its hearing is moderate, sense of smell good and its ability to pick up vibrations travelling through the soil is excellent. It does so using the minute sensitive whiskers on its nose and specialised patches of skin on its body. A well-established mole's home can be extensive, and on more than one underground level. There is a central chamber with many inter-connected hunting tunnels running off it, with near-vertical shafts leading up to the surface. Spoil heaps are flung up above open ground at intervals. Loss of hedgerows and established pastures may have forced moles to turn to parks and gardens as alternative refuges to their traditional habitats of deciduous woodland and well-drained arable land. Moles are sometimes seen on the surface of the ground in very dry weather. They can live up to 3 years.

Not always popular with farmers and gardeners, moles are important aerators of soil – and they eat potentially destructive insect larvae, too.

FEEDING AND BREEDING

Moles cannot survive without food for more than a few hours, and earthworms top the menu. Moles will store several at a time. They also eat leatherjackets (larvae of crane-fly or daddy-long-legs), cutworms, wireworms, other animal food, and carrion.

YOUNG ONES

After mating with several males, a female digs a separate nest hill and gives birth to an average 3 or 4 blind, hairless, pink young around May. The youngsters' skins turn dark blue-grey before their fur appears, their eyes open when they are three weeks old and they leave their nest of grass, leaves and twigs at about five weeks. Male moles play no part in rearing young.

RODENTS – THE LAW

SQUIRRELS

Although it is an offence under the Grey Squirrel (Prohibition of Importation and Keeping) Order 1937 to *keep* grey squirrels without a licence, even if they are injured, and also an offence (under the Wildlife and Countryside Act 1981) to release them, rescuers should not be deterred from undertaking humane actions that will help any individual animal. Euthanasia by a vet, on humane grounds, is allowed within the law, for example. It would be feasible, in theory, to keep grey squirrel casualties that had recovered (but could not be released back to the wild) inside suitable permanent housing, such as strengthened outdoor aviaries, with others of the same species, *provided you had a licence to do so*. In practice, such a licence is unlikely to be granted. You may notice that our squirrel case history, at the end of this chapter, breaks all the rules. That is because it dates back to the 1960s, when attitudes to these regulations were much more relaxed.

As with all wildlife "non-returnables", it would invariably be better for any animal casualty which could not be released to be permanently housed in an established care centre (which had the correct facilities to look after it) rather than treated as a pet in a private home, and your local branch of the RSPCA would be able to advise you further about care centres in your area.

Today's wildlife rescuers should also be aware of the often contradictory demands of "welfare" and "conservation". At the time of writing, the RSPCA has to negotiate a tightrope response to government plans designed to help red squirrels by establishing "greys-free" buffer-zones around selected forest reserves where both types compete. Although their stated policy is that of concern about "any plans that could compromise the welfare of *any* squirrel", if handed a grey squirrel casualty or orphan, the RSPCA and other national animal welfare charities would have no legal alternative but to **euthanase** it. Only if the grey squirrel were temporarily trapped (e.g. entangled in garden netting) and could be immediately released on site could their staff effect any other rescue or treatment.

RABBITS

Releasing native rabbits back to the wild is legal, but releasing non-native rabbit species is not (Destructive Imported Animals Act 1932). However, you would need to consider the future life chances of any wild creature that is a perceived pest if you put it back on cultivated farmland where it is liable to be shot or snared. That means juggling the pros and cons of what's technically "correct" in **rehabilitation** terms (putting back to familiar, established territory) versus what may be more realistically survivable when picking release sites. A rabbit should not, in any case, be released near a warren with which it is not familiar because, if it is a stranger, it is likely to be attacked and killed by the other rabbits. Such are the conundrums facing wildlife organisations throughout the country. And, alas, there are no easy answers, particularly for wild animals whose natural life expectancy is, in any case, very short compared to our own and against which the odds are always going to be heavily stacked.

RATS, DORMICE AND WATER VOLES

It is illegal (under Schedule 9 of the Wildlife and Countryside Act) to release black rats or edible dormice to the wild. Control of the brown rat is permissible by some approved methods, such as spring traps and **poisons**. Although hunting with dogs in England and Wales, and in Scotland, has now been made illegal, this ban *excludes* rats and rabbits.

It is an offence under the Act to interfere with common (hazel) dormice, except under licence (obtainable via Natural England), and EU conservation regulations also protect the habitat of this native species. The Act also prohibits the taking and killing of shrews by certain methods.

Any shelter, or "place of rest", used by water voles is legally protected.

Rescuers should note the often contradictory demands of "welfare" and "conservation"

COMMON HAZARDS FOR SMALL WILD BRITISH RODENTS

PREDATOR ATTACK

Voles are a major prey of foxes, owls and kestrels and, in recent years, american mink that have escaped or been released into the wild. Nearly a fifth of one year's field vole population will be taken by weasels and a further 13% are likely to be eaten by foxes. Foxes will also take rabbits, rats and mice, as will badgers, stoats, weasels, mink, polecats and ferrets. Some rodents eat one another, too (e.g. rats will prey on mice).

Young animals are especially vulnerable to predation. A mother rabbit tries to protect her young during her absence by leaving them hidden in a short, blind underground tunnel in the warren. She'll return to feed them at intervals, re-sealing the entrance when she leaves. But larger mammal predators, like badgers, are often able to smell the litter and dig them out. Mother hares try a different tactic, relying on their young keeping absolutely still, silent and hidden, each leveret in its own shallow dent in vegetation. Domestic cats (of which there are up to 160 per square suburban kilometre in the UK) are efficient predators. They catch up to 200 million small mammals each year, according to one estimate (although this figure has been disputed by some mammal experts). Rodents account for 65% of their mammal tally, while land-living insectivores (like shrews) make up 19%. Some victims are let go, unharmed, but many get killed immediately or die soon after as a result of their wounds. Cat dentition is designed to sever a victim's spinal cord. Dogs usually bite what they catch, then shake their prey, causing additional tearing wounds that rip a flap of flesh away.

SIGNS: predator attacks usually leave few walking-wounded survivors, unless perhaps a victim has been merely "mouthed" and relinquished. But signs indicating injury that might be survivable include skin wounds, fractures (signalled by movement disturbances, pain, swelling), concussion, loss of consciousness, un-coordination, collapse, fast shallow breathing. A fresh bite wound may go very deep but be hard to spot, hidden by fur. Look for drops of bright, fresh blood on the coat. An old, infected wound may have caused a deep abscess. Bite wounds lead to infection because of ever-present resident bacteria on predators' teeth. Head and jaw damage will result in the victim starving to death, if untreated.

Flystrike is another hazard: open wounds are vulnerable to blowflies laying eggs in them in warmer weather. A small mammal unable to move properly and groom itself because of injuries will also attract blowflies around its damp, soiled hindquarters.

Blowfly   Eggs   Maggot   Pupa

TREATMENT FOR TRAUMATIC INJURIES:

Small mammals may be initially looked at, under dimmed lighting, held in a transparent box, to avoid handling causing them stress. Predator bite injuries require antibiotic cover, but rabbits can show adverse reactions to penicillin-based drugs. Rabbits and hares may also be given drug treatment to counteract effects of stress, which can lead to fatal post-capture myopathy (muscle weakness or atrophy affecting the heart) in these species. The casualty would be more fully examined under light general anaesthesia; shock is offset by warmth and replacement fluids, pre-heated to body temperature and given by **injection**, via a **vein** or, if possible, by mouth.

ROAD TRAFFIC AND MACHINERY INJURIES

ROAD KILLS

A Mammal Society survey of common mammal road-kill casualties in 2000–2001 assessed that 11% of road kill casualties were grey squirrels, 5% were brown rats, 3% hares. Some black spots, where major roads and motorways cross habitats, are so bad that the Society fear that some populations of common species, such as hares, now face local extinctions primarily as a result of road kills.

Many male animals are killed on highways in the principal (spring) mating season, when they cross more roads than usual, in search of females. Squirrels get distracted by chasing one another and many get run over in mating periods. Young, inexperienced animals fall foul of traffic when they set off to find territories of their own. Some small mammals are routinely attracted to road verges or central reservations in order to eat insects and other creatures that have been killed by traffic, or to nibble grass or berries growing there. Night-feeders often get "frozen" in headlight beams or become so confused and disorientated that they run towards oncoming traffic.

OTHER MACHINERY

Man-made technology clashes with wildlife routines in many places. Rodents that rear their young amid crops or at field edges are no match for farm vehicles and modern harvesting and hedge-cutting equipment.

SIGNS: include traumatic injuries, (see *Predator Attacks* p. 138); concussion, loss of consciousness, etc. Most rodents, rabbits and other small mammals are too light and fragile-boned to survive a battle with a passing vehicle. But it's worth checking for signs of life, if safe to do so, because some animals may have survived by being flung up in the air, or to the side of the road. The injured mammal should be examined and, if viable, treated and allowed to recover quietly, away from hazards such as predator attack or exposure, before being released.

TREATMENT: is as for *Traumatic Injuries*, above.

Anatomically and physiologically, wild brown rats are just like their domesticated counterparts. They eat anything that's digestible.

Rehydration Therapy and Trauma Management by Veterinary Professionals

Small wildlife **trauma** casualties (if concious)can be given an **oral rehydration** fluid, which has been extra diluted, to offset shock. Commercially available preparations usually contain only water, salt and glucose. A medical product such as Hartmann's, mixed with ten per cent Duphalyte (a blend of **amino acids** and vitamins) may be administered by injection or **infusion** via a **drip**. Such **intravenous** solutions are for more severe cases of dehydration. They contain a combination of saline and glucose, sometimes supplemented with potassium chloride.

If the casualty was a collapsed, unconscious, larger mammal, such as a rabbit or hare, fluids would be given by drip into a vein. In a smaller collapsed mammal, fluids might instead be introduced into the abdominal cavity or into a limb bone, rather than via a drip. A small, conscious mammal casualty might be given very small, gradual doses of fluids, injected under various sites of skin along its back, to a maximum of ten per cent of its body weight, so as not to overload its circulatory system.

Analgesics would be adminstered for pain relief. No further treatment would be given until the animal's condition was stable. Small mammal casualties whose injuries, such as spinal breaks and multiple open fractures of limbs, were not considered survivable upon release in the wild would be euthanased by an injected **anaesthetic** overdose. Otherwise, later treatment would include cleaning and disinfecting of external wounds and **abrasions**, stitching where appropriate, and draining of abscesses. Bone fractures might be fixed, internally (e.g. pinned) or externally. But small mammals' fractures often heal spontaneously without need of stressful intervention. Amputation of a severely damaged limb or tail would be considered if this did not compromise survival. A casualty would need nursing care and hand-feeding for a while.

STARVATION

This is a major killer of small mammals. It's the commonest cause of death among both adult and inexperienced young squirrels, particularly in poor summers. Buried food stores will see adult squirrels through the harshest winter months, but there may be a dearth of food during hot, dry midsummer months. By then, they will have eaten all available young, fresh greenery and tree seeds, and fruits won't be ready until autumn. An undernourished, weaned youngster that hasn't found enough food to build up its fat layers will not have enough energy resources to keep warm while out **foraging** in cold weather.

Starvation can also be the result of people using **insecticides** and **herbicides** in the garden. They kill off the range of insects and weed seeds that many rodents and insectivores (like shrews) live upon.

SIGNS: Rodents, such as woodmice, may become more bold and visible in very cold weather, entering dwellings in search of food and taking up residence under old floorboards. Young squirrels will take whatever extra provisions they can find, from bird tables, dustbins, compost heaps or garden plants and bulbs, etc. But most undernourished small mammals won't survive.

PEST CONTROL

Legal methods include trapping, snaring, shooting and poisoning. Some methods require licensing and/or are restricted to use of a particular type of restraint (such as the so-called "free-running" snare) or permitted kind of poison.

All legal pest control methods used today are supposed to be humane, allegedly killing quickly and efficiently. But "free-running" (as opposed to old-style, illegal, "self-locking") snares aren't as merciful as they sound. They will tighten, then relax, indefinitely, according to how much an animal struggles and how long its panic-induced energies can last.

All traps and snares, unless frequently checked within the stipulated time frames, expose their captives to predators and scavengers, egg-laying blowflies, starvation, dehydration and the elements. Even a naturalist's inspection trap can be lethal to a small rodent or insectivore held inside too long, because these tiny mammals have very fast metabolisms and can't go long without food. Snares are not species-specific. They can maim, rather than kill straight away, occasionally allowing a fatally injured animal to escape, bearing the deep-levels of necrotic **tissue** that will cause it to die slowly of **blood poisoning** some days later.

Shooting that fails to kill outright is ethically unacceptable. Many mammals die slowly as a result of airgun attacks. "Glue traps", bought in hardware stores, kill slowly and cruelly and don't discriminate between species.

SIGNS: A small mammal may be still alive, held by leg or neck in snare or trap. Never simply release any snared animal and let it go – pressure injuries will result in **tissue** die-off (**necrosis**) and fatal blood-poisoning later. Spring traps usually kill outright. But some species (e.g. grey squirrels) may be held temporarily in a multi-capture cage trap for dispatch later.

Tiny pellets that have been fired into their victim create deep, narrow tracts. There may be little external sign of bleeding, but pale mucous **membranes** (e.g. gums) will indicate internal blood loss. Problems when the animal tries to move, such as tissue swelling and pain reactions, indicate possible bone fractures. A survivor may have an old, sealed-over wound that has become infected, deep inside.

POISONING

Small mammals tend to die underground, so probably won't be found. Some rodent-killing poisons (e.g. *Calciferol*) damage kidneys and the digestive tract, leading to **acute inflammation** and bloody diarrhoea.

Others used in rat bait, (such as Alphachloralose) dramatically lower body temperature. A third group (e.g. **Warfarin**) interferes with the blood's clotting mechanism and, if enough is eaten, will lead to internal bleeds into joints and other body cavities. Strychnine is sometimes used (illegally) to poison moles. This gradually paralyses the muscles used in breathing; moles can take two hours to die.

Survivors of non-fatal poisonings may be responsible for a species developing inherited resistance to particular chemicals used in bait. Poisoned bait may on occasion be eaten by mammal species for whom it was not intended. It can also cause harm in the food chain by affecting any predator (such as a bird of prey) which has eaten the poisoned rodent.

Small mammal starvation can result from people using pesticides in their gardens

> **TREATMENT**: (see *Trauma Management* p.140). X-rays are used to determine the extent of internal damage, e.g. to show where shot is lodged. Pain relief and **antibiotics** are given, wounds are cleaned. Some may need to be re-opened, drained and kept open so that they can heal fully, from the inside outwards. Surgery, including amputation, may be necessary. Some encapsulated shot might be left in place, if surgery might cause more nerve damage. Euthanasia is the kindest option for some casualties, but others may be given a second chance. In the wild, animals naturally survive near-misses from traps, and botched shootings. Researchers studying grey squirrel populations on forestry land have found numerous three-legged survivors of extermination attempts.

It is illegal to treat wild rodents that have ingested poisoned bait, although this constraint does not preclude euthanasia by a vet. But, practically, there is little treatment available for any animal in this condition other than injections of vitamin K and flushing the system through with fluids and **activated charcoal**. Darkness, warmth and quiet are vital nursing aids.

LITTER, ENVIRONMENTAL POLLUTANTS AND HAZARDOUS WASTE

It's quite common for a small rodent or insectivore, such as a mouse or shrew, to enter a discarded bottle looking for food, only to find that it cannot escape. Others may follow suit, only to perish as well. Other litter, such as fishing tackle, or broken glass, and containers holding remains of chemicals, such as paint and oil, are also potentially lethal to wildlife.

Glass bottles, with sloping, slippery necks, are death-traps for mice and shrews looking for food.

SIGNS: You may find a small mammal still alive inside a bottle, jar or can, or covered in engine oil or other harmful substance.

TREATMENT: Rehydration, rest, support-feeding and careful cleaning (many chemicals are highly corrosive and burn a victim's skin, as well as its gut when it tries to groom), followed by release onto its former territory. No one can prevent a casualty running into the same problem again, but it is best off going back to the home patch it knows.

FIGHT INJURIES

Male hares and rabbits can seriously injure one another fighting. Moles are also very territorial and aggressive to one another, even outside the breeding season between March and May.

SIGNS: skin **lacerations**; possible flystrike at wound sites, in warm weather.

TREATMENT: (see *Trauma Management* p.140) Care is necessary when stitching rabbits' skin, or giving injections, because their skin is very fragile and prone to splitting. Fracture repair work also has to take into account the brittleness of rabbits' and hares' bones. Non-fatally injured moles are sometimes seen, but treatment is complicated by the fact that they do not react well to anaesthesia – perhaps because their breathing has adapted to the high CO_2 content of the air quality in cramped underground burrows.

RODENT DISEASES AND HUMAN HEALTH

LEPTOSPIROSIS

Different strains of bacteria cause different kinds of **leptospirosis**. One type that can affect people, as well as animals, is chiefly spread by contact with the urine of infected rats. The resultant **zoonotic** illness can vary in severity, but includes a potentially fatal form of **jaundice** due to severe liver disease. The infection can also damage kidneys and cause meningitis. The bacteria responsible can be picked up from contact with infective urine, or from urine-contaminated material. Bacteria can enter the body through pre-existing skin cuts and scratches, or penetrate the mucous membrane that lines the mouth, throat and **airways**. In humans, this kind of leptospirosis infection is called *Weil's Disease*. It used to be a much-feared hazard among sewer workers in the days before antibiotics. The diluted quantities of rat urine found in canals and rivers are unlikely to pose a serious risk.

HUMAN SYMPTOMS: This is a rare but **acute** and potentially fatal illness with throbbing headache, **fever**, chills, aching muscles, eye **inflammation**, possible skin rash, jaundice; it causes kidney damage.

HUMAN TREATMENT: Antibiotics are effective, provided **symptoms** are picked up early.

BUBONIC PLAGUE

Although another zoonosis, bubonic plague is primarily a disease confined to rodents. This type of plague is named after the buboes, or swollen lymph glands, which appear in two-thirds of cases. The rat is not the only reservoir; guinea pigs, marmots, squirrels and prairie dogs can also harbour the disease. In past centuries, human epidemics have occurred when wild rodents' fleas have switched to rats living in cities, then moved on to humans, when all the sick town rats died. Today, most human cases of bubonic plague are the result of people having been bitten by wild rodents' fleas, such as while walking in the countryside. Human outbreaks are chiefly found in parts of Africa, South America and south-east Asia. Up to 50 cases occur in the USA each year.

HUMAN TREATMENT: This must be prompt, with antibiotic drugs.

RABIES

This deadly disease is caused by a virus that attacks the **nervous system**. It may be transmitted via saliva, usually during a bite. It can affect many different species of mammal, especially **carnivores**, but rodents are not considered to pose a particular risk anywhere in the world.

In Europe, the fox population is thought to be a principal **rabies** reservoir. In other parts of the world, public health concerns centre on stray dogs, wolves, jackals, skunks and raccoons. In the UK in 2002, a licensed bat handler in Scotland was fatally infected by a bat bite. But the type of rabies found among certain kinds of bats is not the same as the dog species variety, and in this country, it is extremely rare. However, anyone routinely handling wildlife, in this country or abroad, should talk to their GP about possible rabies risk and inoculation.

HUMAN SYMPTOMS: These include fever, severe headache, hyperactivity, disorientation, **seizures**.

HUMAN TREATMENT: The prompt and thorough cleaning of any bite wound. Rabies virus is very sensitive to detergents, including ordinary soap, as well as to heat and light and it cannot survive long outside the body. Seek medical advice immediately if you suspect that the animal that bit you could have been infected by rabies – for example, if it has been imported or is a bat that has flown across the Channel. Some people have survived, after intensive care, once the rabies virus had entered the nervous system (which may take one to two months, or longer) but they are rare cases. Luckily *post-exposure immunisation* (with ready-made human antibodies against the virus) is highly successful. Ideally, it should be given within two days of an infective bite, or a suspected one. (If the suspect animal turned out, upon **post-mortem** examination, not to have had rabies after all, the course of injections would be stopped.) Otherwise, a pre-exposure vaccination is available for those who are likely to come into contact with the disease.

Bovine Tuberculosis (BTB)

Researchers found **tuberculosis** bacteria in a small number of rats and moles among 5,700 wild mammals, including badgers, studied during the 1970s. Tuberculosis bacteria can affect mammals, both wild and domestic, and humans (in whom it is usually spread by infective airborne droplets from coughing or sneezing).

Other Zoonotic Diseases

These include diseases from largely domesticated animals, rather than wildlife: **toxocariasis** (from infestation of threadworm larvae in the faeces of dogs and cats), and **salmonellosis**, **pasteurellosis** and **campylobacteriosis** (groups of bacterial infections from the intestinal tracts of many animals, birds, amphibians and reptiles, and caught through the ingestion of their faeces). In this country, salmonellosis is most commonly contracted by eating infected eggs and **poultry** products. The bacteria can survive in contact objects, such as bedding and crockery, but are destroyed by heat treatment. These illnesses, which include typhoid, are more devastating to the very young, very old and anyone whose **immune system** is not fully functioning (e.g. as a result of anti-cancer treatment, prescribed drugs or a pre-existing illness).

> **Human Symptoms**: In humans, these include diarrhoea, raised temperature, vomiting and abdominal pain, and can result in shock or even death. In animals there may be the above ➤

> ➤ but symptoms may also include increased thirst, **seizures**, red discoloration of skin or eyes. *Toxocariasis* in humans can be difficult to treat and includes stomach pain, headaches, sore throat, **asthma** and listlessness. In some cases, the larvae reach the eyes and cause sight problems, although blindness is rare.

Rodent Diseases

Rodents, rabbits, hares and other small wild mammals suffer from several diseases, spread by micro-organisms from animal to animal. Most of their illnesses only come to our attention if they reach epidemic proportions and a large number of corpses, or sick animals, are found. Or there may be a sudden, noticeable absence of a particular species in the aftermath of an outbreak. But, in the main, the majority of their diseases go unrecorded. They arouse little interest, unless they are zoonotic diseases (illnesses that can be transmitted to people).

In the wild, rodent lifespans tend to be short and intense, and disease is just one of many potential killers. A wild rabbit that reaches its second birthday is an old-timer. Many small mammals have to eat little, but very often, to keep their energy levels topped up. A few hours without being able to feed, perhaps through feeling unwell or being injured, as will cold, wet or drought conditions which will finish them off. But although an individual who doesn't live in a very large community may be more at risk of being seized by a predator, there are some health advantages to

A wild rabbit that reaches its second birthday is old

Habitat loss is one of the chief reasons for plummeting numbers of Water voles.

Infection rates increase according to the mouse's age and the water content of the soil where it lives.

SIGNS: Jaundice, widespread small bleeds under skin (following liver and blood vessel damage); inflammation in muscles, brain and kidneys. But you would be unlikely to find a small mammal suffering from this illness.

TREATMENT: Wildlife centres usually advise against handling wild rat casualties because of the risk of zoonotic infection. Animals that survive infection can continue to excrete small numbers of bacteria in their urine for many months. Theoretically, antibiotic drugs would be given to kill off bacteria, supportive **fluid therapy** to counter effects of liver and kidney damage, but the latter is irreversible. In the environment, disinfection, **ultraviolet light** and drying out will normally destroy the bacteria.

such a lifestyle. Voles and shrews, which do not live in colonies, appear to be subject to fewer diseases than mice and rats, which often do.

LEPTOSPIROSIS

The bacteria that cause this serious, sometimes deadly, liver-damaging illness in mammals and people (also see *Weil's Disease*, p. 143) are thought to be widely harboured in the brown rat population. Most people who contract the illness do so after being in water that has been contaminated with rats' urine. Although the acid pH of urine tends to destroy any bacteria being excreted by the kidneys of an animal harbouring them, these organisms can survive for longer periods when in water. Woodmice in Britain (not Ireland) are also commonly infected with the **bacterium** Leptospira.

MYXOMATOSIS

A fatal viral disease which occurs naturally (and non-lethally) in South American forest rabbits. It was introduced in Australia to devastating effect in 1950–51, and then, deliberately, in France a year later. It crossed the Channel and proved impossible to contain: it was estimated that the UK rabbit population of 60–100 million, which was severely affecting farmers' crops, was reduced by 99%. The disease spread rapidly, in blood-to-blood transmission via fleas or **biting flies**, moving quickly through the cramped quarters of underground rabbit colonies. Although immunity to myxomatosis in British rabbits gradually increased, it still kills between one and two-thirds of all rabbits affected, and it is thought that Britain's rabbit population is still only around half of what it was before myxomatosis was introduced.

In 1954, The *Pests Act* made it a criminal offence to transmit the disease intentionally , but prosecutions have been few.

SIGNS: Appearing within a week or so, they include swollen eyelids, **pussy** discharge gumming eyes shut. Infection spreads, causing abscesses in eye sockets, ears, neck, head and rear end, signalled by swollen nose and genitalia. Rabbits will continue to eat, even when unable to see. But most will die within 11 to 18 days.

NOTE: *Dermatitis* in hares, resulting in **lesions** and scabs around face and genital areas, can be mistaken for myxomatosis but does not affect the population seriously.

TREATMENT: A vaccine, available for captive rabbits, will protect for nine months. Wild rabbits affected by the **virus** may be euthanased if suffering convulsive fits or showing signs of extreme distress. Otherwise, supportive nursing care is best if the rabbit's immune system appeared to be fighting the virus. One wildcare centre treats survivors of 19+ days intensively with a daily regime of fluids, antibiotics, anti-toxins, drugs to expand airways, plus a pro-biotic to restore gut flora. (Rabbits are prone to digestive problems anyway, and antibiotics destroy the natural gut bacteria balance.) ➤

➤ For anti-flea control, animals are dusted with anti-flea powder and quarantined (specifically safe for use on rabbits). Survivors are kept in permanent, fox-proof pens if their sight is too damaged for release, and neutered.

VIRAL HAEMORRHAGIC DISEASE IN RABBITS (VHD)

This illness came from domestic animals in China, spreading to Britain's wild rabbit population in the early 1990s. Commonly spread by direct contact with infected animals, including carcasses, or via rodents, birds and insects, the virus can survive for a long time outside its **host**. It can also be carried on animal feed, wildlife hospital equipment and handlers' clothing. Most affected rabbits (around 90%) die within a day or two of becoming infected. The disease appears to break out in alternate years among wild rabbit populations. Very young animals, under a month old, remain unaffected, though, and will develop lifelong immunity.

SIGNS: Appetite loss, drowsiness, **depression**, loss of co-ordination, pallor, breathing distress, **haemorrhages** and blood-stained mucous discharge; sudden death from liver failure.

TREATMENT: None appears to be effective. Rabbits which survive acute stage of illness usually develop jaundice and die. Newborn hand-reared wild rabbits in wildlife rehabilitation units may be vaccinated against VHD.

VIRAL HEPATITIS IN HARES

(EUROPEAN BROWN HARE SYNDROME)

This virus, similar to VHD in rabbits, arrived from Germany in the mid-1980s and causes rapid death after attacking the liver and central nervous system. It results in massive mortality among hares of all ages, and appears to be as virulent as VHD. A similar recent hare disease attacks that part of the animal's central nervous system that controls involuntary movement and digestion. Brown hares in Britain are in decline.

SIGNS: You are highly unlikely to find survivors.

Starvation, not disease, is the biggest killer of young squirrels, like this grey.

PARAPOX VIRUS IN SQUIRRELS

Red squirrels are susceptible to this viral disease, with high death rates. Grey squirrels seem to have immunity (although acting as a reservoir host throughout England and Wales). Between 1900 and 1925, Red squirrel numbers declined dramatically throughout the British Isles; culling was even halted in the New Forest. Researchers now believe that stress (overcrowding, food shortages, severe winters, habitat destruction due to timber demands) exacerbated the epidemic's effects on the native red squirrels. It is not yet understood exactly how the virus is transmitted, but it is thought to be by direct body-to-body contact between animals.

SIGNS: Similar to those of myxomatosis in rabbits, they include conjunctivitis, **nasal discharge**, ➤

➤ swelling of lips, mouth and throat, ulcers, weakness, loss of appetite, loss of sight; pox-like lesions around face, eyes, and ulcerative lesions on body. Diagnosis may be by electron microscopy. The illness is almost invariably fatal and you are unlikely to find a sick red squirrel as they are shy and seldom approach human habitation. But there is evidence that some can survive the disease, despite having full-blown symptoms for up to a month.
TREATMENT: This would be by antibiotics, **antifungal** drugs, painkillers and fluids and hand-feeding, if the casualty's sight were affected. It is now considered desirable for red and grey squirrel populations to be kept apart, particularly in areas where greys may harbour the virus.

ADENOVIRUS IN RED SQUIRRELS

This can fatally affect the large intestine and **spleen**. There is also an adenovirus which affects mice.

SIGNS: These include diarrhoea. A diagnosis of virus would be by electron microscopy. Post-mortem examination of intestinal contents would show characteristic grey faecal colouring.
TREATMENT: Supportive therapy, including rehydration fluids and anti-diarrhoeal agents.

LOUPING ILL

This is a viral disease of sheep, but it has also been recorded among woodmice.

VIRAL PNEUMONIA

Rodents are vulnerable to lung-damaging viral infection, as well as to other viruses that harm the brain and spinal cord, but it is not known to what extent these affect their populations in the wild.

UPPER RESPIRATORY TRACT VIRAL INFECTIONS IN RODENTS

Captive rodents (mice and rats) can suffer from these, so perhaps wild ones do, too. If untreated, secondary bacterial chest infections (signalled by rattly breathing) will lead to fatal **pneumonia**, but affected wild rodents would probably be caught by predators before they reached that stage.

SIGNS: Depressed state, passivity; breathing difficulties. Note that it is normal for a common dormouse to seem torpid at some times of year (they are the only British rodents that may appear passive when handled). Apart from when they are hibernating, these dormice are sluggish during the day, active mainly at night. (They require a special licence for handling.) However, such passivity in any other rodent would be a sign that they were ill. Our other (non-native) dormouse species, the edible dormouse (Glis Glis), is not naturally "snoozy", approachable and easy to pick up.
TREATMENT: Antibiotics for secondary bacterial infection; supportive therapy; nursing.

PRIMARY BACTERIAL INFECTIONS IN RODENTS

All rodents are susceptible to the same types, such as infections by Salmonella and Campylobacter micro-organisms. Some types are also infectious to man (also see Rodent Diseases and Human Health, p. 143). Rodents are also vulnerable to infectious **anaemia** and brucellosis. Like people, rats and mice often live in crowded social groups, allowing diseases ample scope to spread and refine themselves. Their susceptibility probably lies behind their high level of use in medical research laboratories.

SIGNS: You are unlikely to come across a sick **rodent** in the wild suffering from bacterial infection.
TREATMENT: Antibiotic therapy, although the disruption caused to normal gut fauna would pose major problems in rodents.

BACTERIAL INFECTIONS IN RABBITS AND HARES

Lice are responsible for one bacterial disease which causes **septicaemia** and is common in the environment. Other infections include secondary bacterial wound infections and abscesses, a sexually transmitted illness and a **tuberculosis**-type disease that result in general wasting and internal abscesses.

SIGNS: Wasting, diarrhoea, inflamed lesions and dull coat; animals in poor condition would be unlikely to avoid predation.
TREATMENT: Appropriate antibacterials.

PARASITES – INTERNAL

WORMS, FLUKES AND PROTOZOA

Usually, it is the already sick animal that runs into deadly problems with **parasites**. But some rodents, such as water shrews, may carry a high internal and external parasite burden in the wild, yet remain apparently healthy. It is thought that parasites tend only to cause severe adverse effects when mammal populations become over-dense. When a small wild animal is taken into temporary captivity, getting rid of internal parasites like **worms**, **flukes** and **protozoa** (microscopic single-cell organisms) must be done in sensitive stages to avoid challenging its system too greatly. **Toxins** released by the bodies of killed parasites before they have been excreted can cause a dangerous reaction in a patient already weak, injured or ailing.

> **SIGNS**: There may be few, unless the parasite population has gained the upper hand, causing weight loss, depression, poor-looking coat; **anaemia**.
> **TREATMENT**: Isolation of new admissions; worming; possibly antibacterial in drinking water or by injection, depending on patient's condition.

ENTERITIS AND HEPATIC COCCIDIOSIS

Both rabbits and hares can be affected by severe gut problems, probably caused by a common intestinal parasite that can run riot. Lesions develop on their internal organs and animals quickly become thin and die. Coccidiosis can be very troublesome in rehabilitation centres. An animal infected by these parasites would pass egg cysts onto the grass when it defecated, and these could be eaten by the next host (which could be the same animal as the first, because rabbits and hares routinely eat their own faeces in order to fully digest their food). Parasitic egg cysts would then hatch within the host's intestinal wall, and the whole parasite life cycle repeat itself.

Red and grey squirrels may also suffer fatal illness from coccidiosis. Three different types of microscopic organism are potential trouble-makers. Two cause wasting because they damage the large intestine and stop it absorbing food. Another type affects the bile ducts, as well as causing excessive urine production. But a number of factors could lie behind the development of this illness, such as bacteria and environmental toxins.

> **SIGNS**: Diarrhoea is often the main symptom, young animals being particularly badly affected. Rabbits or hares with diarrhoea often fall victim to flystrike in warm weather, with flesh-eating maggots burrowing into the skin around the damp tail area. Emaciation (severe weight loss), dehydration, depression, appetite loss and, in some cases, liver enlargement, may also be present. Diagnosis would be by identification, under microscope, of tiny eggs found in faeces.
> **TREATMENT**: For uncomplicated coccidiosis, this includes a sulphonamide in drinking water, scrupulous removal of droppings around feeding area; rehydration and supportive nursing for ➤

→ more severe cases. Some animals may suffer long-term liver damage, and would need extended care and dietary regulation if they were to stand a chance of recovery.

PARASITES – EXTERNAL

FLEAS, MITES, TICKS AND MAGGOTS

Again, there are plenty waiting to live off rodents and their relatives. Woodmice, for just one example, can carry numerous different sorts of **mites**, three species of lice and two species of blood-sucking **ticks**. As for fleas, 22 different flea species have been found in relation to woodmice in the British Isles. Some fleas hang around the nest, as well as their host. Only a third of these fleas are commonly recorded and it isn't entirely clear for which of these the mouse is the true host.

Squirrels' fleas like to switch hosts, too. The red's fleas are found on greys, and vice versa. Sometimes, both kinds of squirrel will be living in the same wood and using the same drey to sleep in, at different times. Rabbits may be badly affected by fleas, too. Fleas are the main vectors of myxoma virus.

TREATMENT: A suitable insecticide, in powder or pump spray form, would be used against flea or mite infestation, once the casualty was stable. **Pyrethrum** powder is safe for use on rodents and other small mammals; other drugs, such as fipronil (*Frontline*) might be used, on veterinary advice. →

→ Ticks, which latch onto skin for a blood feast, are carefully removed by hand (using a dab of anaesthetic, or petroleum jelly to suffocate the tick, or a specially designed tick hook) taking care to leave no tick mouth parts embedded. Maggots are carefully tweezered out, and antibacterials used for infected flystrike wounds.

SKIN FUNGAL INFECTIONS

Woodmice carry the **spores** of **ringworm**, which is not a worm, but a zoonotic skin fungal infection. Different types of ringworm cause skin inflammation and intense itchiness at various sites in the body.

SIGNS: Affected animals may show patches of hair loss (but not always); a carrier will appear to have normal fur. Ringworm spores remain viable in the environment for a considerable time. Care must be taken when handling any mammal that may be carrying them.
TREATMENT: A course of antifungal drugs may be possible. (In humans, treatment is by **topical** ointment or, if more persistent, by **systemic** antifungal drugs taken orally.)

FLIES AND MAGGOTS: "FLYSTRIKE"

This can affect any wildlife casualty, but rabbits are especially susceptible. Even perfectly healthy animals may be attacked around their anal and genital regions. The blowflies that lay their eggs there are particularly

Usually, it's the already sick animal that runs into deadly problems with parasites

attracted to faecal contamination. Once hatched, maggots will attack healthy, as well as necrotic, tissue.

SIGNS: Maggots and clusters of small, white eggs are visible in the wound.

TREATMENT: Eggs and maggots must be meticulously removed by tweezers, or flushed out, and the area cleaned. Possible anti-larval treatment applied topically, or by injection. Non-steroidal anti-inflammatory medication is given to counteract possible endotoxic shock, plus antibiotic therapy and supportive care.

Twenty-two flea species have been found in relation to Wood mice

OTHER PROBLEMS

HYPOTHERMIA

Core body temperature can become too low when a casualty is injured and unable to seek shelter, or when an infant gets separated from its nest and littermates. It is a dangerous situation and the animal will die unless its body heat can be gradually brought back up to normal temperature. A young hypothermic mammal won't feed and will rapidly lapse into unconsciousness.

SIGNS: In a wet and cold environment, the body feels chill to touch, its extremities very cold; sluggish movements, slow mental reactions; there is loss of consciousness, as breathing and heart rates slow.

TREATMENT: This must be by gradual warming of the animal's total environment, e.g. housing the casualty under an overhead heat lamp. Some ➤

➤ wildlife centres recommend immersing the animal in a bath of water at normal body temperature, provided the casualty is thoroughly dried afterwards. Too much sudden surface heat to the body – for example via a heatpad – would cause a sudden rush of blood to the skin and underlying **tissue**, further reducing blood supply to heart and brain. It might also cause burns. Covering the casualty in heat-reflecting material, such as a **space blanket** or bubblewrap film, is an effective way of conserving body heat, but take care not to overheat the animal.

HABITAT LOSS

This is one of the most serious of all threats to wildlife in Britain. Unprecedented new housing pressures are likely to mean "tighter" cities and fewer brown-field sites. New-style houses tend to have small, tidy gardens, too, often with paved or other hard-surfaced areas that offer little to sustain small wild mammals that like to live in, or on the edges of, woodland. They venture only small distances during their lifetime, going from their home base into nearby gardens to look for food. They need to escape quickly back to thicker cover to shelter and hide from predators, to sleep in safety and to breed. If one food-rich garden is suddenly split off from their home territory by a new road, a busy housing estate or an impenetrable fence, it might as well be on Mars for all its life-supporting value to small wild mammals.

TOOTH TROUBLE: (MALOCCLUSION AND LOSS) IN RODENTS AND RABBITS

Tooth problems are more often seen in pet rabbits whose teeth have not been worn down enough, resulting in gross overgrowth. It's a life-threatening condition, if allowed to continue, because the curving, constantly growing teeth can eventually penetrate the animal's skull cavity. But malocclusion (teeth that don't meet properly, so the biting action can't wear opposing surfaces down) may also be seen in young, or hand-reared, wild rodents and rabbits and hares. Then, it's usually the result of congenital jaw misalignment or, possibly, a past, healed traumatic injury, such as the teeth or jaw being broken in a fall.

Tooth loss in carnivorous non-rodents, such as stoats and weasels would be life-threatening, too, because they would be unable to hunt their prey. They would need to rely on scavenging and carrion to survive – if they could still chew.

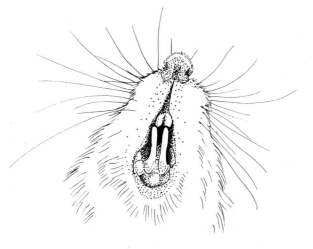

A healthy set of rodent teeth

SIGNS: Missing or broken teeth, or teeth "missing" each other when the animal eats. Incisors should be capable of wearing each other down, as surfaces meet in a grinding action.

TREATMENT: The casualty should be kept in captivity while growing replacement front teeth. If they regrow misaligned, they would need to be clipped and filed regularly. In this case a casualty could not be released into the wild.

METABOLIC BONE DISEASE IN SQUIRRELS

Found most commonly among young squirrels kept in captivity and reared on the wrong diet – too much phosphorus in the calcium:phosphorus ratio. Calcium, which is essential for the healthy formation of bones and teeth, makes up more than 90% of their bodies' hard matter. It also plays a vital part in the blood clotting mechanism, transmission of nerve impulses and the contraction of muscle.

SIGNS: Weakness, weight loss, spinal curvature; fits; early death.

TREATMENT: Use of suitable substitute milk formula for bottle-fed squirrel youngsters (such as Esbilac); mineral and **vitamin supplements** on food to give correct calcium content; and in juvenile squirrels an avoidance of peanuts and sunflower seeds, which inhibit calcium intake. Muscle-relaxing anticonvulsant to control fitting; possible intravenous injection of calcium.

WHEN TO RESCUE ORPHANS AND DISPLACED NESTLINGS

You'll need to take both animal and trap, snare wire or bottle, along to the vet or wildlife rescue centre

Baby hares are sometimes picked up by mistake because they seem to have been abandoned in a field. But if you find a single, tiny young rabbit out in the open above ground, it will probably need rescuing, because it should not be out there on its own. Likewise, a very young squirrel which may have fallen (or been shoved) from its nest, and may be injured and very cold, won't survive without help. Baby squirrels often lose their homes when breeding nests are accidentally destroyed during woodland management or roof and loft work. Late-born squirrels may find it impossible to survive the winter. Any young rodent or other small wild mammal that is unweaned and not fully furred, and without a parent, will not be able to fend for itself.

Follow the usual "Home Alone?" wildlife rescue code for "orphans" and check things out. Watch, from a distance, to see if the youngster is in transit, being taken from one nest site to another, and has been temporarily set down. Its mother may come back and pick it up. But don't wait too long. Sharp-sensed predators will be close by, waiting to snatch up waifs and strays. And the smaller the animal, the more quickly it will succumb to hypothermia if is becomes hungry, cold and wet.

All rescued orphans need warmth (not roasting), a constant environment, clean bedding and regular feeds. Use common sense when deciding whether to rescue a juvenile small wild mammal and don't take on a task that you are not prepared to follow through. You may decide to take on the time-consuming business of hand-rearing and releasing the animal yourself, when it is fit and old enough. Or you may opt instead to take it to a reputable wildlife rehabilitation centre. It is your responsibility to make sure that its future is safely assured and that it will be properly and responsibly cared for. Your aim – where the law allows this – is for each youngster to resume a natural existence, and go back to the wild. If that is not going to be possible, it may fall to you to provide suitable permanent accommodation and, if necessary, obtain a licence to do so.

If the animal is caught in a trap, snare or litter, it is important to rescue it, but equally vital not to just let it go because it may be too injured or weak to survive without intervention. The classic case is that of snare wire that has so damaged a deep line of cells in the animal's flesh that the tissue will die off and fatal septicaemia set in after the animal is released.

Trap or snaring equipment needs to be carefully removed, under anaesthetic, the animal treated with drugs to counteract toxic shock and other problems caused by bacterial action in the wound, if it's to stand a chance of surviving

Even if you find a small mouse or shrew trapped in a bottle, merely letting it out won't do. That is liable to present a predator with a weakened, easy target for lunch. In both these cases, you need to remove both animal and whatever is trapping it (snare wire or bottle) and take them together to the vet's or wildlife rescue centre for them to deal with.

There are good and bad ways of releasing rodents trapped in narrow-necked glass containers if you want to ensure that the victim does not perish in the rescue attempt. Place the bottle, can or whatever is holding the rodent or insectivore prisoner, inside a high-sided secure container, so that you can check for injuries. Later, if the neck of a glass bottle needs to be broken, the occupant must be at the further end. Then it may be possible to cut off the bottle neck using a heated wire, or a little boiling water, and giving the glass a light tap.

OTHER EMERGENCIES

Even an emergency situation, such as a small mammal that has fallen into water from which it cannot escape, will require the casualty being held in captivity for a while so that it can recover. Obvious signs of injury or sickness will be easy to spot (animal unable to move properly, flies and maggots around tail end, visible blood and wounds, etc). But a rodent or other mammal that has been "catted" is also a rescue candidate because, unless treated with antibiotics, the bacteria resident on the cat's teeth will kill it soon, even if any original bite damage was not immediately fatal.

Bites and scratches from wildlife casualties

Follow sensible hygiene and cleanliness protocol when handling any wildlife casualty. Clean your hands with antibacterial wash or other (animal-safe) disinfecting solution and do not eat, drink or otherwise put your fingers in or near your mouth while handling the animal. Use lavender or tea tree essential oil, or similar disinfectant, on fresh skin abrasions and bites.

HOW SHOULD I DEAL WITH A CASUALTY

Bites incurred when a small casualty is handled can be painful (especially if a biter's teeth are backwards-slanting and you draw your hand away quickly) and it's not always the largest set of jaws which hurt the most. The saliva of shrews contains a venom which causes localised pain and inflammation on humans, even when a nip doesn't break the skin. Wearing thick gardening gloves may give you good protection but they are inappropriately clumsy and heavy-duty for handling the smaller, delicate wild mammal casualties.

Small rodents can be caught in a soft-rimmed bird-catching net, lightly held by the head and neck with your fingers, and dropped into a container. The see-through plastic pet boxes sold for domestic rodents are ideal for transporting and for temporary accommodation, enabling the animal to be observed and fed without permitting escape. Never pick up a mouse by its tail, other than the very base, because the skin will slough off later. Also avoid touching the mole's nose area. Moles can be very gently and briefly "scruffed" by loose skin around the back of their neck, provided you also support their body. Rescuers are not advised to handle wild rats because of the risk of zoonotic infection and if they are caught, indirect methods are preferable. Handlers should wear goggles, mouth-covering masks and very thick, impenetrable gloves.

Wild rabbits and hares are best "scruffed", too, but their hindquarters must be supported with

Never hold a rabbit by its ears – scruff loose neck skin and always support its bodyweight to protect its delicate spine.

your other hand. Never pick up a rabbit or hare by its ears, so that these are taking its full weight. Don't let them fall or twist in trying to escape (which will damage their backs). Holding the animal close to your body, but away from your face, will minimise kicking. Keep hands-on intervention as short as possible. Stress is often fatal to wild-living lagomorphs through heart failure or knock-on effects of disrupted digestion.

Squirrels may "hold their breath" when captured and this stress-induced behaviour can prove fatal. Use a net, sack or cat-carrier squeeze-cage to confine them, if possible, not your hands. If you do pick a squirrel up, avoid squeezing it around the abdomen, as you could kill it. The correct way to hold it is by making a circle of your thumb and forefinger (like the gesture for "excellent!") to gently support the squirrel's neck and head, as if it were being embraced by a neck brace or collar. As you lift the animal, catch hold of one front leg between the fore and middle fingers of that same hand. Mammal researchers use special "handling cones" that cover the squirrel's entire body when they wish to move them. There are also squirrel live traps which you can leave pre-baited. In an emergency, you could roll a squirrel casualty into a small towel, leaving its head free. But watch where you put your fingers. Squirrels can bite deeply, even through leather gauntlets, and they have very sharp claws – how else do you think they can hang upside-down from branches and tree trunks?

TRANSPORTING

A SMALL RODENT

Make sure that a mouse or other very small casualty is held inside a container that it cannot jump, or chew its way out of. A see-through plastic box of the kind pet shops supply for small rodents is the best option for transporting, as well as temporary housing. An upturned glass jam jar, with a piece of cardboard slid underneath, (for escape-proof transfer) makes a good temporary holding bay for a small rodent if you need to take a good look at it. But remember, it needs to breathe. Provided that it's well-ventilated, a smooth-sided plastic food container with lid makes a good DIY carrier, too. It must have air-holes in its lid or, better, low down around its sides. These are easy to produce in plastic, using a heated skewer (in gas flame for couple of minutes). Or use a cardboard shoebox as a temporary carrier and make air-holes with the tips of sharp, closed scissors. But do customise your container before you put the casualty into it! Lay some kitchen towel, or crumple a little newspaper, inside the box, so the casualty does not slide about in transit, and has somewhere to hide.

A LARGER RODENT OR LAGOMORPH, E.G. HARE, RABBIT OR SQUIRREL

A bigger animal can be transported inside a metal-mesh cat basket, the bottom of which is covered with newspaper and (or) a layer of "Vetbed"-type fabric which cushions the animal and also allows any fluid to drain through it. Some cage carriers are designed as crush-cages, with a sliding panel which pushes an animal against the side of the container when operated from above. This would enable it to be given an injection (e.g. of anaesthetic) without being directly handled. A lightweight towel, laid over the top of the carrier in transit, without unduly restricting airflow, will darken the environment and help keep the casualty calm. Keep yourself, and other people quiet, and keep domestic animals away while transporting the casualty, to avoid stressing it further.

Even if the casualty is unconscious, or acting in a very lethargic way, don't carry it loose in your car, or hold it, uncontained, in your hands. It may suddenly "come to" and escape. It may be advisable to put the casualty and container in the vehicle boot, not on a seat (where it may roll off if you corner sharply, or stop suddenly, injuring the animal, or releasing it inside the vehicle).

FEEDING IN CAPTIVITY

ORPHANS IN CARE

If the orphaned or displaced nestling is very young, it will need to be fed on milk. This does not mean cows' milk or human baby formula. Every mammal mother produces milk that is tailor-made for an infant of that species, and giving the wrong "mixture" is likely to severely upset digestion (causing diarrhoea) and may ultimately even kill the young animal you are trying to save. The fat content of dolphin's milk is almost 80% of its total makeup, while that of a brown rat is half of that. A rabbit's is around 50% fat. So the bottlefed baby mammal will need to be given the most suitable powdered milk formulated for young animals that you can obtain. In practice, this usually means ingredients made up to suit puppies or lambs, and wildlife rescue centres are always swapping notes on what brand worked best for them when hand-rearing that season's orphans. Seek expert veterinary and wildlife advice on milk replacers, additives (minerals and enzymes) and suitable weaning foods.

BOTTLE-FEEDING

Oral rehydration fluids are normally given for the first couple of feeds. Whichever milk replacer is then used (e.g. Esbilac, goats' milk, Multimilk, Lamlac), it is important that it isn't changed during the period during which that infant is being bottle-fed, unless there are clear signs that it is not being tolerated.

Bottle-feeding, when the baby's fully opened mouth is smaller than a dried pea, presents all sorts of problems, too. Larger babies, such as hares, rabbits and squirrels, may be fed with a kitten-feeding bottle, or a small (needleless) syringe. Great care must be taken not to depress the syringe plunger too quickly, or there is a danger that the youngster will be flooded with milk. If any trickles down the wrong way and gets into its airways, it will choke or later develop **inhalation pneumonia**, a common killer of artificially-fed wildlife infants which have been inexpertly given liquid feeds. Milk must always be warm (not hot). Usually, the infant mammal will turn away when it has had sufficient for that feed.

Very small rodents and insectivores, such as baby woodmice and shrews, may be too tiny to be fed by syringe. Instead, it's possible to use a fine hair paintbrush of the soft, tapering kind found in watercolour paint sets, dipped in formula milk, for them to suck. Believe it or not, this method does work.

Hand-feeding requires patience and skill, particularly when a young wild mammal is recovering from an illness, injury or veterinary surgery. It is sometimes difficult to tread the fine line between coaxing and forcing. While some young animals will readily take to a strange giant foster parent proffering

Bottle-feeding, when a baby's open mouth is smaller than a dried pea, presents problems

a plastic nipple, others would appear to prefer starvation to letting a drop pass their lips. But lightly stroking the side of the face or mouth often succeeds in triggering the sucking reflex, as it does in human babies. Place the animal in a comfortable, supported upright position (many animals will only feel relaxed and secure if their feet are touching something solid) and afterwards gently rub its back to bring up excess air it has swallowed while feeding. Usually, just-fed infants will then go to sleep. Don't keep disturbing an otherwise healthy young mammal, other than for a routine feed. They need their sleep.

FEED LITTLE AND OFTEN

Small rodents, such as mice and voles, need feeding every hour, from early morning (first light) until it gets dark, then every two hours throughout the night. Baby shrews need feeding every hour – both day and night. This is what is meant about wildlife orphan fosterers needing commitment, patience and

Wood mice and other small rodent young need hourly feeds by day, then two-hourly during the night.

stamina! The good news (for human handlers, as well as rodent mothers) is that both mice and voles will begin to take solid foods, like clover, chickweed and dandelion, even before their eyes are fully opened. Baby squirrels require four or five daily feeds, rabbits and hares need only twice-a-day top-ups. Hares' milk is very concentrated and nutritious and leverets would only be suckled once a day in the wild. In captivity, baby rabbits and hares are very prone to bacterial gut infections (which are often fatal) because their guts lack the natural protection that an enzyme in their mother's milk would give them. It is vital that their bottle-feeding equipment is sterilized and that only boiled water is used to make up feeds.

TOILETING

Demanding though bottle-feeding may be, it's every bit as vital to take care of the other end of the animal, too. This involves bottom-wiping, not after the animal has defecated or urinated, but *before*. Using a moistened cotton bud or soft flannel to gently wipe around the urinary and anal openings mimics the way the young animal's mother would stimulate the infant to pass urine and faeces. It must be done after every feed. Neglecting to do so will lead to the animal dying if its bladder is not emptied. (Bowel movements are usually less in need of encouragement.)

WEANING

Wild mammals tend to wean themselves quite quickly, if offered the right food choices. The widest possible variety of foods would be offered, mirroring the range the animal could expect to find in the wild, plus fresh, clean water from a drip-feeder, or a very shallow lid, so that the youngster cannot drown in its water bowl. Additional, filling starter solids for a variety of small mammals include (human) baby rusks and crumbled-up digestive biscuits. Many rodents obtain all the liquid they need from their normal daily food. Often, this will include fresh berry fruits.

FEEDING ADULTS

RABBITS AND HARES

In their natural environment they eat grasses and a wide variety of plants including dandelions, clover, coltsfoot, carrot and turnip tops, cabbage, grain and cereals, plus fruits such as apples and soft fruits in season. In captivity they require a well-balanced, high-fibre diet of grass, hay, vegetables and weeds. This may be topped up by a small amount of rabbit food mix (from pet shops), supplemented by some fresh green foods, plus vitamin and mineral supplements. Adult rabbits and hares may be given vegetables such as carrots, broccoli, kale, cabbage and spring greens. They need clean water daily, in a heavy bowl that they can't easily kick over.

RODENTS

Complete diets for rodents are available in pellet form, but unless a rodent is going to remain in permanent captivity, it's probably not worth encouraging it to accept commercial petfood. Stick as closely as possible to the natural menu in the wild.

SQUIRRELS

They are given nuts, in shells or out, but not salted. (Sunflower seeds and peanuts would be offered very sparingly because they hinder calcium absorption and lead to bone disorders in squirrels.) In captivity, fresh carrot and cabbage go down a treat. They would also be offered, fresh each day, a selection of: chopped apples, pears, grapes, grains, berries, fresh shoots, plus some bread, commercial rabbit mix and chick pellets. They could have new growth from native bushes and trees, grasses, lichen and bark. They need some extra calcium (added to drinking water, in powder form or as boiled pork long bones) as well as vitamin supplements. Clean water, regularly changed, is supplied from gravity water bottles.

RATS

In the wild, rats usually get their moisture from fruit and vegetables, but in captivity, rats, mice and other rodents should be given drinking water daily, in a gravity water bottle with metal spout or a shallow container. Specialist feed suppliers and pet shops sell a dry food mix containing corn, wheat, cereals, flaked maize, dried crushed peas and biscuit for fancy rats. They would also eat non-sugared breakfast cereals, wholemeal bread, rice, table scraps, fresh fruits and vegetables, spaghetti and a small amount of meat. Ideal daily greens (to provide folic acid) are apples, carrots, tomatoes, celery, cabbage, swede and broccoli. Don't give citrus fruits, which are too acidic for them, or lettuce. Like rabbits, rats eat their own droppings to maximise absorption of minerals. Rats are able to provide their own vitamin C.

MICE

All varieties will eat grains and seeds, plus clover, dandelion leaves, grass and flower buds, most

Native/hazel dormouse – it sleeps for up to three quarters of its life and is disappearing fast in Britain.

can trigger diarrhoea in rodents. Harvest mice will eat millet, linseed, rape, birdseed, growing grasses, wild (hedgerow) flowers and fruits, insects – and a little flaked fishfood.

Common dormice eat hazelnuts, some unsalted peanuts, growing hazel or sycamore twigs, sunflower seeds, ripe fruits (berries, including strawberries, grapes, apples and bananas), corn and canary eggfood. Non-native edible or fat dormice eat a similar diet, plus some dry puppyfood, kale, pecan nuts and spinach.

VOLES

In captivity, give seeds, whole oats and some commercial mouse food mix from pet shops (as for mice, above) plus fresh green food (leafy twigs), buds, hay, young grass shoots, chopped grass and clover, chickweed, dandelion, garden flowers according to seasonal availability, and chopped carrot. Feed only in small amounts and only give vegetation that has not been sprayed by **pesticides**; wash fruits and vegetables.

INSECTIVORES

Shrews in captivity must have a constant supply of food and water round the clock. They can be given (cleaned) white maggots, mini-mealworms, waxworms (all available from specialist pet shops and aquaria) as suitable substitutes for their natural, foraged diet. Add a little fresh meat, food for insect-eating birds, dried catfood pellets crushed up, and egg.

Moles will eat earthworms, mealworms, waxworms, insects, slugs, meat-in-jelly dogfood, food for insectivorous birds, and chopped (supplied frozen) young mice (fed to birds of prey or snakes in captivity).

vegetables and acorns. In woodland, their natural diet consists of seeds, buds, seedlings, nuts, fruits, snails, insects, beetles, spiders, woodlice and their eggs and larvae, plus fungi, moss and some bark.

In captivity, mice will eat seeds (e.g. wild birdfood mixes), dry porridge oats, crumbled digestive biscuits, plus a little insectiverous mix. Mouse or hamster mix from pet shops, with added vitamin and mineral supplements, may be added. They also eat apple, pear, tomato, cucumber, parsley, cabbage, spinach, ant eggs (if you can find any) and all kinds of insects. Woodmice eat seeds, rosehips, berries and insects. Mice may be given a tiny amount of tinned dogfood. Offer root crops like carrot, turnip, swede, a few brussels sprouts, peas, spinach or cauliflower leaves. Avoid lettuce, as it

TIME FOR RELEASE: WHEN AND WHERE

Rodents, rabbits, hares and small mustelids, like stoats and weasels, are extremely territorial and must be released as close as possible to where they were found. Otherwise, they are likely to be quickly predated and males are likely to be challenged and chased away.

The red squirrel and the native hazel (or common) dormouse are both endangered species and should be released in accordance with one of the ongoing re-introduction programmes, at specific sites, to maximise their chances of survival. The Mammal Society (see *Useful Organisations*, p. 163) can give advice.

Woodmice, voles and shrews should be released into hedges, or into dense, wild undergrowth at the edges of gardens, at night, as far as possible away from people, predators, traffic, litter and other hazards. They should go back on their former home patch.

Rabbits and hares would probably be best released on non-farmland, to avoid controversial clashes with farmers (and the hand-reared orphan getting promptly shot). Some farmers welcome hares, however, and are keen to see their numbers re-established, so do make enquiries first. Rabbits and hares need good grassland, and cover away from busy roads. Blind rabbits are un-releasable, but will do well in captivity.

Grey squirrels cannot, by law, be kept without a licence, and it is illegal to release them back to the wild (although they are notorious for their ability to gnaw their way out of containers and escape).

Feral mink can only be held in captivity under licence and it is against the law to release them (under Schedule 9 of the Wildlife and Countryside Act 1981).

➤➤ WAYS TO GET INVOLVED ➤➤➤➤➤➤➤

◆ Keep cats in overnight. Don't let them outdoors again until well after dawn, and put a bell on a stretchy collar around their necks. That way, they'll be out of commission during the two main hunting peak times.

◆ "Garden for Wildlife" and don't use chemicals that kill the insects many creatures feed on and introduce toxins into the food chain and environment. Use natural pest control methods (e.g. encourage ladybird beetles to breed in your garden via custom-made nestboxes and let nest-building birds pick off the insect life you don't want, too).

◆ Tall, rough grasses and prickly low-level plants give small wild mammals vital shelter when they have to venture out for food – the same goes for amphibians, insects and ground-feeding birds. Campaign so that your local public parks and commons are tended according to "gardening for wildlife" principles too, instead of mistakenly over-tidied.

◆ Pick up and bag potentially hazardous litter you see, even if you didn't leave it yourself. You'll be doing wildlife a real favour and improving the scenery for people to enjoy, at the same time.

◆ Discourage rodent "pests" in places where you don't want to see them by not leaving food. Don't feed bread to waterbirds on ponds; dispose of takeaway and other food litter where it can't be got at later.

◆ Get an urban woodland planted. Even a small copse or linear strip of native trees, with underlying shrubs, is a wildlife haven, especially if it links existing habitats.

◆ Be a conservation volunteer for a Wildlife Trust. Even inner cities have valuable oases of wilderness that need protecting and improving for wildlife.

◆ Become an ace wildlife photographer – without going on safari. There are some reasonably priced light-triggered cameras on the market. You'll be surprised at the range of wildlife that enters your garden at dawn, dusk and overnight.

HOW SHOULD I APPROACH A RODENT CASUALTY?

Important: make sure that you keep your anti-tetanus immunisation up to date, if you are handling wildlife casualties that could scratch or bite.

1 Make sure that you know the difference between a young rabbit and a juvenile hare (leveret) and don't rush in to seize an animal that is not in danger. A baby rabbit crouching in the open, on its own, is a likely "rescue", a leveret in the same position probably isn't. Wait and watch, if you can.

2 Safeguard your face and hands from a possible bite. It is best not to attempt to pick up a rat or squirrel by hand. Be prepared for a mouse to jump higher than you thought possible, and to move in any direction very quickly. Don't let your arms, face or chest get in the way of a rabbit or hare's powerful back feet and claws because a surprise kick will make you drop the animal. If a small mammal is close to a road, always approach from the carriageway direction, so that it does not head straight under an oncoming vehicle.

3 Animals in this species section are prone to get exceedingly stressed by being handled. It's best to catch them indirectly, whenever possible, using a box, net, tube, etc. If the casualty is unconscious, pick it up and put it in a safe container immediately. If it is conscious, it may be possible to direct the animal into a container without touching it. Most rodents will instinctively try to run and hide in a dark place, so offer them a bolthole in the form of a container with solid sides, then cover and seal the entrance.

Casualty Kit

✔ A couple of old, clean, thick cotton towels – for trapping, holding casualties, covering containers. Hot wash them between uses

✔ Sturdy gloves – leather gardening or rose pruning gloves, welder's gloves, etc. – will help you pick up small mammals when there is no time to fetch a container

✔ A tough, clear plastic container (from a pet shop) suitable for a small rodent

✔ A metal-mesh (ideally not plastic coated) cat carrier – for squirrels and rabbits, etc.

✔ Cotton wool and lint

✔ Blunt-ended scissors

✔ Plastic, blunt-ended tweezers, surgical forceps (from chemists)

✔ **Styptic** shaving pencil, or blood-stopping powder, for minor bleeds

✔ Small mammal-safe disinfectant – e.g. Hibiscrub, which you can dilute with water

✔ Small, needleless syringe (keep supply unopened until use, dispose of after use) from chemists

✔ Rehydration powder; bottled mineral water or clean filtered or boiled tapwater, to mix up

USEFUL ORGANISATIONS:

The Mammal Society

15 Cloisters House, 8 Battersea Park Road,

London SW8 4BG

02380 237874

www.abdn.ac.uk/mammal

Natural England

1, East Parade, Sheffield, S1 2ET

0114 241 8920; www.naturalengland.org.

People's Trust for Endangered Species,

15 Cloisters House, 8 Battersea Park Road,

London SW8 4BG

020 7498 4533; www.ptes.org.uk

The Royal Society for the Protection of Birds (RSPB)

HQ: The Lodge, Potton Rd, Sandy, Beds, SG19 2DL

01767 680 551 Wildlife enquiries 01767 693 690

www.rspb.org.

The Royal Society of Wildlife Trusts (RSWT)

The Kiln, Waterside, Mather Rd, Newark, NG24 1WT

01636 677711; www.wildlifetrusts.org

TRUE OR FALSE?

1 London house mice use the Tube.

2 Hares seen boxing one another are males, squabbling over territory or female partners.

3 Hazel dormice are the only small mammals in Britain to have a completely furry tail.

4 Grey squirrels, like many contortionists, are double-jointed.

5 The term "rat run" was inspired by the brown rat's habit of always using the same route when out looking for food at night

ANSWERS

1 True, but they don't take the train. They scamper beneath the tracks when all is quiet, looking for commuters' discarded food waste.

2 False – usually, the sparring pair will be a male and female, and she will be using her front paws vigorously to fend off his advances (for a while, at least). The phrase 'Mad as a March Hare' refers to their lively, marching up-on-hindlegs movements during courtship.

3 True. It helps preserve body heat and save energy when food is scarce and the dormouse has to build a hibernation nest under woodland leaves.

4 True. They are skilful acrobats who can run as quickly down a tree as up it, thanks to their sharp claws – and their double-jointed ankles which allow their feet to face either forwards or backwards.

5 True. A brown rat doesn't tend to vary its foraging route, for safety reasons. In the countryside this regular too-ing and fro-ing will wear visible tracks through tall grass. A brown rat may travel up to 5km on each expedition to find a meal.

The Labours of Hercules

Hercules was strong, hence his name. He'd had to be, otherwise he would never have survived his premature ejection from the nest. A young groundsman found the very young grey squirrel lying in a gutter alongside the sports field early one morning. Perhaps the youngster had been blown down when high winds shook the tree overnight. Maybe he'd been snatched by a predatory bird or even kicked out by an adult squirrel. No one would ever know how he got there. The groundsman plucked the tiny cold animal from the wet grass, popped him in his pocket and took him home.

Luckily for Hercules, his saviour was well used to handling small and helpless creatures. He bred budgerigars in the well-kept aviaries at the bottom of the garden and occasionally he'd had to hand-rear chicks. His family had homed three stray cats and a "Battersea" dog and were always first port of call in the neighbourhood for pet feeding duties at holiday time. Hercules was warmed, dried and initially hand-fed from a doll-size baby feeding bottle on a milk substitute. Later, he was switched to solids and frankly spoiled rotten with a rich array of tempting morsels to suit the discerning rodent palate. He grew big and strong enough to set himself free from his caging and join the household indoors. He could come and go as he pleased.

His manners were perfect, he enjoyed being handled, evidently appreciated the use of human heads and arms as staging posts in his travels from one room to another. He never bit, unless it was by accident when he took a nut with his eyes closed. He fitted in with the dogs and cats, ignored the budgies and lived, as they say, the life of Riley. Then his male hormones kicked in. He was on a mission.

Unfortunately, Hercules' quest for a tree hole to call his own led him through many a half-opened bedroom window and loud were the shrieks in the suburban street when his explorations included dressing tables, curtain rails and fitted wardrobes. It was always a mistake to try to hasten Hercules'

exit, let alone confine him, and soon his popularity
rating began to plummet. But miraculously, given
his neglected education in the field of "wilding up",
Hercules discovered the delights of the poplars beside
the brook that ran along the backs of the houses and
he learned how to be a squirrel.

He still kept in touch with the
groundsman and his family, visiting
the garden now and again. But he
couldn't stop by for long. After all,
he had a mate now and soon there
would be a family of his own.

SNOWDROP AND THE GOOD SAMARITAN

*I*t was not an uncommon sight: a badger lying motionless at the roadside. It had been hit during the night while looking for food, retracing the ancient West Country tracks of its ancestors.

Over the next few days, many people drove past the grizzled body. Scavenging crows began to eat one of its eyes. Eventually, one motorist decided to stop and take a closer look. He wasn't sure if the badger was alive but he thought he'd seen movement. He lifted it into his car and took it to the Secret World wildlife rescue centre in Somerset, founded by Pauline Kidner and famous for rehabilitation work with badgers. It was still clinging to life and was passed to a vet experienced in treating wildlife trauma victims.

The vet felt guilty when he learned where the casualty had been found. He'd driven past the badger three times himself. Examination showed she was badly concussed and dehydrated and so small that she was taken to be a half-grown cub. One eye was damaged beyond saving and there were serious head, back and leg injuries, too. She was put on a drip and stabilised, her ruined eye later removed.

Back in the wildlife centre, Snowdrop, as she was named, curled herself into a tight ball in the corner of a recovery pen. She seemed to have lost the will to live. She was attractively marked, but so thin that her skin hung in folds from her scrawny body. It was a battle to get her to take any food or drink. In desperation, staff injected rehydration fluids under her skin as an emergency life-saving measure.

Days passed and she clung on to life. Pauline, a trustee of the Badger Trust (formerly the National Federation of Badger Groups), and a very experienced rehabilitator, was beginning to think that putting Snowdrop to sleep now would be the kindest thing to do. First, she thought, she'd try another tack: syringing liquid food – Complan, honey and egg – into the corner of the badger's mouth. It was a slow, sticky process, but it worked. Snowdrop gained weight and began lifting her head with interest to see who was coming into her pen. However, it was felt that she'd been away from her original territory too long to be put straight back

to the wild. (She would no longer smell right to other badgers in her group, and would be attacked.) Instead, she'd go out with a new, mixed group into a carefully chosen location the following year.

One February morning, Pauline had a surprise. Snowdrop, by now fat and glossy, was not alone. Between her paws, she was holding two tiny cubs.

Through a natural process called delayed implantation, female badgers can put their pregnancies on hold for several months. Despite her injuries and very lengthy convalescence, Snowdrop had successfully maintained a pregnancy that had begun before her road accident. When she was released, she was accompanied by her cubs, Dawn and Dusk. The kind motorist who stopped to check if Snowdrop was alive had saved not just one, but three badger lives.

BADGER FACTS

POPULATION DISTRIBUTION

Recent genetic studies suggest that the badger group of mammals originated around 18 million years ago, much earlier than had been thought. Until relatively recently, badgers were incorrectly categorised biologically as members of the bear family. Indeed, small badger cubs can look like miniature teddies and when an adult puts its stout front paws and forearms over its eyes and rolls up defensively, thinking that is the best way to deflect danger, there's something bearlike about its appearance, too. But, in fact, badgers belong to another species – the **mustelids** – a group that includes otters, weasels, stoats, martens, polecats and skunks.

Badgers are widely distributed throughout Europe and they are common in many other parts of the world. However, marking variations in Siberian or Chinese badgers make them look slightly different to the ones you would see (if you were patient and lucky) out **foraging** on a moonlit damp summer evening in Britain.

The first national census of Britain's mammals, done through the Mammal Society in the mid-1990s, put the pre-breeding population of badgers at around 250,000, with a probably stable population. But there is no room for complacency: government culling policies, intensifying new housing developments and road expansions, along with climate changes that result in long periods of heat and drought could jeopardise that population status quo in the future.

Badgers in Britain were exceedingly widespread at one time, digging their setts (underground tunnelled homes) in any suitable, well-drained hillside within walking distance of reliable food sources like earthworms, roots and beetles. Their distribution is now much patchier. The South West contains about a quarter of the country's badger population. Other areas, such as the Fens and the far north of Scotland, are not ideal terrain for making setts. But some parts of the country are notorious for badger-digging and baiting, and such persecution accounts for patches of rarity in the UK badger distribution. Continual **habitat** destruction and road-building that bisects wildlife pathways have caused local populations to dwindle or disappear altogether in other places.

IDENTIFYING BADGERS

The Eurasian badger is the species found in Britain. It is one of our largest wild mammals: a big one could weigh up to 22kg. Like most of its close relatives worldwide, the Eurasian badger possesses the kind of bold facial markings (mask) that warn other animals not to mess with it. A badger's face is normally white, with two parallel black strips running from the top of the head down to the muzzle, making it a dramatic signal to other animals, even in dim light. These days, badgers in Britain have no mammal enemies (apart from human diggers and baiters), but bears, wolves and big cats would once have been potential killers.

Other noticeable badger features include long, industrial-strength black claws to dig with, strong-smelling musking **glands** for scent-spreading (one branch of the family goes under the vivid name of Stink Badger) and an acutely sensitive, wide, flexible snout, for locating and nosing out anything edible.

Badger eyesight is not brilliant, but their sense of smell more than makes up for it.

A badger in good condition looks powerful and compact. It has a thick-looking neck and tough skin covered in dense bristly hair (winter coats tend to be thicker and paler than summer ones). Its coat and build are useful for withstanding inter-badger fight injuries. A healthy animal carries a good store of subcutaneous fat for part of the year, which is designed to see the animal through hard times such as drought (when rock-hard soil takes earthworms off the menu) and extreme cold (when badgers tend to hole up underground to conserve energy). It is thought that badgers don't fully hibernate but are relatively inactive between November and February.

The fur on a badger's back has brindled, pepper-and-salt colouring. Individual hairs contain different levels of pigment along their shaft. Fur underneath its body and on its legs and throat is usually black and sparse. Natural pigment variations mean that some individuals may have a gingerish tinge to their coats, while others look entirely black. A few may be true albinos. Semi-albino badgers are commoner, their coats nearer apricot and cream than pure white, their eyes pigmented (i.e. they will look brown, not pink).

Adult males (boars) tend to be 70–90cms long and weigh on average in autumn 11kg, but some tip the scales at up to twice that weight. Females (sows) may be smaller and lighter (6–14kg) but are hard to tell apart from males in the field. Both sexes have a short tail and a broad-in-the-beam body behind a relatively slender snout. Their legs are short and sturdy. This overall shape is ideally tailored to a tunnelling

existence. Although it may look dumpy and shambling at times, a badger can move with lightning speed and turn with surprising flexibility. It can climb, swim and run fast.

A badger's head is supremely well-engineered for strength, which is why some casualties survive being hit by motor vehicles and even trains. A raised crest of fused bone runs along the top of the skull, protecting the badger from crushing attacks. The badger's lower jawbone interlocks with the upper portion of the skull in a wrap-around hinge, which means that the lower jaw cannot be dislocated, or fall off when the badger dies and becomes a skeleton. This skull design anchors very powerful facial muscles in place, making the badger's bite particularly effective. One rescuer, unlucky enough to muff his handling of a frightened casualty, described the experience as akin to shutting a hand in a car door. However, badgers usually opt to avoid conflict unless cornered or attacked.

Skulls of very juvenile badgers occasionally turn up on spoil heaps, but how they got there remains a topic for speculation. It's known that a dominant sow may be responsible for the deaths of the offspring of less dominant females in a group. But it is also possible that such skeletal remains may be the result of interference from dogs, or sett gassing, at a much earlier date. Skulls may then surface when part of a sett comes into re-use and gets cleared out by the new inhabitant.

Badgers are easy to identify, but they may be hard to see in the first place. Centuries of persecution have resulted in a natural wariness of man. Studies show that animals living in suburban areas come out of their setts far later at night than those in rural parts. Unless it

The South West holds about a quarter of the country's badgers

is used to your regular presence, a badger that picks up your smell will speedily head off out of sight.

HABITAT

Although badgers have adapted to living in our suburbs and most big cities have their badger populations, ideally badgers like to build their homes on hillsides, away from people. They are most likely to choose a quiet wooded area, with chalky or alkaline soils, because they are easier to dig out and water drains more easily from them, making the sett less likely to become flooded. There'll invariably be a good supply of earthworms in such places because badger **territory** and group sizes are determined by the quality and availability of food in an area. Tunnel openings tend to have low-growing foliage cover nearby.

A badger sett is a highly developed, far-reaching network of tunnels and chambers, excavated deep underground and accommodating up to around 15 animals. Like a big old country house, parts of the sett may come into use while others get shut off from time to

The badger's bony head crest can save it from skull fracture.

time. New wings and extensions are added over the years by new generations. The whole network of used and disused setts, main living quarters, subsidiary setts and annexes, can extend hundreds of metres below the ground, and there will be numerous entrances. Many established badger "cities" are several centuries old, their presence signalled by placename suffixes like Brock or Brox, which are Old English names for badger. One Derbyshire sett is mentioned in the Domesday Book, which dates from a decade or so after the Norman Conquest, more than 900 years ago.

New setts are dug as far away as possible from human disturbance. Slopes are favoured because the dug-out soil falls away from the tunnel. Badgers may shift scores of tonnes of earth in the process of homebuilding. It remains visible as huge spoil heaps outside main entrances. Fresh, dry bedding, such as straw and hay, is periodically gathered and taken underground. This provides vital insulation during winter, especially for cubs. Old bedding is regularly brought up to the surface and discarded on, or near, the spoil heap. Toilet areas (latrines) are sited at a distance from main living quarters. Sometimes, the droppings are covered up with soil but otherwise, dung deposits are left exposed, their musk-enhanced scents acting as potent territorial markers.

NOTES FROM THE UNDERGROUND

Unlike foxes, badgers aren't famous for their vocalisations. But they can and do make a wide range of sounds. Fighting or distressed badgers growl, yelp and scream loudly. In happier moments, they utter low grunts, soft whickerings and purrs. Playing or mating may elicit louder cries and badgers can be very noisy eaters, too.

Before the days of radio-collar tracking, fibre-optic cameras and glass-sided artificial setts, badger watchers were literally in the dark about many aspects of badger life because the animals spent such long periods deep underground. Even with the aid of such recent windows on their world, there remain question marks over the badger's winter lifestyle and inter-group and cub killings. But it is now generally believed that badgers do not hibernate, in the strictest sense. They conserve energy during very cold weather by building up a generous fat store beforehand. They stay underground in a torpid state (with lowered heartbeat rate) for lengthy periods when temperatures drop really low. But this is not true **hibernation**.

BREEDING

Although a Eurasian badger could theoretically live to ten years or more (ages of 14 and 15 have been recorded at monitored setts, and even 19 years in captivity) a UK badger's lifespan in the wild is more likely to be *two or three years*. It's estimated that 60% of cubs die in their first year. Many don't survive long enough to leave the **nursery** sett. Starvation is thought to be a major cause of death for both adults and youngsters.

Badgers live in social groups (clans). Typically, a clan consists of five badgers, with a dominant male, but numbers can vary from two to 30 animals or more and some single-sex groups have been reported. The dominant boar will mate with several sows in his clan and also impregnate females in other territories, if he can. Less dominant young males have to wander further afield to find receptive females if they want to pass their genes on. Badger procreation, like other badger activities, entails a fair amount of biting. Newly mated sows often have neck-chewing scars, while males often bear the marks of run-ins with rivals on their necks and rumps.

Badgers give the lie to the old maxim about it being impossible to be a bit pregnant. They can be, through a fascinating natural reproductive trick called delayed implantation. This means that a pregnancy can begin at a "normal" rate, then be "put on ice" until a later date. While matings occur at any time of year, all cubs are born around the same time, early the next spring. This start-stop-start **gestation** can stretch a pregnancy from its basic two months to ten months or more.

Badger pregnancy begins (as in other members of the weasel brigade as well as in the cat family) after mating has triggered ovulation in the female. But then the newly fertilised cells can stop developing. They stay inside the mother's uterus as primitive, early-stage **embryos**, in suspended animation, waiting for the best time to continue growing. They get all the nutrients and oxygen they need to stay alive via the blood-rich uterine lining.

Once given the biological green light, gestation continues. If the sow is healthy and food conditions remain good, her embryos mature into **foetuses** and the fully-developed cubs are born about seven weeks later. It's been suggested that, as the sow begins to live off her stored body fat reserves in colder weather, steroid hormones get released into her bloodstream, activating the next stage in cell development in her unborn

Pregnancy can stretch from two to ten or more months

Most commonly, two cubs are produced. They are blind and helpless at birth.

cubs. In our case study at the start of the chapter, Snowdrop's body needed to recover fully from its traumatic injuries before her hormonal status was sufficiently balanced to trigger this process. Obviously, delays cannot be indefinite. Poor health, harsh weather and poor foraging conditions would ultimately result in embryonic cells dying and the switching off of that particular pregnancy. This breeding pattern looks complex (particularly when you throw in the fact that impregnated female badgers can continue to mate and ovulate). But its energy-saving value is easy to see. It enables a mother to produce viable offspring only when she, and the environment, are best able to nurture and support the cubs.

Cubs

Births peak in February, but they can start as early as January and occur as late as May. Cubs are born deep underground, in a special chamber prepared by the sow and thickly lined by her with bedding. Dry straw is a favourite material but grass, hay and moss are also used. (Human debris like plastic rubbish and baling twine, intermixed with bedding, can be particularly hazardous and cause cubs to become strangled.) Usually, a pair of cubs are born but litter numbers can range from a single cub to five. The cubs' bedding is scented by the sow – using a musky, oily secretion from a gland under her

tail – so that, when they emerge, they will smell familiar to other adults in the group and not be attacked by them.

Badger cubs are born with their eyes closed, their faces looking blunt and foreshortened. Their first coat is a dingy white with very little fur underneath. The distinctive head stripes appear gradually and faintly. Cubs' eyes don't open until they're about five weeks old. But smell, not sight, will always be their most important sense. Adult badgers' long-distance vision is poor and cubs are particularly short-sighted.

Cubs are weaned at around 12 or 13 weeks, but their mother brings them up above ground before then. She always emerges from the sett first, to reconnoitre, and the cubs will quickly backtrack down the entrance hole at the first sign of disturbance.

The cubs grow fast. By the age of three months, they will normally have increased their weight to *ten times* their 100g birthweight. By the time they are a year old, they're likely to weigh over 9kg. Equal numbers of males and females are born, but twice as many male cubs die before they are one year old.

Communal Living

Unlike the gruff Badger in Kenneth Grahame's *Wind in the Willows,* the real-life badger isn't such a loner. It is likely to be sharing home with a dozen or more other badgers – although it is true that badgers don't care for visitors from outside their own familiar circle. They may also "sub-let" their setts, either regularly or temporarily, to other species: foxes, rabbits, rats, woodmice and weasels.

Individuals within the clan are subject to a pecking order, underlined by much biting, barging, playing, mutual grooming and occasional social exclusion. But the hierarchy and relationships in it shift from time to time. Older badgers drop down the ranks as their teeth get worn down (the grit in all those earthworms is a recipe for dental disaster). Their status falls as they start coming off worse in disputes on a regular basis. Clan membership alters, too, when individuals die or newcomers arrive. Outsider badgers may come in from other colonies which have died out. Or they may have been forced to move because their environment has been damaged or severe drought has reduced food supplies. There is considerable social to-ing and fro-ing in early Spring when young subordinate males move out of their home territory in search of females further afield. That's when badger road accident deaths peak as animals cross unfamiliar terrain.

FIGHTING

Adult male badgers become highly territorial and can be very aggressive to one another when defending their "patch" and the fertile sows in their group. Fights usually involve each animal trying to bite the rump of the other, forcing the weaker animal to retreat. Severe bite wounds that become infected can lead to death through starvation and/or **blood poisoning**. But many healthy badgers bear the scars of old, healed fight wounds on their rears. Researchers have also observed that, after a fight, the loser does not necessarily disappear. He might move out to the edge of the sett or be tolerated as a fringe member of the group, allowed to hang around with the rest when they feed at night. A badger may be permanently marginalised in this way or fully accepted back in the group later.

EYESIGHT AND SCENT MARKING

Badgers' eyesight is relatively poor. They rely on their sense of smell to pick up information about their environment and to recognise familiar places and fellow clan members. To help them do this, they transfer their own body odours onto key objects around their living quarters and onto other badgers' coats. Glands inside the anus transfer the badger's scent onto its droppings as they are passed. Another gland (visible externally, near the root of the tail if the animal is lying flat on its back) squirts a sweet-smelling, musky, fatty liquid directly onto other badgers and onto landmarks around the sett.

Although clan members will routinely and affably back up to others in their group, then squat and "musk" one another, the over-riding scent they all wear will be that of the dominant clan boar. It ensures that the whole social group smells much the same (rather like wearing a uniform, or company logo, in human terms) and avoids unnecessary fights and injuries.

FEEDING HABITS

Badgers are our largest **carnivore**. They have a wide diet which varies throughout the year according to seasonal availability of a particular food. Insects and small animals are eaten, as well as plants, including fungi, nuts, fruits, berries, seeds, grass, clover and roots, tubers and bulbs. But earthworms are a mainstay of badger diet, and they account for almost half of what a badger consumes. On damp, warm nights, when these kinds of **worm** come to the soil's surface (e.g. to mate) badgers will seize the opportunity to tuck in. An adult may eat 200 worms during a single night. Badgers'

Now wash your feet, please – if you're a rehabilitator

It's rare for a wild badger to launch an attack on a human. But it can happen if that person's smell puts out the wrong message. Rehabilitator Pauline Kidner had been in a recovery pen with some orphan cubs. Several had "musked" her shoes, a normal social marking that takes place within a badger's clan and an honour to which fostering cub-rearers grow accustomed. Then she noticed that she had a visitor. A wild badger was heading her way across nearby fields.

Pauline sat quietly, as the newcomer snuffled right up to her feet. She assumed that he would soon turn tail. But the visiting boar was a young adult, around the age when males have to fight one another for dominance and territoriality is all. Confused by Pauline's acquired musky odour, the young boar mistook her for another badger. He decided that she must be driven from his area and took several bites out of her ankles. When she fell sideways, he bit her sides and wrists, and even pursued her when she tried to scrabble up onto farm equipment out of his reach.

By the time she had managed to get back to her house to ring for an ambulance, she had lost a lot of blood. "I'd forgotten that, working with badgers, you start to smell like them," says Pauline. "But the only people who have ever had problems being bitten like this are rehabilitators," she adds.

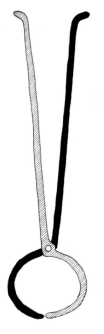

Long metal tongs were used by baiters when "bagging" a cornered badger.

worm-seeking expertise ensures that they know exactly where and when they can vacuum up the maximum number of earthworms from any particular grassy site.

During droughts, when the earth is packed hard and worms don't come up to the surface, badgers suffer a two-fold deprivation. Not only do earthworms form an important part of badgers' nutritional intake, but their water-filled, segmented bodies also provide badgers with one of their most important sources of moisture.

Badgers consume a great range of insects and their larvae. They frequently dig out wasp and bumblebee nests in search of grubs and adults. Coarse, dense hair must offer a badger some protection, but probably the sensitive nose and less bristly underbelly must get stung! Small mammals such as **rodents**, rabbits and hedgehogs are also taken, both alive and as **carrion**, and the hedgehog's prickles and curling-up muscles are no defence against a badger's strong paws and long claws. They also eat the occasional bird or nestling, as well as frogs, toads, slugs and snails.

BADGERS AND THE LAW

(also see *Rescuers and The Law*, p. 232)

After centuries of persecution and in the teeth of opposition, badger-baiting was outlawed in 1835. Today, a badger is legally protected against deliberate cruelty by several acts, including the 1992 Protection of Badgers Act. It is a criminal offence to use a dog to enter a sett or to disturb or harm a badger. It is also illegal to have possession of a live badger (unless handling a badger wildlife casualty with the aim of getting medical attention for it). Nevertheless, at least 10,000 badgers are being killed each year by baiting and digging.

Badgers also continue to be illegally shot, gassed and **poisoned**, sometimes by illegal use of **pesticides**. Destroying badgers can only be done under licence, for specific purposes such as disease prevention. In practice, few licences are granted each year. The chemical deterrent to keep badgers away until recently has been Renardine, but its use is no longer permitted.

Sentences for those found guilty range from fines to up to six months in jail. Diggers and baiters may have their dogs confiscated or destroyed and be disqualified from keeping dogs in future.

The badger's home is also protected. It's against the law to damage, destroy or prevent access to a sett. Interfering with it (or moving badgers) for the sake of building development can only be done under licence from a government's statutory nature conservation body, such as Natural England*.

While badgers certainly have a bulwark of supposed legal protection in the statute books, in the field, it can be tricky to make a criminal charge stick. Existing fines are well within the budget of organised groups who see the outlay as part of the cost of their illegal "sporting" activities.

Challenging a supposed badger-harmer or catching them red-handed can be difficult and intimidating. Who's to tell if the excuse of a spade-toting dog-owner that they are "only trying to rescue" their Jack Russell, stuck down a hole, is genuine? It doesn't help that most nefarious activities around badger setts take place in the middle of the night, when little backup help or potential witnesses are around and the local police force's Wildlife Liaison Officer is not by the phone. Badger crime may slip through a legal loophole, too, no matter how much evidence you gather or how accurate and

*formerly English Nature

well corroborated eye-witness accounts might be. The Home Office does not accord badger crime sufficiently high status to make it a recordable offence. This may sound like a small technicality, but if an offence has not been recorded, it cannot be investigated. (On the other hand, weapons offences that may accompany badger persecution activities, are recordable.)

PROBLEMS CAUSED BY BADGERS

DIGGING AND FORAGING PROBLEMS

Badger excavations sometimes undermine buildings and roads, or cause cracks. Their digging, trampling and foraging can damage crops. Their feeding technique of delving below soil and nosing for grubs can create holes in the ground that are hazards to horses and riders.

A crop growers' solution is to make targeted food items less accessible. Soft fruit and other crops can be protected with electrified fencing. Although this can be expensive, it is very effective. Nine-string electric wires are the deterrent recommended by conservation groups.

Poultry, pet rabbits and guinea-pigs should always be housed in predator-proof caging. Badgers have been known to kill fowl and may surplus-kill in a confined place. They eat young rabbits in the wild, having dug open their blind-ended tunnel, and would probably attack a flimsy hutch when hungry. Livestock or pets that are inadequately housed will be targeted by other carnivores, such as foxes, cats and rats, not just badgers.

The Agricultural Advisory Service and local badger groups advise on problems arising from badger activities

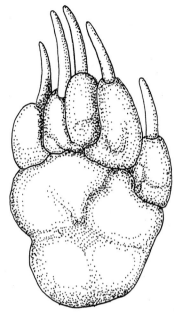

Long front claws are used for digging and defence. Those on the back feet are shorter.

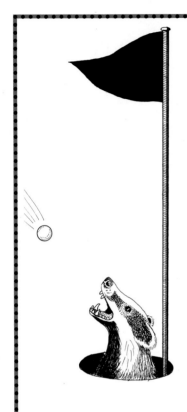

Green Problem? Green Solution!

Legal obligations apart, these days a frustrated builder, farmer or motorway surveyor with a deadline or a business to run is more likely to seek ways of accommodating badgers and their setts than try to have them moved or eliminated. One Surrey golf course is typical. Its management team saw the local badger community as nothing but a nuisance, creating divots and leaving smelly droppings on the perfectly manicured turf. Then a visiting group of Japanese golfers expressed delight at the prospect of seeing British wildlife at close hand. Suddenly, the holy terrors of the fourteenth hole had a new role: the course's management recast them as a valuable tourist attraction and advertised badger-watching-cum-golfing trips.

which clash with human livelihoods, or landscaping and garden schemes. There are a number of specialist badger consultants throughout the country who will also offer advice, for a reasonable fee. Literature is available from the Badger Trust to help householders, farmers, builders or engineers sort out specific on-site problems. Usually, things can be resolved without any need for badgers to come to harm. Destroying a badger (often a foraging single male is targeted) is only ever a short-term solution to a nuisance problem. There will always be another itinerant male waiting to take the other's place. Set against any damage they may

do, it's worth remembering that badgers themselves can be effective pest controllers. They keep rabbit numbers down (by reducing litters) and consume the larvae of **invertebrates** that would otherwise eat plants and roots.

COMMON HAZARDS FOR BADGERS

Major natural hazards include starvation and dehydration in spells of extreme drought, fight injuries that turn **septic**, severe dental wear-and-tear problems leading to starvation or septicaemia, and occasional loss of cubs to other predators or through internal badger group attack. But other life-threatening dangers, from road traffic, digging, baiting, snaring and shooting to gassing and destruction of habitats and food resources, are directly people-linked.

Badgers are becoming rare or absent in some parts of the country (South Yorkshire, parts of Derbyshire and Wales) because a minimum 1,000 animals a year are being culled by the Department of the Environment, Food & Rural Affairs, who are investigating possible links between badgers and increased incidences of cattle TB.

ROAD AND RAIL ACCIDENTS

It has been calculated that RTAs (road traffic accidents) account for half of the deaths in monitored badger populations. The annual toll for the country as a whole is reckoned to be 40–50,000. Unfenced roads in the South West alone claim 1,000 lives. But published figures may be underestimates. Not all road-kill bodies are found. Many animals will have struggled into deep undergrowth or have been flung some distance.

Attempts to separate badgers from traffic routes such as underpasses are often prompted by the dangers posed to human road users of hitting such a large animal – a particular danger to cyclists and motorcyclists. But it's not always easy persuading badgers to deviate from traditional routes.

Because of their strong build, adult badgers sometimes survive road hits that would instantly kill other wildlife. Some have recovered and been released back to the wild after being struck by trains. Only a minority of survivors are found. Most die later, as a result of **shock** and dehydration. But some survive and recover naturally. Veterinary **post-mortems** on badgers have found old, healed **lesions** on livers and **spleens** caused by road accidents earlier in life.

Apart from being hit by trains, badgers get killed when rail lines become newly electrified at ground level. There are no figures for such deaths. Hidden, long-term population problems also occur as a result of rail companies installing high-voltage electric fencing (750 volts) along sections of track. Such a system on the South East network ten years ago had the effect of fragmenting and isolating local badger populations. The long-term effects of this will be to impoverish foraging for the groups and reduce genetic diversity.

SIGNS: An unconscious casualty by the road, or severely burned near a rail track; a slow-moving badger out in open in daylight. Thickness of coat and general body shape may conceal the severity ➤

➤ of injuries. Concussion is likely. Badgers involved in RTAs often suffer severe mouth damage;broken teeth, pulp cavities exposed.

TREATMENT: (Also see *First Aid*) Life-saving on-site measures (using an open-mesh Baskerville muzzle if head injuries are not severe). Most painkillers used for domestic animals are suitable for wildlife and non-steroidal anti-inflammatories are often given.

TREATMENT FOR SEVERE HEAD INJURY: includes **intravenous** drugs to reduce brain swelling. The sooner this is done, the greater the chance of avoiding permanent brain damage.

TREATMENT FOR BROKEN BONES: **Simple** bone fractures are repaired when the casualty's condition has stabilised, using standard veterinary surgical procedures. **Complicated** breaks pose more problems because they must heal perfectly to take into account the rigours of life in the wild. Bone repair techniques used in modern canine hip surgery have been successfully applied to badgers. Such work requires a long post-operative recovery stint in captivity, specialised care and excellent healing results if the badger is to be released. **Amputation** of a limb would not usually be considered for a badger.

TREATMENT FOR INTERNAL INJURIES: These would be treated on veterinary advice, depending on the estimated chances of survival.

TREATMENT FOR TOOTH DAMAGE: Dental problems must be treated or the released animal would suffer painful abcesses and might die. No badger would be released if it had lost several teeth.

DELIBERATE DESTRUCTION

BOVINE TUBERCULOSIS (BTb)

The most widespread controversy currently surrounding badgers is their possible role in transmission routes of **bovine tuberculosis**. This problem came to a head in 1971, when a badger suffering from BTb was found dead in south-west England. Since then, thousands of badgers have been culled, and millions of pounds of taxpayers' money have been spent, and still there is no resolution. Meanwhile, BTb has surfaced in some herds where cattle re-stocking took place in the wake of the Foot and Mouth crisis, but where there are no badgers around. It has been suggested that the **perturbation** caused by culling could actually increase the likelihood of badgers transmitting the activated disease organisms.

Moreover, BTb exists in a wide range of wildlife species, not just badgers. A 2004 **Defra** report reveals that it affects five out of six deer species in the UK, with **infection** detected in between one and 15% of sampled deer. There are between 1.25 and 2.6 million wild deer in Britain, compared to around 300,000 badgers.

Current solutions to the badger-cattle problem are focused upon improving husbandry and farming practices, with particular attention to addressing the health risks of long-distance transportation of cattle, increased livestock testing and avoidance of possible cattle feed contamination (e.g. where other species can eat it or foul it).

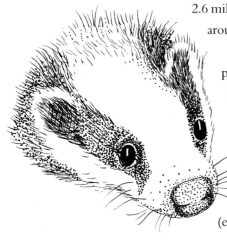

Since 1975, around 30,000 badgers have been killed (and tested post-mortem) in a bid to halt bovine TB.

Over the last 25 years, more than 30,000 badgers have been gassed or shot under licence after the former Ministry for Agriculture, Fisheries and Food concluded that they were a reservoir of bovine TB infection and posed a risk to cattle.

GASSING: This is now illegal, but badgers used to be routinely and legally destroyed while underground (along with any rabbits and foxes down there) as part of successive governments' badger slaughter policies. Cymag crystals were used, giving off lethal fumes of hydrogen cyanide gas when in contact with damp soil around the tunnel entrance. Originally, this method was thought to be more humane than trapping, snaring and shooting. It was much later concluded that badgers did not die quickly and painlessly from inhaling the fumes, although foxes and rabbits apparently did.

SHOOTING: Legalised shooting continues in certain areas, as part of the experimental culling programme aimed at halting the spread of bovine TB from cattle in the West Country to new areas. Badgers in designated zones are first held in cage traps before being shot through the head. Ireland has been culling badgers since 1997, in some cases using wire snares to trap them first.

Badgers are also shot, illegally, by private individuals. Any badger that survives the initial **trauma** of being hit by a high-speed projectile (bullet, pellets, arrow, etc.) and hasn't died from **asphyxia** (not getting enough oxygen in the blood) is at risk of dying from secondary infection via bacteria that have invaded the wound. Airgun slugs and shotgun pellets may seem less serious but often result in prolonged suffering and slow death (infection, starvation).

SIGNS: Damage to soft **tissue**, including nerves, muscles and blood vessels, multiple bone fractures, depending on the ammunition and weapon used. Pain is signalled by hot, swollen areas of tissue. Airgun slugs and shotgun pellets both cause puncture wounds that may not show much, unless an eye has been damaged. Tiny entry holes may be hidden by the coat, without much bleeding, but tracks will go very deep.

If a bullet has passed through a part of the body, without killing the badger outright (unlikely), you may be able to see both entry and exit wounds (the latter are larger) but won't know what internal damage exists. Internal **haemorrhage** may be signalled by pale mucous **membranes** (e.g. gums), or severe shock, and a **collapsed** animal. An injured badger may be out in daytime, moving awkwardly, or not using a limb. It may have lost the sight of an eye. It may look weak and lethargic, its coat may be dirty; it may smell bad. Puncture wounds often become infected, invaded by maggots or soil-borne **pathogens**.

TREATMENT: If treated before complications of **secondary bacterial infection** have overwhelmed the casualty, many badgers suffering puncture wounds will be able to recover. Fluid replacement therapy is used in place of the blood transfusions a human shooting victim would receive. Veterinary drugs would be administered intravenously to counteract the toxic effects of long-standing bacterial infection. Maggots and necrotic (dead) tissue would be removed; pain relief administered with possible ➤

➤ surgery later, depending on the type, location and level of damage. After initial assessment and pain relief, some animals may be **euthanased** on veterinary advice if not expected to fully recover.

Some fractures heal well naturally if the badger is kept in a very small area, with restricted movement, for a period. Other fractures, depending on their location, the badger's general state of health and likelihood of it being able to function normally in the wild, need the bones repositioning and kept stable. Young badgers apparently tolerate external metal bone-fixing frames and bandages better than adults.

SNARES

It is against the law to set a snare with the intention of trapping a badger. But snares that are set for animals such as rabbits, for pest control, can lethally injure many other species instead. They are not always checked as often as welfare guidelines advise. The cutting and pressure injuries they cause when an animal tries repeatedly to escape are horrendous and animal welfare charities like the RSPCA have long campaigned against the use of all snare types.

Never attempt to remove any wire from the badger's body yourself, or cut through it and let the badger run off. Both badger and attached snare should be taken together to the vet. Always contain the animal in a cage before cutting the securing line.

Snares set for other species can snag, and fatally injure, passing badgers.

SIGNS: A trapped badger will be suffering from exhaustion, dehydration and severe injuries caused by tightening wire cutting into body (illegal snare type); or half-strangled as a result of a drag snare tangling with other objects, e.g. tree branches, fencing, etc., as a powerful badger fights to escape. Injuries to limbs and jaw are likely. Even if no external injuries are visible (unlikely), a badger must not be released without a full veterinary examination and in-hospital surveillance. Necrotic (dead) **tissue** caused by pressure injury from the snare that goes undetected would cause a badger's inevitable, painful death later from blood poisoning.

TREATMENT: X-rays*, **sedation**, **fluid therapy** (via **drip** into **vein**); removal of embedded or entwined wires, constricting netting, etc., done under general anaesthesia; **broad-spectrum antibiotics**, analgesia (painkillers), intensive nursing care.

* *It is important that those treating badgers suffering from injuries caused by shooting and snaring keep records, such as X-rays, which could be used as evidence in future prosecutions.*

BITE INJURIES

Despite their thick coats and stores of fat around neck and rump, a proportion of young badgers die each year from bite injuries inflicted by **other badgers**, after wounds have turned **septic**. An elderly boar is likely to die after losing successive fights if the injuries get infected. (**Flystrike** is a serious warm weather hazard). Badgers may also be found suffering from **dog bites**.

SIGNS: These include a badger seen above ground during the day, seeking shelter in or near human habitation (e.g. farm outbuildings), scavenging (e.g. domestic animals' leftovers); weakness, **emaciation**, uncoordination; or found **collapsed**. Wounds may be visible, often on the rump, sometimes on the chest. Injuries may be seen in male and female badgers, young and old alike, but male fight injuries peak around the mating period. Secondary bacterial infection can make the wound look enormous, but it can heal quickly in animals in good condition. Some old males present with several rump wounds, all at different stages of healing.

TREATMENT: Minimal hair-clipping. The wounds are flushed out with saline, possible administration of a general **anaesthetic** for ease of examination, or painkiller drugs. **Topical** water-based gel is used on wounds. These are usually not closed surgically, but kept clean and allowed to heal naturally.

Antibacterials are given short-term; non-steroidal anti-inflammatories are given for pain relief; opioids may be used before and after surgery.

If bite wounds were inflicted by other badgers, it has been noted that they heal more efficiently than those inflicted by dogs, and require minimal, but daily, topical treatment, as well as cleaning.

POISONING

Because of their omnivorous diet, badgers are vulnerable to accidental poisoning from chemicals originally put down to kill rodents or insects. They may also fall victim to poisons deliberately (and illegally) put down to kill them.

SIGNS: These may include haemorrhaging, vomiting, diarrhoea, twitching, convulsions and **coma**.

TREATMENT: It's usually impossible to identify the poison. But if it were known, a specific **antidote** could be administered in a few cases. More often, so much time will have elapsed that much of the toxic agent will already have been absorbed. Sometimes an **emetic** may be given to empty the stomach. Otherwise, fluids and supportive care are given to relieve symptoms while the poison is naturally excreted. Veterinary protocol recommends that badgers which do not respond quickly to therapeutic treatment be put to sleep. If illegal use of poisons is suspected, vets may contact the Central Science Laboratory, where a Wildlife Incident Investigation Scheme is run by **Defra**.

HABITAT DISRUPTION

Badgers are cut off from their food sources when meadows, woods and other foraging areas are lost to increasing urban development. Research has shown that badgers are very susceptible to starvation (which is a major cause of badger deaths) if their foraging areas are lost. With the increased traffic flows that housing, industrial and road developments bring, badgers are at risk of getting run over. They may suffer more disease as the effects of stress and overcrowding weaken their **immune systems**.

Extraction of rock, coal and ores in the countryside is often disruptive to wildlife sites and can fragment badger clans and territories, too. Dutch research has shown that fragmented clans are especially sensitive to the death of any adult member and if contact with other badger groups is cut off and normal dispersal patterns (e.g. for breeding) are blocked, a clan may not be able to survive.

Where relict badger populations do remain, stranded in a sea of new housing, there are "problems with the neighbours". Some people worry about badgers causing subsidence. They may see the animals as dangerous, liable to rush up and bite them, menace the children or family pets in the garden. They may consider badgers as a potential threat to human health in other ways, such as through confused messages about bovine TB transmission. Setts within easy reach of human habitation are soft targets for diggers and baiters, too. Even well-meaning badger watchers who just want to visit setts may force the retiring badger to move elsewhere.

DIGGING, TERRIER WORK AND BAITING

Some 10,000 badgers a year are killed illegally as a "sport". Digging and baiting continue to such an extent that badgers are becoming rare in parts of Britain. Nationally, at least 11% of main setts are believed to be affected by diggers. Digging entails opening up setts to expose a badger to a terrier, sent down to find it, once it has been cornered in an underground tunnel. The practice has traditional links to fox hunting and to the custom of working with dogs to flush out and kill animals such as foxes, rabbits and rodents as a

The first attempt to have the baiting of badgers banned was in 1800.

method of "pest control". Dug-out badgers are often deliberately injured, usually with a spade, then held in captivity for later use as the "bait", in baiting.

Baiting involves a badger being set upon by dogs, either to hone the dogs' fighting skills or as money-making entertainment sponsored by onlookers' bets. Baiting has been illegal since 1835, but there are signs that it is on the increase. Great secrecy surrounds the whereabouts of these illegal fights, which are often staged in urban areas.

The odds are considerably stacked against the badger by giving it such handicaps as a broken jaw or leg. Dogs are often severely – even fatally – injured in the fray, and subsequently abandoned. Penalties for those found guilty of breaking the law in this way include prison terms, fines, confiscation or destruction of dogs.

LAMPING is another form of persecution where a badger is dazzled by a spotlight and dogs are set upon it.

BADGER DISEASES – AND HUMAN HEALTH

A **zoonosis** is an illness that people and animals can share. In common with other wildlife, badgers can carry bacterial illnesses which may affect humans, too, in certain circumstances. But transference is unlikely, even for those who customarily handle or treat badgers, if standard clinical cleanliness protocols are observed. Veterinary staff would follow specific procedures relating to surgery in the light of zoonotic risks from particular badger diseases.

LEPTOSPIROSIS (WEIL'S DISEASE IN HUMANS)

Badgers have been recorded as carrying the bacteria which cause this serious, potentially lethal liver- and kidney-damaging illness, perhaps as a result of eating infected **rodents**. But the chief source of this **infection** in humans is ingestion of – or open skin contact with – water contaminated by **infective** rats' **urine**.

Any mammal may contract the **rabies virus**, although in the UK badgers are not considered to be a primary **host**.

SALMONELLA

Salmonella bacteria are often cultured from badgers, but this doesn't pose a significant risk to rescuers and rehabilitators. Salmonella poisoning in humans is usually associated with faecal contamination linked to domesticated animals, most frequently chickens, and consumption of animal-sourced food products. Young babies and children, older people and anyone whose immune system is compromised by illness or medical treatment (such as chemotherapy) are at most risk from effects of these illnesses.

> **HUMAN SYMPTOMS**: These include gripe, vomiting, diarrhoea, and dehydration.
> **HUMAN TREATMENT**: This is usually by antibacterial drugs and **rehydration**. Avoidance includes hygiene measures (e.g. hand cleansing, using soap or antibacterial liquid, not eating or drinking while handling animals, not sharing feeding areas, dishes or utensils with animals).

ANTHRAX

Badgers are known to be susceptible to **anthrax**, a serious bacterial **infection** primarily associated with cattle, although it affects other animals, too. People can also become infected by anthrax, (a dreaded potential weapon of biological warfare). There are two strains: one affects the skin, the other attacks the lungs. One of the chief worries about anthrax is the ability of the bacteria to survive for many years in soil, or in animal products, as **spores**. They lie dormant but remain capable of causing infection when animals graze on land contaminated by them. The disease, although potentially fatal and still a problem in some parts of the world, is a very rare health threat to people in Britain.

TUBERCULOSIS

Not one, but a whole group of diseases, tuberculosis used to be a very common contagious infection worldwide. Under the name of consumption, it killed off many a character in romantic opera and classic novels. Until after the Second World War, it was one of the commonest causes of death in the UK. Today about 30 million people worldwide have active tuberculosis and about three million die of it annually. The disease has been making a reappearance in the developed world amid the poor hygiene, inadequate diets and chaotic lifestyles of those sleeping rough, and the alcohol or drug-addicted in big cities such as New York and London, and is also on the rise again in the Third World where it may be the first sign that someone is HIV positive. Drug-resistant TB strains in humans have emerged in recent years, too, as a result of sufferers not completing courses of prescribed drugs.

The **bacilli** may enter the body through a cut, by inhalation (an infected person suffering from a cavity in the lung can spit up 4,000,000,000 bacilli in 24 hours), or by ingestion.

BOVINE TB (BTB)

This is the cattle version of the disease. In people, the infection route of BTb is most commonly via the digestive system, not the lungs. Some people became infected years ago through drinking untreated (green top) milk, if it contained undetected infective TB bacilli. Their bodies may have naturally halted the infection (they may not even have known they had TB). But in later life, as their immune system weakened, dormant bacteria in their bodies could become reactivated. Milk pasteurisation (a heating process that destroys disease-causing micro-organisms in the milk) is now standard.

> **HUMAN SYMPTOMS**: include the gradual onset of poor overall health, loss of appetite and weight, recurrent fever, night sweats, cough. Chest X-rays reveal damage in the upper lobes of lungs.
> **TREATMENT**: is by a range of antituberculous drugs; untreated, TB spreads to destroy tissue permanently and cause scarring.
> **Prevention** includes vaccine (prepared from an artificially weakened strain of cattle TB).

BADGER DISEASES

TUBERCULOSIS IN BADGERS

Badgers, like other mammals, can be affected by the bacterium (*Mycobacterium bovis*) responsible for bovine TB. Like humans, badgers infected with TB can suffer from a delayed revival of the active disease. A common trigger would appear to be an infected bite wound in a male badger. Such an injury can set off an accelerated, severe re-emergence of active TB.

TB is a significant infectious killer of badgers in the wild. In infected areas, it is thought to account for a tenth of badger population deaths. It is feared that artificial breaking up of social patterns through culling (causing stress and territorial fighting) may increase disease transmission in badgers.

It is still not clear if, and how, badgers might transmit BTb back to cattle. Observations on pastureland within badger clan territories have shown that badgers tend not to have any close physical contact with grazing cattle. Cattle can catch BTb from each other, however, all too easily, via inhaled droplets from the mouths and noses of other, infected, cattle when they are kept in close proximity. Latest Defra control measures include more frequent testing of cattle and post-movement testing with on-farm isolation.

In the vast majority of cases, no one can tell, simply by looking at a badger, if it is infected, or if the infection is active and capable of being passed on. Lesions are usually formed internally, on the animal's lymph nodes and lungs. Post-mortem tests on tissue samples of dead badgers are the only reliable way of proving whether a badger has TB or not.

> **DIAGNOSIS**: It is difficult to test for TB in badgers because bacilli are excreted only intermittently. A one ml. serum test, taken from blood of a sedated adult badger, or cub, is one helpful test.
>
> Otherwise tissue samples from dead badgers (sent away for culture to approved laboratories) are the only reliable way of telling if badger is infected. Lesions on lungs, kidneys, and other organs, including large abscesses with necrotic tissue, will be visible on post-mortem. A triple-testing policy is used for releasing cubs which are due to be ➤

translocated away from the area where they were born. Animals are classified as TB positive on the basis of a single positive result from blood tests taken during rearing, and put to sleep. This is done to avoid introducing TB into disease-free areas.

SIGNS: There are usually none externally. Signs of general ill health, weight loss, cough, etc., can all be effects of other problems or illnesses (e.g. starvation, secondary bacterial infection, lung worms). An infected injury or trauma such as snaring or captivity stress are known to hasten the progress of the disease if bacilli are already present.

TREATMENT: Those treating sick badgers should be aware of potential zoonotic infection risks. Infected badgers can excrete TB bacilli for up to three years. Vets operating on badger casualties with severe chest injuries, in particular, advise against repeated use of post-operative chest drains. Euthanasia is usually recommended for reasons of animal welfare, as well as a TB transmission risk.

PARVOVIRUS INFECTIONS

Canine **parvovirus** is a killer which replicates in the growing cells of its host's gut lining or developing heart muscle. It is highly contagious, very resistant to disinfectants, can survive up to six months in contaminated **faeces** on the ground and can be carried around on animals' coats, and people's shoes.

Parvovirus originated in the 1970s in domestic cats, then spread to dogs. Since then, a variant of canine parvovirus has severely affected Britain's grey and common seal coastal populations on more than one occasion. Canine parvovirus is also believed to affect fox cubs being treated in rescue and **rehabilitation** establishments. (New admissions are isolated before being housed with other cubs.) Several places now vaccinate fox cubs and badger cubs reared in captivity **prophylactically** against canine parvovirus before release.

In the late 1990s, clinical signs were observed in sick badger cubs at a rescue and rehabilitation centre, and several died. But, at the time, vets were unable to isolate the virus and prove parvo was the killer. However, other members of the **mustelids** group of animals are known to be susceptible.

SIGNS: Initially none while the virus is destroying only a few cells in the gut or heart. This is followed by sudden-onset vomiting, **enteritis**, large quantities of foul-smelling, bloody diarrhoea; dehydration, shock, and secondary bacterial infections. Death may be rapid, even if **symptoms** are mild.

TREATMENT: If a youngster is found to be infected by canine parvovirus, or a related strain, it can continue to shed virus in large quantities even when appearing healthy. Treatment includes rehydration, antibiotics and supportive nursing. Strict barrier nursing, disinfectant bath outside the pen to prevent spreading by contaminated footwear, disinfection of feeding bowls, towels, etc.

PREVENTATIVE MEASURE: Inoculation with an **attenuated** parvovirus vaccine, of at-risk badger cubs in captivity.

DISTEMPER

Canine distemper (formerly called hardpad) is a virus related to the human measles virus. It causes brain and spinal cord **inflammation** and has been found in badgers in continental Europe, but not in Britain. The virus is inhaled via the nose and throat, and destroys cells in the digestive system, lungs, skin and central **nervous system**.

SIGNS: These vary from mild illness and diarrhoea (in animals whose immune systems recover quickly) to severe vomiting, diarrhoea, dehydration, **fever**, **pneumonia**, **paralysis**, thickened, cracked skin on pads and nose, and permanent signs of **nervous system** damage later.

TREATMENT: No treatment will kill the virus once in the animal's body. Antibiotics are given for (usually common) secondary bacterial infections; intravenous fluids.

DENTAL DISEASE

Badger casualties often show signs of tooth damage, which may be linked to earthworms in their diet, as well as the result of injury.

SIGNS: Teeth may be broken, worn down, or diseased.

TREATMENT: Veterinary dentistry to remove teeth; treat abscesses. No badger would be released if it had had four **canine teeth** extracted.

PARASITES

INTERNAL

In common with other wild mammals, badgers may play **host** to a variety of internal **parasites**, including worms. The best known affect mainly the intestines. Often when another problem arises, such as starvation, traumatic injury or secondary bacterial infection, the balance between internal parasites and their host goes awry and the animal suffers an abnormally large parasitic burden. In young animals, an overload of parasitic worms can occasionally prove fatal, blocking the gut. Worms may cause loss of blood and seriously interfere with food absorption. In the lungs, they provoke respiratory symptoms, such as coughing.

SIGNS: These include worms and eggs in excreta, rough coat, poor condition, diarrhoea, vomiting, weight loss, **anaemia**, **chronic** cough. Ripe **tapeworm** segments break away and are shed from the anus; egg cases look like grains of cooked white rice and move when fresh.

TREATMENT: In captivity, many internal parasites may be easily treated with standard appropriate veterinary-use drugs (of the kind prescribed for domestic animals). Lungworm treatment is complicated by the fact that the worm-killing drug does not resolve the inflammatory reaction in the host's body to the toxicity of the dead worms; pro-active treatment would include corticosteroids to reduce inflammation, and antibiotics.

A certain **endoparasite** load is considered normal for a wild-living animal in good health and a released badger patient can expect to encounter the usual suspects again before long. Newly hatched **roundworm** larvae are killed by sunshine, and, to a lesser extent, dryness, but the eggs can be quite disinfectant-resistant.

EXTERNAL

Badgers enjoy a good scratch. This is often the first thing they do – communally – upon emerging from their sett at dusk. A close-up examination of their fur and underlying skin would probably reveal why. Scratching can lead to secondary infection by bacteria which enter the skin via moist, weeping open areas.

Badgers are not generally subject to persecution by the skin **mite** that causes **sarcoptic mange** in foxes and dogs, although there have been instances of badgers found with mange here and on the Continent. Sarcoptic mange is spread by direct contact with shed skin cells containing living mites and their eggs. These accumulate in sleeping and nursery areas but it is thought that badgers' habits of shifting from one part of a sett to another and clearing out old bedding helps them avoid external parasitic build-ups in their underground homes.

Badgers may become unwitting hosts to badger-specific varieties of fleas and biting lice (their most common external parasite) and three types of tick (shared by sheep, dogs and hedgehogs) picked up in their environment. Apart from the skin irritation caused by any insect or eight-legged, spider-like creature that punctures the skin and makes a meal of its host's blood, many external parasites can also spread disease between mammals, including those caused by viruses, bacteria, **protozoa**, **rickettsia** (parasitic micro-organisms that live in mites themselves) and worms, because of their direct access to bloodstreams. Fleas, for example, play a role in tapeworm transmission and ticks can spread zoonotic diseases.

SIGNS: Visible, moving fleas and flea-dirt; crawling **lice** on coat (lice exit if the host's body temperature drops); scratching, hair-loss, self-inflicted skin wounds; samples of parasites are clearest on close examination of the underfur of the badger's coat. A tick looks like a small grey-green grape when the parasite's abdomen is full of ingested blood; otherwise flat.

TREATMENT: This consists of standard veterinary-use treatments, such as Frontline and careful manual removal of all ticks. Great care must be taken not to leave any portion of tick's mouthparts behind, where they will lead to abscesses. Dabbed with a little methylated spirits or Frontline, a tick should slowly release its grip, enabling it to be pulled away. If lodged near an eye or genital region, liquid paraffin should be used instead, the tick removed after a ten-minute wait. The small wire hook designed for the job works well, but must be used with a smooth, gentle continuous action.

"Castor bean" or "sheep" ticks are common in Britain, and although they only visit mammals (man included) over a few days in spring or autumn in order to feed, they can pass on diseases (also see *Lyme Disease*, p. 188).

Cubs due for release are triple-tested for TB

Lyme Disease (a zoonosis)

This is caused by a **bacterium** carried by a particular tick normally found on deer. Sensible hygiene should be observed when removing ticks to avoid the (small) danger of transmission to the handler.

> **Symptoms in Humans**: A flu-like illness, swelling and redness of knees and other large joints. Diagnosis confirmed by blood tests.
> **Treatment**: antibiotics, non-steroidal anti-inflammatories and possibly corticosteroid drugs.

Flystrike can be a particular curse in the warmer months

Flies and Maggots – "Flystrike"

An injured badger may become targeted by blue, black and greenbottle flies which lay their eggs on open wounds. Their hatching maggots feed on the flesh, thereby releasing bacteria into the host animal's system. The animal becomes seriously ill, eventually dying of **toxic shock**. Flystrike is most noxious in summer.

> **Signs**: Small white flies' eggs and maggots are visible in the wound area and also around the rear if the badger has suffered severe diarrhoea or has toileting problems following spine/**pelvis** injury.
> **Treatment**: After wound cleansing, dental irrigators are often used for flushing out small maggots; therapy with **ivermectin** is given, plus anti-bacterial cover for severe cases, and non-steroidal anti-inflammatories to provide both pain relief and anti-toxic therapy.

Other Problems

Badger Fallen Into Pit

Occasionally, healthy badgers tumble into sunken areas from which they cannot escape: empty swimming pools, slurry pits, and so on. If they are unhurt and have only been trapped for a night, they can be rescued and released. The best time to let them go again is dusk. But if they are cold and hungry, or if it's raining or heatwave weather, the sooner they get back to their sett, the better. Offer some raw mince, or peanuts, beforehand, or leave a little food out in the area, in case they come back later.

Cubs in Peril?

Very Young Cubs Alone

If you see a very young cub alone above ground before the end of March, or beginning of April, and its mother does not appear and pick it up, it's likely to have got there because it was disturbed.

February is peak time for cub births. They don't normally make their first cautious trip above ground (at dusk) until they're around 8–10 weeks old. They won't go far at first, only onto the soil spoilheap at the sett entrance. The first danger signal from the sow will send them scooting back down below.

Not until the early summer months will mother and cubs be exploring their group's territory together. By July, when the cubs are four or five months old, they will be much more independent, venturing further away from the sett to find and eat their own solid foods, such as earthworms and beetles.

OLDER CUBS ALONE

Sometimes, bigger, newly weaned cubs are found, having strayed from their own territories. But they are in danger, too. They are at high risk of being killed by dominant males who find them "trespassing" on their home ground, or by sows from the same or another clan. Even in normal circumstances, there is high cub mortality. 50–60% of all cubs don't live beyond their first year. In a year of drought, when earthworms may become unavailable, juvenile badgers are extra vulnerable to starvation.

SIGNS: A cub above ground that seems very immature, very small, with eyes still shut (eyes open after five weeks) its coat still thin and silvery, with very faint black stripes, and no discernible teeth (milk teeth come through at around one month). The cub is cold to the touch, emitting distress cries.

WHAT YOU CAN DO: Watch and wait. See if the mother returns. But be prepared to take the cub for emergency help. No one would advocate removing a young wild animal from its environment unnecessarily, but leaving a very young lone badger in a vulnerable position risks its death from starvation, **hypothermia** or **predation**. It may be killed by another adult badger. Ring an individual or organisation with badger know-how for advice about cub problems (also see *Useful Organisations*, p. 196). Don't leave them to sort themselves out "naturally".

TREATMENT: Prompt gradual warming (indirect heat from overhead lamp, covered heatpad or ➤ hot-water bottle. Use a towel or bubblewrap or your own body heat as temporary first aid measure. Rehydration therapy and shock treatment (via a drip, if unconscious); feeding with puppy milk via a needle-less syringe or kitten-feeder bottle if the cub is well enough. The cub is cared for in captivity for several months, then **soft-released** in an artificial new "clan", with initial support-feeding on site.

CUBS IN CARE

The Secret World wildlife rescue centre in Somerset (also see *Useful Organisations*, p. 195) receives about 60 to 70 orphaned cubs a year. Inevitably, it is not always possible to establish whether a new admission is a true orphan or one of "Nature's rejects" which would not have thrived or survived in the wild. Congenital health problems often don't emerge until the cub has been in care for a week or two.

But the most common problem facing badger "orphans" is hunger. The sow may have become a victim of baiters or been killed on the road. (March is peak month for adult badger road deaths.) Other youngsters may have been pulled from the sett by dogs.

Each admission must be given a full health assessment, (also see *Bovine TB tests*, p. 184) and any necessary medical treatment. Most need to be hand-fed with milk replacements (e.g. half-strength Esbilac) by bottle until they are old enough to be weaned at around 8–10 weeks.

Fosterers note: cubs push out a large scent-marking gland, situated alongside their anus, when they feed. It is not a sign that they have piles or constipation problems! Young cubs must be stimulated to excrete after feeds. The sow would normally lick her cubs' rears to do this in the wild.

Older cubs are weaned on to foods such as Weetabix, porridge and scrambled egg. At 10 weeks, they are given a wide diet that includes minced meat, puppy food, dead day-old chicks, peanut butter sandwiches, cooked chicken and some fruit.

Later, all cubs destined for release must be put into socially engineered groups, with the right sex ratio, to create a viable artificial clan on release. Suitable new territories must be found well in advance. If that were not complicated enough, great care must be taken not to allow the cubs to become imprinted upon humans while being cared for.

A group's sex ratio is two males to four to six females

ORPHAN CUB RELEASE

Cubs are put back into the wild according to the guidelines in the Badger Trust's standard protocol (also see *Useful Organisations*, p. 196). They are only released if a series of blood tests has shown that they are not a BTb risk.

Cubs get released in stages. Human contact is systematically reduced, their food thrown into their enclosure. The naturally weaned youngsters teach the bottle-fed orphans how to fend for themselves. Sometimes orphan cubs are introduced early on to sows with cubs of their own, or to those who have lost their cubs. A young adult whose history was unknown (i.e. there was no chance of reuniting him with his clan) might also get released with a new "family" into an artificial sett on virgin territory. This would be his best chance of being accepted in a new group.

Small colonies of youngsters are sent out together (although not natural littermates or fellow clan members originally) and released into artificial setts. This usually happens when they are six to eight months old. Great care and much research goes into siting such setts, usually in conjunction with the RSPCA and with the active co-operation of landowners. New groups are usually made up of five to eight individuals, with at least two males in the group and between four to six females, so that the breeding ratio is appropriate.

Support feeding in the area would continue for a while. Interestingly, although such groups of badgers usually abandon their new artificial home and escape the confines of temporary wire fencing in double-quick time, they often choose to dig a new sett of their own in the vicinity. Their progress would then be monitored.

WHEN BADGERS NEED HELP

LIFTING AN UNCONSCIOUS BADGER

This is obviously the easiest kind of casualty to handle, though expect it to be heavy. Fully grown adults can weigh between 9kg and 12kg depending on time of year. And expect it to come round unexpectedly (e.g. in the warmth of a vehicle). Don't bother with thick gloves or towels to protect your hands (they won't) but use a blanket, towel, survival blanket, bubblewrap, etc., to conserve the badger's body heat.

If you move an unconscious badger, try to keep the casualty in the same position in which you found it. If possible, ease it onto an improvised stretcher. This will help to avoid moving any broken bones or disturbing any blood clots that have formed. (Also see *Badger First Aid*, p. 195).

A Conscious One!

Badgers aren't gratuitously aggressive, but their powerful bite can sever a finger. So keep your hands (and any other part of you) out of range. Badgers can switch direction and move with considerable agility and speed. They are not easy to lift with a dog-grasper because they are heavy and have thick, strongly muscled neck areas (ideal for sliding backwards out of tight corners). Unless you are an experienced wildlife handler, scruffing – picking a badger up by the loose skin on its neck – is probably out of the question if you ever want to play the piano again.

Handling an adult badger is not a job to tackle on your own because of its weight and habit of unexpectedly coming back to consciousness. One rehabilitation centre tests the reflexes of badger casualties with a dab from the head-end of a soft-bristled broom. If the animal does not react to this, the broom is used to securely pin the neck and head to the ground while a grasper is put in place. If you do lift a badger, always support its rear.

But if you don't fancy doing this, you could offer a casualty a safe dark tunnel to hide in, such as an empty dustbin, or large end-opening metal-framed pet carrier. If the badger is obviously badly hurt, suffering from multiple fractures and unknown internal injuries, getting it to a vet will be its only possible chance of survival. Left where it is, it may be further injured by scavenging birds or it may stagger into the road.

Approaching

Always work your way towards a casualty quietly and in a low-key manner. Don't look directly at the animal's face. Approach gradually, at an oblique angle. Although it can be helpful to have other people as back-ups (blocking off possible escape routes), a single figure presents less of a threat. Move confidently, with smooth movements and don't talk, or make noises to the animal – they won't soothe it.

Using a Grasper

Unlike the technique used for foxes, dogs and cats, which are all more lightly built than badgers, conscious badger casualties may be "grasped" with the noose firmly over the neck and one front leg. Once firmly secured in this way, the rescuer is advised to pick the badger up by the rump – at arm's length – and put into the basket/carrier immediately. Badgers have heavy bodies and you must support the whole animal when lifting.

A dog grasper has a padded noose that is quickly retractable.

Containing

A badger is likely to move towards what it sees as a safe bolthole. This could be an upturned, empty plastic dustbin or other strong darkened container, such as an end-opening cage. If the badger is accurately held in a dog-grasper's (releasable) noose, the bin can be stood upright, noose quickly removed, and the lid put on. The badger will probably curl up in the bottom but must not be left in there too long. Get further help immediately. Keep the casualty in darkened conditions, and minimise noise and disturbance around it. Keep people away and discourage frequent condition checks.

TRANSPORTING

Transport the badger in a container that is strong enough to prevent its escape, without interfering with its breathing. It is against the law to carry a wildlife casualty loose inside your vehicle. Putting an unconscious animal in the boot can create problems. If it regains consciousness, it may cause considerable damage (e.g. to wiring) with its strong claws. Attempting to unload the casualty from the boot could result in its escape.

Telephone in advance and warn a veterinary surgery of your arrival and its estimated time, giving details of the badger's condition. If arranging for someone else to pick the badger up, give clear directions. Stay on site to guide the wildlife ambulance or other rescue vehicle. Position the casualty so that it cannot roll or jolt when the vehicle brakes or turns a corner – facing front to back may be best.

The most common problem facing badger orphans is hunger.

At the vet's surgery, the badger may be more easily examined if it is given an open-mesh muzzle (i.e. treated like a domestic dog with a tendency to nip when stressed). The practice to which Secret World take their trauma admissions do not normally anaesthetise badger casualties in order to examine them. They prefer to see the animal's responses when it is able to move around.

TIME FOR RELEASE? WHEN AND WHERE

Ideally, a badger should be released back to its territory quickly, at the exact spot where it was found. But this isn't as simple as it sounds. A rescued badger must meet a number of criteria if it's going to cope and get a second chance of life back in the wild.

Only those badgers considered to have made good recoveries are sent out again. In rescue and rehabilitation terms, this means that their condition must be practically 100% perfect. A badger's lifestyle is physically gruelling and only the best equipped will survive. That rules out any injuries which, though physically healed, would compromise the badger's ability to run, feed, defend its territory, and reproduce. Limb amputations, complicated jaw fractures, asymmetrically healed pelvic fractures in females, severe toe and claw damage, loss of sight or hearing, would all rule out release.

Some charities release badgers with poor sight. But, says Pauline Kidner, this may not be humane: "*We had a cub with very poor eyesight. It coped very well while being hand-reared in our kitchen. Out in a pen with other cubs, it still seemed fine. But there were four breeze blocks stacked in the corner of the pen. We went down one night and there was this cub, stuck at the top of the pile. It had climbed up somehow. But then it couldn't get down again because it had no means of knowing how high up it was."*

A rescued badger adult or cub that recovers quickly, and has not been away from its clan and sett for very long, may be returned to that territory with relative ease. But it depends how long it has been away. If its familiar clan scent has faded or if it has had other smells superimposed upon it, the animal won't be made welcome on its return. Instead, it is likely to be attacked and driven away, as if it were a stranger.

Some badgers can be "turned round" by a treatment centre within hours. But these are the lucky minority. Most casualties need longer to recuperate. Bone fractures, of the kind suffered by most road accident victims, require two to three months in-patient care.

Although dusk is usually the recommended time for release, many badgers are now being sent back out into their home areas very late at night. It is hoped that this will avoid repeats of the very injuries that brought them into care in the first place, because road traffic is usually lighter during the small hours. Released badgers need to be monitored to check how they are coping. A system of inner thigh tattooing, under licence, may help with this.

NON-RETURNABLES

An elderly badger with broken or heavily worn teeth, low bodyweight, in poor condition, or one that had been driven from its sett because it was suffering from disease, or bearing scars of several territorial bite wounds at various stages of recovery, would not be sent back to the wild. It would most probably be put to sleep

for humane reasons. But some elderly badgers end up as permanent residents in wildlife sanctuaries or hospitals with the suitable facilities to care for them. They would live with other resident badgers for company.

The Badger Trust, Secret World Wildlife Rescue and the RSPCA have devised a protocol to help those handling badger casualties. (See *Useful Organisations*, p. 196)

Casualty Kit

✔ A big old clean blanket, bath towel (cotton is easiest to wash and re-use) to cover and wrap around unconscious casualty
✔ Smaller cotton towels, flannels, to use as pressure pads
✔ Bandages, lint, cotton wool
✔ Grasper (dog-size)
✔ Disinfectant suitable for animal use
✔ Blunt-ended scissors
✔ Wire cutters for snares (but take the attached snare to the vet, along with the casualty)
✔ A waterproof sheet, or paper, to put under the casualty in the vehicle
✔ A strong metal animal travel kennel or carrier
✔ A baskerville dog muzzle, medium size (a badger's skull is wide at the top)

Inner-thigh tattoos may help in long-term monitoring

▸▸10 Ways to Get Involved ⟫⟫⟫⟫⟫⟫⟫⟫⟫⟫⟫⟫⟫

◆ Treat yourself to a badger-watch weekend (see adverts in magazines such as BBC Wildlife) or enrol in a Field Studies course to become a brock boffin; it's amazing what can be seen under the microscope and in the field.

◆ Join a local badger group and discover the most effective ways to tackle badger crime and cruelty.

◆ Become a wildlife hospital volunteer to be hands-on with badger rescue and rehabilitation.

◆ Campaign for more road underpasses on known badger routes. Make sure fencing gets put in, too, because badgers won't use new lifesaving routes otherwise. Measures are more likely to get the go-ahead if you can gather evidence to show they'll potentially save human lives.

◆ Keep a watch over badger clans and setts in your area.

◆ Carry a first aid kit, **space blanket** or bubblewrap in your car. They could help all roadside trauma victims.

◆ Drive more slowly, especially at dawn and dusk, when badgers go on their rounds.

◆ Attach a sonic warning device to your car. It might help signal vehicle's approach to wild mammal about to cross.

◆ Always check to see if a prone badger is still alive. (Stop or park safely, and make sure you can be clearly seen by oncoming motorists if you're on foot. Keep a Day-glo, fluorescent jacket or gilet in the boot for roadside emergencies, use warning triangle, hazard lights, torch, etc., or get someone else to flag down the traffic before it reaches the scene).

◆ If badgers visit your garden, provide clean water daily. You could also offer a little complete dried dogfood, plus **vitamin supplements**, when weather conditions are harsh.

BADGER FIRST AID

AIRWAYS. Wear latex gloves. Clear obvious blockages from mouth and nose (vomit, mud, netting) to maximise oxygen intake. Try not to disturb blood clots if the casualty has serious head and facial injuries. If possible, check that the tongue has not fallen back, blocking the throat. Pull the tongue forward if necessary.

BREATHING. If there is a heartbeat, make sure the casualty is in the best position to help its breathing: on its side with head and neck extended. Do not hamper breathing by putting anything over its face

CIRCULATION. Feel for a pulse, detectable under front left armpit. Keep the body horizontal to maintain effective blood circulation. But if there is much blood at the nose and mouth, try to ensure that the head is slightly lower than the body during transportation. This will help blood drain from the **airways**. If the animal vomits, this position will help avoid fluid inhalation, too.

Stop obvious external bleeding by applying pressure at the site with a clean absorbent pad. Add more pads on top if blood soaks through. Direct pressure from a clean finger or thumb can be effective in the short term.

DO note where you found the badger and the circumstances in which you found it

Do note all **signs** of injury or illness. Details count and can save precious time, e.g. fluid coming from ears can indicate skull fracture. What you notice may aid a prosecution

Do get professional help as soon as possible. The badger is likely to need rehydration and must be treated immediately

DON'T give badger casualty anything by mouth. You could choke it

DON'T put a muzzle on (even in an open-mesh plastic box) until at the vet's surgery, in case it escapes

DON'T cut away any restriction, e.g. snaring wire, yourself. Bring all ligatures and traps to surgery along with the casualty

USEFUL ORGANISATIONS:

Badgerland The Old Post Office, 10 Badger Lane, Blackshawhead, Hebden Bridge HX7 7JX. 01422 846846; www.badgerland.co.uk

The Badger Trust PO Box 708, East Grinstead, RH19 2W8
08458 287878; www.badgertrust.org.uk

League against Cruel Sports
Sparling House, 83–87 Union Street, London SE1 1SG
0845 330 8486; www.league.uk.com

Secret World Wildlife Rescue Centre
New Rd, East Huntspill, Highbridge, Somerset TA9 9PZ
01278 783250; www.secretworld.org

Scottish Badgers 01386 624 851; www.scottishbadgers.org.uk

The Royal Society of Wildlife Trusts (RSWT)
The Kiln, Waterside, Mather Rd, Newark, NG24 1WT
01636 677711; www.wildlifetrusts.org

True or False?

1 Litters of badger babies are produced by several females, called sows, in each group.

2 Badger droppings come in a whole range of colours.

3 Like hedgehogs, badgers often react to the threat of oncoming traffic by standing still.

4 Badgers' bulky, low-slung bodies make them very slow-movers, above and below ground.

5 Badgers sometimes send a member of their group into exile.

6 Badgers don't normally need to drink much water.

7 Body fat and dense hair is all a badger needs to keep warm in its underground sleeping quarters.

8 A badger needs to eat around 200 earthworms each night.

Answers

1 False – Generally, only one female in the clan will reproduce successfully, giving birth underground to up to five cubs in January or February.

2 True – and not simply because researchers may have fed them (harmlessly-passed) coloured plastic marker pellets. If badgers have been feeding on earthworms, the main item in their diet, their faeces will be brown. Droppings will be yellow if corn was on the menu, purple if the badgers have been feasting on berries.

3 True: although badgers can pick up the vibrations that herald the approach of a vehicle, their defence tactic is as unsuccessful as that of the hedgehog. Up to 50,000 badgers are killed on our roads each year.

4 False: they may be squat, pear-shaped and carrying a lot of subcutaneous fat at certain times of year, but badgers are extremely flexible – and fast. They can spin, twist, climb and run at remarkable speed and they are competent swimmers, too. Great care must be taken when dealing with badger casualties because they can turn-tail, even in a confined space, quicker than most people would expect.

5 True: Individuals may be ostracized, either temporarily or permanently, and excluded from the clan. They are forced to dig a new outlying sett on the edges of the existing one. However, the outcast may be tolerated at closer quarters when the group feed at night, provided they behave passively and do not challenge the clan's existing pecking order.

6 True – for much of the year in the UK, badgers can obtain enough water for their needs from earthworms, whose body segments are full of water. But in drought conditions, when they cannot find worms because they have retreated too deeply into the soil, badgers can suffer severe dehydration, and die unless they can use an alternative clean water source, such as a pond, in their foraging area.

7 False: badgers collect fresh bedding at regular intervals and it provides them with vital insulation during winter. The bedding must be dry, but badgers will make use of a wide range of materials, from dried wild grasses, leaves and bracken to straw and hay. If it contains agricultural binder twine, this can strangle or fatally injure cubs when they become tangled in it. Old, dirty bedding is ejected onto spoil heaps of excavated soil at sett entrances.

8 True: and when conditions are right (damp, still evenings, short cropped grassland), this number can be taken in just a couple of hours.

BOG BEAN

Sometimes, sows sleep so soundly that they don't even know when their cub has been pulled out from under them. But there's no point in blaming your dog, the rescuer told the dog's owner, who was very upset. Maybe the mother had been killed and the cub's crying had attracted the dog in the first place…

Bog Bean appeared in a garden, freezing cold, one February morning. He was two days old and covered in lice and fleas. However he did well at the wildlife centre, bottle-fed on puppy milk. No problems at all. He was joined by six others, including one that had been taken from its sett by a Jack Russell. Even though tiny, their eyes and ears still sealed, these two cubs interacted with one another straight away.

By the time he was released, Bog Bean was fit, full-sized and in fine fettle. He was also very people-shy, which was reassuring for his rehabilitators – and very surprising, considering how much handling he had received. He was in with a good chance.

WANTED: STAG LODGE – ROSE GARDEN OPTIONAL

*D*eer senses are much sharper than our own. Their hearing is considered to be five times better, their sense of smell 20 times superior. It's not surprising, therefore, that they're difficult to sneak up on. But the walker had almost tripped over one that day, a little red deer calf curled up in the rough grass. The animal looked very new to the world, yet he was instinctively keeping very still. Knowing that mother deer leave their offspring silently hiding while they forage, the man immediately backed off and quietly retraced his steps so as not to cause alarm.

He decided to check again, a few hours later, to make sure that the hind had returned to feed her baby and that both had moved on. Moving softly and watching from a distance, he could see that the calf was in the same position and there was no adult deer in sight. With nightfall approaching, the man called a wildlife hospital for advice. Fearful that the calf would fall victim to hypothermia or predation, the unit decided that intervention was the safer option for now and the young deer (by this time, very cold and dehydrated) was taken temporarily into care. They planned to put him back at the same site within 24 hours, his energies restored, for his mother to find him. Sadly, despite every effort, this did not happen.

The rangers who managed deer on the parkland suggested that shooting him was the most humane option. Getting tame as a result of "imprinting" on humans and then having problems reintegrating with the herd were probable reasons why park staff weren't keen to reinstall a year-old male red deer (Britain's largest deer species). Incorrectly handled, he could grow into more than just a "cheeky" handful, begging for food from picnickers and walkers. He'd want to engage in rough play fights with people, too. As a sexually mature stag, he could be unpredictably violent at times, using antlers and hooves and his considerable body weight to "see off" any perceived threats to his territorial foraging and harem rights.

So the calf was admitted to the wildlife hospital to be reared. He was very hungry. He was kept indoors at first and bottle-fed on a supplemented deer-milk replacer (deer milk has more fat and protein than cow's milk) every three or four hours. He needed to be toileted after every feed, his bottom wiped with a warm, wet tissue. This mimicked a mother deer's normal actions in the wild, to encourage defecation. He could nibble succulent leafy foods early on, but it took ten weeks to wean him fully. Most importantly, all hands-on care was limited to one individual to minimise risk of imprinting.

When the "orphan" was old enough to be transferred outdoors, it was hard, but necessary, for other staff to ignore the distant Bambi gaze and persistent bleats for more rose-stem treats. He was given an open stable within a large, quiet pen in a corner of the hospital grounds. The nearest neighbours were birds, foxes and squirrels from the adjacent wildlife reserve. He was soft-released on a private estate with a small, established collection of deer and has settled in well. For one young deer orphan, a new billet had proved a better solution than a bullet.

RESCUING THE REST

Opportunities for wildlife rescue are around us all the time, and most of them, of course, are very undramatic: the stranded earthworm, migrating toad on the roadway, or exhausted bumble bee you almost put your foot on as you hurry along the pavement. It is no great effort to preserve wildlife, even in such humble forms, rather than heedlessly squash it!

Perhaps you will only encounter tricky-to-deal-with mammal casualties, like otter or deer, once in a blue moon. Some species need specialised handling techniques and expert initial care if found injured, displaced or sick. But this isn't as daunting as it sounds. There is often much that the lay person can do to help. Your most vital contribution

may lie in having spotted that there was a problem in the first place. Giving precise location details of a casualty and staying with it to prevent further harm can also be invaluable. You may be a casualty's only hope of help if time is short and no one else is around. Wildlife writer and wildcat expert Mike Tomkies, for instance, lived in a Scottish wilderness with scarcely any contact with the outside world. As the only potential rescuer on hand, he once extricated a red deer that had become entangled with a fallen tree in an icy brook. It was a case of him having a go, or watching the animal, already weak with **hypothermia**, slowly drown.

So here – in case of emergency and in rough order of size – is a rundown on rescuing some of the rest.

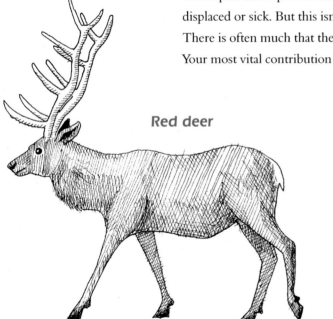

Red deer

Reindeer

Fallow deer

Our largest land mammals, red deer migrated to Britain from Europe 11,000 years ago, when we were part of the same land mass.

A Swedish herder re-stocked the Scottish Highlands with once-native reindeer in 1952 after the landscape, rich in lichens, reminded him of Lapland pastures.

Common in southern England, fallows are fugitives from royal hunting parks.

DEER

Thanks to deliberate introductions and haphazard escapes, we now have seven species of free-living deer in the UK. One of the biggest is the red deer, our largest native mammal. At the other end of the scale is the little muntjac, about the size and weight of a medium-sized family dog. It is so secretive and can live in such relatively small woodland areas that its presence is sometimes not even suspected. No one deer variety is found everywhere in the country, but some are in the process of spreading into new areas. Inter-breeding occasionally occurs, producing fertile hybrids (e.g. red deer and sika crosses).

Three deer types are natives: **roe**, **red** and **fallow** deer (the last became extinct here before the end of the last Ice Age and were most probably re-introduced by the Normans for hunting purposes). More recent newcomers hail originally from Asia: the Chinese and Taiwanese **muntjac**, the **sika** and the Chinese **water deer**. There is also a small population of introduced wild tundra **reindeer**.

Deer antlers are made entirely of dead bone, and are shed and re-grown by the males each year. The furry skin (velvet) that covers growing antlers does have a rich blood and nerve supply, however, until it dies and is ready to be shed or scraped off. For this reason, the so-called "harvesting" – i.e. artificial premature scraping off of antler velvet from the antlers of farmed deer – is a cruel procedure.

Sika

Roe deer

Chinese water deer

Muntjac

Our Sikas descend from introductions to an Irish estate in 1860.

Mainly found in Scotland and southern England. The buck has a rasping "cough" and the doe's reply is high-pitched.

Although they are found in our eastern wetlands, Chinese water deer are now almost extinct in China.

Introduced from the Far East and Britain's most widely distributed deer.

IDENTIFYING DEER

RED (estimated UK population around 316,000*) are large deer. Males (stags) have huge, branching antlers with many points. Scottish *Monarch of the Glen*-type red deer weigh on average around 80kg, standing 1.5 metres at the shoulder. But they come much bigger than that in central Europe, where they can weigh up to 300kg. The Highlands are their traditional stamping ground, but they also occur living wild in England and Northern Ireland. They are also being farmed commercially for meat.

Roe (est. pop. 300,000*) are small deer with reddish or grey-brown coats (shades vary according to the time of year). Their antlers have fewer than three points. They are found mainly in Scotland and the south of England, but are absent from Ireland. Roe favour woods and dense cover, but may also be seen **foraging** on the fringes of arable land, where there are hedges and clumps of trees into which they can escape. If you are in a wooded area on foot, you are unlikely to see a fit, healthy roe deer, even one that is very close, until it decides to break cover, because of its effective camouflage and ability to "freeze".

Fallow (pop. c. 128,000) are the only deer that develop antlers which are flattened (palmate) at the ends. Their coats, reddish-brown on top, paler underneath, have white-cream spots. You can find them throughout the UK, but they're commonest in southern England and are a favourite parkland species (e.g. Richmond and

---

* Population figures are 2004 revised Mammal Society estimates.

Bushey parks on the outskirts of southwest London). Truly wild herds (most of which can be genetically traced back to the original parkland herd from which they are descended) are very people-shy and tend to be nocturnal.

Chinese muntjac (pop.128,500) are extremely small, hump-backed deer and their tiny, spiky antlers grow in a backward sloping direction. They have enlarged **canine teeth** which stick out like "tusks". Muntjac can breed at any time of year and, not surprisingly, are spreading fast from their southern England stronghold where they initially escaped from captivity. Highly secretive, they can live in an area unnoticed by the general public.

Sika (pop.26,600 and increasing) are another exotic introduction from the Far East. Males have smallish, branching antlers. Sika have some spots on their coats, like fallow deer, and they also look somewhat like smaller versions of red deer. But they sound quite different to either. One sika call resembles somebody rudely blowing a raspberry!

Chinese water deer, (pop. 2,100; includes 1,500 free-living, recently increased. UK now has 25% of world's population). These are small Asian newcomers, which have escaped from deer parks and become feral. They don't possess antlers, but like muntjacs, they do have "tusks" (not real ones, but long, visible top **canine teeth**) which they use for digging up roots and tubers. These deer tend to be solitary. Females can produce up to six young at a time (twins and triplets being the most common number).

Reindeer (around 80). Long domesticated by the Lapps of north Scandinavia, reindeer have distinctive grey-white coats and both sexes have antlers. They have been re-introduced into the Scottish Cairngorm mountains where, a very long time ago, they were native.

COMMON HAZARDS

Deer, in common with other hoofed animals, can be susceptible to a number of ungulate-specific diseases (like **foot-and-mouth**), as well as bacterial diseases such as TB and **enteritis** shared by other mammals. They may suffer health problems caused by **parasites** and fly-strike. Some deer are prone to a severe form of arthritis which destroys and distorts their joints. Zoologists, however, have found that, to date, wild-living deer in this country are generally very healthy. In the wild, they can live into their teens, or longer. There have been more disease problems among captive deer.

CWD: (CERVID WASTING DISEASE)

In America, both farmed and wild deer, and elk, have been affected by this **chronic** wasting disease which is similar to BSE, or "Mad Cow Disease" among domestic cattle in the UK. Wild elk in the States are similar to our own red deer species. Despite drastic attempts by game ranch owners to eradicate the disease – destruction and burial of all associated livestock, repeated disinfection and subsequent re-stocking with wild-caught animals – the disease has re-emerged on previously infected sites. It has also been transmitted to free-living deer populations, albeit in low levels, in a couple of states. The disease is thought to be passed via exchange of body fluids. One theory suggests that it may have first been caught from deer that were in close confinement near scrapie-infected sheep.

TRAPPED DEER

Deer occasionally get themselves accidentally trapped – when fighting males' antlers interlock, or when an individual gets caught in fencing. Deer that appear to be trapped in a confined space – such as in a garden – should be observed from a distance because rescuers may panic and disorientate them. A stressed deer will pant and breathe with its mouth open – so back off any animal that does this. It is likely that the "trapped" deer will be able to find their own way out – the same way they came in. If the deer is genuinely caught in fencing or other foreign material, it will need to be sedated before being freed, to avoid the struggling animal creating fresh injuries, or making existing ones worse.

ROAD TRAFFIC ACCIDENT VICTIM (RTA)

This is the most likely deer casualty you are likely to find. Deer cause around 40,000 road accidents a year in Britain, according to the RSPCA. **RTA** injuries (bone fractures, muscle injuries, body wall ruptures) are the most common reasons for admission of deer to wildlife hospitals. But deer may also suffer wounds as a result of gunshot, dog bites, snare and fence wire injuries.

ABANDONED DEER?

Sometimes, worried observers report an abandoned or orphaned baby deer (called either a fawn or a calf, depending on its species). But, because it is normal in the wild for the doe to leave her offspring hidden in low vegetation while she goes off and forages for food, it is vital to check that the orphan really is an orphan before attempting to "rescue" it. Mistakenly rescued

The UK now has 25% of the world's population of Chinese water deer

newborn deer may be safely returned to the spot where they were found up to 24 hours after being removed.

EXHAUSTION

It is not unusual to find a male red or fallow deer suffering from exhaustion and debilitation during the **breeding season** (autumn), when they are at their most active, yet are eating much less than during the summer. Deer can lose ten per cent of their bodyweight over the winter, even though good food is available, but this is normal behaviour.

TREATMENT AND REHABILITATION

One of the chief bugbears of wild deer rescue is stress-induced heart failure (post-traumatic cardiomyopathy) which can occur some time after the initial **trauma**. It is believed that deer have not evolved physiologically to deal with the muscle and blood changes induced by such drawn-out periods of stress – as opposed to the stress of a brief getaway sprint – that rescue and hospitalization involves. Rescuing a deer can trigger irreversible metabolic changes leading to heart and kidney damage. Close confinement can often be the last straw. A common result is that a hospitalised deer casualty which looks to be well on the road to recovery suddenly drops dead.

Hospitalised casualties are kept under dimmed light in extremely quiet surroundings away from other wildlife casualties, and they may be sedated. They are released back to the wild as speedily as possible. Where possible, they might be given any necessary veterinary treatment in the field, to avoid bringing them into a wildlife or veterinary hospital at all. Even if injured,

some deer that remain mobile and able to feed may be left free with the herd and monitored from a distance.

"Sick", **collapsed** deer – which may be suffering from combined effects of bacterial **infection**, malnutrition, excess numbers of parasites, etc. – are likewise kept in for as short a time as possible. They may be put on **rehydration** fluids via an extendable **drip** to allow some freedom of movement, given long-acting antibiotic cover and a short-acting corticosteroid to counteract **inflammation** and **shock**.

Accident victims, even those suffering from a broken leg (if only one limb is affected) may be released straight away. Follow-up studies have shown that some deer casualties which were given no surgical treatment at all, and others which had a badly broken leg amputated and **sutured** before being immediately released had done better than those deer which were kept in care. Deer appear to be able to manage in the wild with only three legs, provided there is no **infection**; healthy active animals have been observed that have naturally shed a damaged, necrotic limb at some time in the past.

ABANDONED YOUNG

These are hand-reared on deer milk replacer – cows' milk with added whole egg, cod liver oil and glucose – and later fed a mixed, succulent vegetarian diet that includes cabbage, carrot tops, root vegetables and leafy branches of native broadleaf trees. It is vital to restrict human contact. Contact is restricted to one sole carer in the early stages only, to avoid the animal **imprinting** on humans. (An imprinted fully-grown male deer of one of the larger species which is not wary of people will be a danger to the public and, sadly, to itself. It will soon get itself shot for being too "aggressive" towards people.)

Identification of very young deer can be difficult. Soft release – with the recovered youngster penned but able to communicate with wild herds in the area – is considered the best way to socialise young hand-reared, or previously hospitalised casualties.

It should be noted that it is against the law to release muntjac into the wild, except under licence, in certain parts of the country. If released, this must be within half a mile of where they were found. Other types of deer are released in open woodland glades with thick cover nearby. Those kept in enclosures are given gradually tailed-off support-feeding after their gate has been left open. In captivity, deer could live up to 20 years, but in the wild this would never happen.

Close Encounter

A royal parks warden who tried, single-handedly, to free a stag whose horns had become jammed behind railings provides a good illustration of what can happen if a rescue attempt goes wrong. The unfortunate man became trapped himself when the stressed animal tried to butt him (it was during the rut, a time of year when deer are particularly ungrateful for human company, however well-intentioned). A prong of antler pierced the warden's arm. He remained pinned against the metalwork, closer to the casualty than either would have liked, until a colleague cycled by and fortunately managed to release them both. Never try to do such rescues alone!

❖⟩HOW TO GET INVOLVED ⟩⟩⟩⟩⟩⟩⟩⟩⟩⟩⟩⟩⟩⟩⟩⟩

◆ Get to know deer better. You don't have to go to the country to see them: the Wildlife Trusts have reported regular sightings in the suburban woods and parks of Britain's cities, and, even in London, Richmond and Bushey parks support big herds of fallow deer. On the outskirts of towns and cities, more and more suburban gardeners are beginning to spot muntjac in the shrubbery. Go on an early morning or dusk walk (but keep off-lead dogs away from deer herds) – and don't forget binoculars. Remember, too, that deer have keen senses of smell and hearing.

◆ If you are driving, take note of Deer Warning signs and slow down. Deer are most likely to be encountered on the road at dusk. One deer crossing the road is also likely to be followed by a second, close on its heels. One current theory suggests that (highly prevalent) arthritis may be hampering the mobility of badly affected individuals, making them too slow to avoid traffic. The RSPCA is helping with a study aimed at drawing up a national register of deer-related road accidents. Hopefully, this will lead to the development of more preventative measures.

HOW SHOULD I DEAL WITH A DEER CASUALTY?

(Note: Although there is a link between wild deer, **ticks** and the transmission of **Lyme Disease** to people, this is considered to be a very slight risk in Britain. Wild deer may carry **bovine** TB and there is a very slight risk of infection from handling.)

1 Wild deer casualties should be treated rapidly and released immediately if possible. However, deer are not easy casualties to deal with. They can become extremely stressed when caught and immobilised or transported to a wildlife hospital. This kind of intervention may lead to heart damage that is likely to kill them later – even if their original injuries were in themselves survivable. If they are quiet enough for people to pick up, they are probably terminally ill, have massive injuries such as spinal fractures – or are very young indeed.

2 If a deer appears to be sick, injured or collapsed, veterinary assistance should be sought straight away. The deer will need to be carefully observed from a distance, before possibly being sedated using a dart gun or pole-syringe, and kept immobilised. Any essential handling or containment must be done as quietly, quickly and efficiently as possible, in order to minimise stress and the effects of **shock**. In some cases, it may be decided that it is better for the deer to be humanely destroyed by a vet on site (e.g. if more than one limb is broken, or if it has suffered complicated organ or neurological damage with a poor prognosis).

3 Any adult deer that allows people to go right up to it is unlikely to go on to recover from its injuries or illness. Even severely injured road casualties are unlikely to remain at the roadside but will drag themselves off into the protection of undergrowth. Most manage to travel a certain distance away from the accident scene, despite their injuries (although they may succumb fatally later, hidden from view).

4 Some types of adult deer are large and heavy – several kilos of super-efficient muscle power that will do its best to get away – making for another rescue headache. Sharp antlers and hooves which can easily injure the handler if the animal struggles in panic are another problem to watch out for. You will always need backup help: do not attempt a rescue by yourself.

5 Covering the deer's head (without obstructing its breathing) will have a calming effect – except for muntjac, which tend to panic more when they cannot see. Masking for other types may be done using a towel, or blanket, and the animal may be hobbled and wrapped in something that will restrict its movements (e.g. blanket, cargo net or coat). It is important to keep noise to the minimum and avoid the casualty being troubled by onlookers, dogs, etc. Restrained deer casualties may themselves make a lot of noise – some deer will scream loudly and persistently in these circumstances .

USEFUL ORGANISATIONS:

The British Deer Society

The Walled Garden, Burgate Manor, Fordingbridge,

Hampshire SP6 1EF

01425 655434; www.bds.org.uk

The Game Conservancy Trust

01425 652381; www.gct.org.uk

The Mammals Trust UK

15 Cloisters House, 8 Battersea Park Road,

London SW8 4BG

Tel: 020 7498 4358

www.abdn.ac.uk/mammal

www.mammalstrustuk.org

OTTERS

Otters are a fully protected species of wild animal in Britain under the Wildlife and Countryside Act, making it an offence to kill or trap them or to disturb breeding areas. They are our top wetland predator, inhabiting mainly freshwater systems. Formerly widespread throughout the British Isles, otter populations went into freefall in the second half of the last century and had all but disappeared in the 1980s, apart from pockets of survival in the South West, the Welsh Marches and Scottish Borders. Numbers also sharply declined in France, Germany, Switzerland and the Netherlands. The finger of blame has pointed to **organochlorines** (used in agricultural pesticides and seed dressings) and, more recently, polychlorinate-biphenyls (produced by certain industrial processes) contaminating waterways, killing off the fish which are otters' main food source. **Habitat** destruction through the canalisation of rivers,

and other man-made damaging factors, were evidently also causing major problems. In the UK, otter hunts were voluntarily curtailed through lack of quarry, and by the time otter hunting was banned in 1978 in England and Wales, there were few otters left to hunt.

Over the last twenty years, however, environmental improvements and **rehabilitation** programmes by such organisations as the Otter Trust (also see *Useful Organisations*, p. 212) have combined to put otters back on the map in Britain. Once particular chemicals were banned, or withdrawn, improvements began to be seen. A recent study has recorded a significant decline in **pesticide** and other harmful compound residues in the body tissues of British otters. However, environmental **toxins** and heavy metals are particularly harmful to animals which are in poor condition at certain times of year.

In England, there are records of otter cubs being born at all times of year.

IDENTIFICATION

The only otter native to the British Isles is the Eurasian otter, although an otter found as a casualty may conceivably be of another species – hailing from Asia or the USA maybe – that has escaped from captivity. There are 19 species of otter worldwide. If it is an Asian otter, it will be slightly smaller than a British native.

EURASIAN OTTER

This is a large mammal: a male "dog" otter can be 120cm long and weigh 14kg. It is a fairly solitary, opportunistic predator. It ranges over wide distances (regularly covering up to 18 km of river) hunting its prey.

Otters have thick, mushroom-brown fur (which looks much darker when it is wet and slicked down). Their long flexible bodies carry very little fat, relying on their fur for insulation. They have webbed skin between their toes and thick, tapering rudder-like tails to help them swim powerfully. Their heads are short, with wide muzzles and deep-set eyes. Their external ear parts, which are small and round, can be flattened like mini-submarine hatches when the otter dives and swims underwater. Their nostrils can shut when the otter is submerged in the same reflex-action way.

Otters can look ungainly, walking on land, because their back legs are longer than their front ones. But they are breathtakingly graceful in water, where they move with amazing speed and flexibility, and otters at play are mesmerising gymnasts.

DIET

70–95% of the otter's diet is fish. The rest includes crustaceans, frogs, rabbits and small mammals and occasional birds, e.g. duck and moorhen, snatched by surprise underwater attack. Otters can see well under clear water. In murkier, darker conditions, they rely on long sensitive facial whiskers to locate their prey.

HABITAT

Otters need access to fresh water as their lifestyle is semi-aquatic, but they can travel up to 40km from their waterside homes. They live on the banks of freshwater rivers and lakes, and are also found on the sea coasts. Otters tend not to sleep in the same bed two days in a row. They follow well-defined traditional routes and regular paths, seeking shelter in nests hidden among reeds, in caves and hollow trees or in a "holt" whose entrance is among submerged tree roots.

Otters are **mustelids** (like badgers, stoats and weasels) and use strong-smelling oily liquid from anal **glands** to communicate with other otters and mark their **territory**. They can be hard to see in the wild. But their "calling-card" droppings (spraints) are easily identifiable by their strong fishy odour.

Otters are making a comeback. They need miles of good, unpolluted river water to hunt in and plenty of tangled, undisturbed bankside vegetation in which to breed.

Otters are said to be back in about a third of their former habitats now. The Wildlife Trusts have launched programmes designed to put otters back in various rivers, including the Thames, where wild ones were last known to have set up home in the 1970s. There are also **signs** that otters are becoming more habituated to human noise and the urban built environment, frequenting the beaches at Whitby and Scarborough and turning up in cities such as Bristol and Newcastle. One even used an abandoned car in a scrap yard on the Tyne as a breeding holt. Others regularly cross beneath busy main roads during their nightly foragings. In remote parts of their range, such as the Western Isles, otters have never been very shy, hunting by day, although this could owe as much to differing fish behaviours in coastal and inland waters as to lack of persecution.

BREEDING

In the wild, otters produce one litter a year. (In England, this may be in any month.) The young wander off when they are about a year old to find their own territories – which is when many road deaths occur.

COMMON HAZARDS FOR OTTERS

Otters could live for ten years or more. In practice, in the wild, their mean life expectancy is just over three years. A study of dead otters by the Otter Trust found that a third had been killed on the roads, and a third killed deliberately by people. The rest had been killed accidentally – by dogs, electrocution, getting trapped under ice, and caught in fish and eel traps.

WATER POLLUTION AND SCARCITY

Because otters spend most of their lives in and alongside waterways (and coasts), they are vulnerable to **poisoning** and burns caused by water pollution. They may be found suffering from a combination of internal and external damage, such as that caused by ingestion and immersion in corrosive and toxic liquid spills like oil and petrochemicals. Britain's waterways take in massive amounts of road run-off and agrochemical seepage. Otters may suffer **systemic** damage directly (e.g. internal bleeding and inflammation of the gut) through swimming in polluted water and attempting to groom, and indirectly, by eating fish that had themselves been contaminated by pollutants such as heavy metals, etc. If an affected animal is found alive, it may be showing signs of **nervous system** damage – brain damage from mercury poisoning has been suspected in otters in parts of Scotland and England, but no **clinical** tests have been carried out to prove it.

Even low levels of background pollution in waterways can have very bad effects on whatever lives there – causing mammals to become **sterile**, for instance, or lowering their **immune system** efficiency. Mammal predators become particularly vulnerable to accumulated pollutants stored in their body fat, when they are released into their bodies during times of starvation and stress.

Lack of water is another problem. Excessive water abstraction from rivers continues apace and threatens the fresh water sources that otters need to survive. Increased recreational activities on waterways also mean fewer safe havens for otters

Excessive water abstraction, more leisure activities, mean fewer otters

ROAD DEATHS

RTAs are still a major problem hampering the population recovery of otters, especially in the south-east. An estimated 100 otters died on Britain's roads in 2001 – either young animals looking for new territories, or adults whose territories were bisected by main roads. Some road accident-victims may have been lured to explore new territories by the prospect of a raid on a commercial fishery (where they are often seen as public enemy number one as a result of their ability to rip open an entire stock overnight).

Severe, traumatic injuries from RTAs usually involve bone fractures. In otters, broken bones are always repaired by internal fixing methods. Animals suffering single limb or tail **amputation** may be able to continue hunting, and may theoretically be releasable. But they are likely to suffer fight injuries, back on their old turf, owing to their loss of dominant status.

On the bright side, a recent increase in the numbers of otters being brought into veterinary practices for emergency medical attention may be an indicator of good population recovery overall.

Otters need sharp teeth, in tiptop condition, to hunt with or they can't survive.

INFECTED BITE WOUNDS

This is a common problem treated by vets. They may be the result of dog attacks, but biting also forms a normal part of otter territorial fighting behaviour. Dog bite injuries tend to present differently, often covering the entire body and including crushed ribs and internal bleeding. Otter bite injuries tend to be focused on the opponent's head and rear end and some of the following injuries would not enable a casualty to be released back to the wild upon recovery: accidental castration of a male during a fight, or the loss of teeth, a foot or several toes. Otters might be released if they had lost one eye, however.

ABANDONED CUBS

Distressed cubs which have become lost or abandoned are usually suffering from exposure, dehydration and starvation. They are not independent for many months.

DENTAL DAMAGE AND TOOTH DISEASE

These are common problems – an untreated tooth root **abscess** will spread infection into the bone and ultimately kill the otter. Otters often arrive at wildlife hospitals with broken canine teeth (e.g. from fighting, road accidents). It is considered better for the animal's longterm survival if the tooth can be repaired rather than extracted. However, *severely* shortened or blunted canine teeth would prevent an otter hunting and it could not be released after treatment. Old male otters are sometimes found in very poor physical condition (including the passing of black, tarry **faeces**) and this condition is thought to be stress or starvation-related.

INJURIES TO FOOTPADS

These occur from broken glass and other hazardous litter. Such injuries require in-hospital treatment and monitoring in order to prevent severe infection gaining hold, leading to multi-organ failure.

REHABILITATION AND RELEASE

At the wildlife hospital, the otter may need to be sedated before being fully examined. Surgery may be undertaken once the otter's condition is stabilised and, where possible, prescribed drugs will be given (e.g. palatable **antibiotics**) in feeds, in order to minimise handling and stress.

The otter will be housed, in quiet surroundings, in a smooth metal hospital cage in which it cannot damage its teeth (trying to bite wires or bars). A recuperating otter patient is usually kept in a steep-sided enclosure (which it cannot climb out of) with access to water, and would go to a specialist otter sanctuary prior to release.

Otters going back to the wild may be held in a pre-release pen for a couple of weeks. Food is left on site, after the otter has gone out, for as long a period as the otter needs it – i.e. until they no longer return for it.

ORPHANS

Otters regularly leave their cubs in the breeding holt for periods of time. But the cubs would not normally come out of the holt until they were around eight weeks old. Any cub out in the open that weighs less than 1.5kg (a large bag of flour) will be a likely candidate for rescue. It is likely to be **dehydrated** (its body lacking moisture) and hypothermic (dangerously cold). A test of dehydration is to gently pinch a small section of skin. If it stays peaked ("tenting") and doesn't spring back into shape in an elastic way, the animal is dehydrated. A small cub may leave the holt too early through hunger (e.g. mother dead).

Warmth and **electrolytes** would be the first things given to abandoned or orphaned cubs. Once they were stronger, they would be fed on replacement milk – puppy milk topped up with rich oily extras like whipping cream and cod liver oil, from a cat-feeding bottle. Later (when their eyes are open) they are given a solid diet of finely chopped fish – especially eels – minced meat, egg yolks and dead day-old chicks. Later, they are fed whole fish (white fish needs a **thiamine** supplement). However, in the wild, cubs are normally dependent on their mother for a very long time – 10–12 months – so replicating a natural upbringing and rehabilitation is not easy. It is usually undertaken by specialist otter care centres like those run by The Otter Trust and The Vincent Wildlife Trust.

Not only is it vital to avoid imprinting the young animals on humans, but they must not be released in well-stocked otter territories, or there will be fights.

▸▸HOW TO GET INVOLVED ▸▸▸▸▸▸▸

- ◆ Join your regional Wildlife Trust (see *Useful Organisations*, p. 212).
- ◆ The Field Studies Council (see *Useful Organisations*, p. 212) runs weekend residential courses at its Shropshire HQ, on which you can learn everything you ever wanted to know about otters, from head (e.g. examining bleached skulls from their specimen collection) to tail (analysing droppings under the lab microscope to check what was for dinner). You will walk the talk – crossing fast-flowing rivers in waders to track an otter's routes and hideaways – and, if you are lucky, you may even catch a glimpse of an otter out hunting, during a night-time watch. (You'll need to wrap up warm, wear dark clothing and be prepared to sit very still and completely silent for a long while, but it's well worth it.)

How Should I Deal with an Otter Casualty?

1 Otter casualties can inflict a slashing bite and can move and turn around quickly, especially when frightened and trying to escape. They are also vulnerable to potentially fatal metabolic damage caused by stress. They should be subjected to a minimal amount of handling. Never pick an otter up by its tail, or hold an otter near your face. An otter casualty can be held temporarily by a (dog) grasper and simultaneously gripped by the loose skin over its rump, with your other hand, but this should be done by an experienced wildlife handler only.

2 It may be necessary to loop the end of the grasper around both neck and one front limb in order to secure the casualty – the tension must be firm enough to prevent the otter wriggling free but not so tight that its body is dangerously constricted. Lifting and carrying must be for the minimal distance unless the rest of its body is supported, too. Unlike badgers, otters have enough loose skin around their neck and shoulders to be grasped by hand here. The grasp must be positioned up near the head. Otters may also be caught in a soft-rimmed net. The otter must be put into a secure container as quickly and smoothly as possible, to avoid causing further pain or injury. Even if unconscious, the casualty should not be carried loose inside a vehicle.

3 It is important to note exactly where the animal was found and picked up. Normally, it will be released in the same place when it is fully recovered. Of course, if a territorial fight was the reason for the otter becoming a wildlife casualty in the first place, there is no guarantee that it won't run into its dreaded enemy again. Although many fish farmers would probably prefer local otter casualties to be released far away from their stock, that's not how wildlife **rehabilitation** works. As a matter of fact, many fish owners like otters and there are a number of husbandry-related measures which can be taken to protect the fish and various fishing practices (e.g. the type of net used) which will not trap and drown otters accidentally.

Useful Organisations:

The Field Studies Council (FSC)

Head office: Montford Bridge, Preston Montford, Shrewsbury, SY4 1HW

0845 3454071; www.field-studies-council.org

International Otter Survival Fund (IOSF)

Includes Scottish and International Otter Projects

7 Black Park, Broadford, Isle of Skye IV49 9DE

01471 822 487

The Mammal Society

15 Cloisters House, 8 Battersea Park Road, London SW8 4BG

Tel: 02380 237 874

www.abdn.ac.uk/mammal

People's Trust for Endangered Species,

15 Cloisters House, 8 Battersea Park Road, London SW8 4BG

020 7498 4533; www.ptes.org.uk

The Royal Society of Wildlife Trusts (RSWT)

The Kiln, Waterside, Mather Rd, Newark, NG24 1WT

01636 677711; www.wildlifetrusts.org; also operate several otter watch and conservation schemes which encourage the participation of budding naturalists.

Bats

Bats are the only mammals to truly fly. They're also one of the very few British mammals to go into complete **hibernation**. Bats – and their roosts – have full protection in law under the Wildlife and Countryside Act, 1981, and anyone who damages, injures or disturbs either bat or roost will be breaking the law, and if successfully prosecuted, ordered to pay a fine.

IDENTIFICATION

Of the 16 bat species resident in the UK, six are classed as "endangered" and a further six are "vulnerable". Because of threats to their numbers, bats are a Biodiversity Action Plan species and both bats and their roost sites are strongly protected by law. There is an efficient network for reporting offences nationally.

There are disagreements over the exact number of bat species that do live here. The mouse-eared bat may be extinct, some think, or it could still exist as a tiny, relict population. Foreign visitors also arrive from time to time, from Europe or America.

The most common British species include:
HORSESHOE BAT (two varieties; can fly quite slowly)
NOCTULE (large, by bat standards – size of a swift and UK's biggest bat – high-flying)
SEROTINE (large, needs big entrance to roost)
DAUBENTON (pale underparts, flies low over water)
LONG-EARED (Brown, Grey, slowish flight)
PIPISTRELLE These are the smallest – weighing the same as a ten pence piece and measuring 4 or 5cms long. There are two species of pipistrelle and, although they may be tiny, they account for some 80% of house-bat colonies in Britain. If you live in London, pipistrelles are the ones you're most likely to see in any borough. Generally, female bats tend to be slightly larger than males.

Some bats have flattened, "piggy" faces, others have more of a snout. Some possess very long ears, others have short, broad ones. But unless a bat is dead (or captive), so that you can get close enough in a good light to study its features, your best bet for identifying a particular individual is to note when and where it flies and to interpret its calls via specialised bat-detector equipment – each kind of bat will register its echolocation calls on its own "wavelength" of clicks.

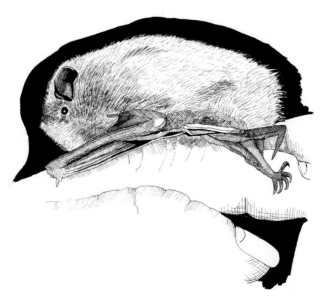

Common pipistrelles - not nearly as common now - can be told apart from recently-discovered Soprano relatives by vocal pitch. They "broadcast" on 45kHz, the Sopranos on 55 kHz.

A bat's own listening equipment is exceedingly sophisticated and well-developed, whether or not a particular type of bat has huge external ear parts. All bats have a kind of internal sonar system (akin to a ship's depth-sounding equipment) which they rely on to target their prey in mid-air and to avoid collisions with obstacles on their flight path. The bat issues a rhythmic series of "shouts" – mostly at sound levels outside the range of human hearing – and waits for the sound of its voice to hit something solid and bounce back. Depending on the speed of the echoing squeak's return and its quality and direction, the bat is able to mentally shape an accurate, second-by-second sound map of all the objects around it, including its moving target prey.

Bats have large, folding leathery wings and strong, curving claws on their "thumbs" which enable them to crawl and climb. They latch firmly onto a roosting site and hang there, upside-down. Despite appearances, bats actually have the same skeletal structure in their hands as we do. The difference is that their fingers have become vastly elongated and a wide webbing of skin is stretched between all the finger bones.

HABITAT

In Britain, the further north you go, the fewer varieties you will encounter. The greatest number of species occurs near the south coast. It's thought that this is because the climate is warmer here, and there's a greater variety of farming methods, a larger amount of insects available and, possibly, more roost sites.

Bats have lived close to Man for a long time, being adaptable enough to spot a desirable residence when it presents itself. They may make their homes in inhabited buildings, getting in via tiny cracks and resting in crevices in clean, undisturbed roof spaces, under weatherboard cladding and large curved tiles and behind brick or stone walls. They also choose traditional, natural **habitats** to variously sleep, breed and hibernate in, where available, such as large old trees with holes and splits in them, and quiet caves. Some bats cluster underground, in old mines, tunnels, large cellars or former ice houses. Others live near water (rivers, like lights, attract insects). They will prefer a clean roost, dry in summer, slightly moist and cool in winter, to a cobwebby old draughty belfry any time.

You may have bats staying in your own home, without realising it, at least for part of the year. Sometimes bats in residence can be noisy, squeaking away at all hours. Or they may draw attention to themselves by leaving copious (but dry and inoffensive) droppings made of powdery insect shell remains below their "upstairs front door". But, more often than not, you won't have a clue that they are there – unless you go looking for that old suitcase in the attic, maybe, or start work on a loft conversion.

Bats like to live alongside their cronies. The whole colony (which can consist of hundreds of individuals) moves as one. Its members will subtly shift position in unison according to temperature variations at a site during different times of the day or night. Bats want to keep warm in summer, but need to cool their body temperatures right down during winter while hibernating. Their body heat echoes that of their surroundings – but if the outside temperature becomes too extreme (e.g. if there is danger of their freezing),

Bats' body heat depends on the temperature of their surroundings

the bats must rouse themselves and move home. For this reason, it is advisable to put up more than one bat box, in slightly different places, e.g. to catch the warmth of the sun at different hours of the day, if you are trying to encourage bats into your home or garden. Then they can choose to vary their positions. Bats don't use bedding for insulation, relying solely on their choice of shelter and their own energy-storing reserves to sleep comfortably.

DIET

Bats feed on night-flying insects, which they catch on the wing, hunting around dusk, or shortly after it gets dark. Lactating females hunt just before dawn, too. Bats spend the bulk of their lives inside their roosts, conserving energy, and can live for a very long time – up to 20, or even 30, years.

BREEDING

Bats breed once a year, giving birth (normally to one) in the summer. The young are suckled, like other mammal babies. In the winter months, bats all disappear from the scene. They go into **hibernation**, clustering in special winter roosts (where temperatures are low, but not freezing, and humidity high) alongside other bats. They live off their fat reserves, occasionally emerging from their torpor for brief spells, until their spring awakening round about April.

COMMON HAZARDS

Bats can, theoretically, live for 20 years or more – an unusually long time for so small a mammal. In the wild, **predation** and starvation are the most common causes of death. Blood-sucking insect parasites can be a common cause of disease, even death, in bats. Youngsters, in particular, can become severely debilitated as a result of **mite** infestation.

HABITAT DISTURBANCE, DESTRUCTION AND MISMANAGEMENT

Many bats are the victim of ignorant, negligent or wilfully maverick decorating and construction work, or ill-advised, mistimed tree work that destroys or damages roosts. Some timber treatment chemicals are fatally toxic to bats, either instantly or after a prolonged period of suffering and illness. Exact numbers of bats harmed or killed are not known – instances are not reported and evidence is easy to dispose of. The RSPB estimates that several thousand bat offences are committed every year, which could have serious conservation implications, with the building trade identified as the worst offender.

Mistakes are also made in the way parks and open spaces are managed. Often, insufficient thought is given to bat roosting sites and breeding patterns when grounds maintenance and tree-surgery work is carried out. Intensive agriculture has also led to bats' decline.

Recently, environmental professionals, tree surgeons, bat conservators and other interested groups have joined in linked training and strategy courses, so it looks as if it will be harder and harder to "accidentally" harm bats and their roosts. Sadly, even a slight poking around and exposure of a roosting site can be enough to disperse a colony and guarantee that they will not return. Anyone who inadvertently opens up a roost should stop work immediately on site and seek advice

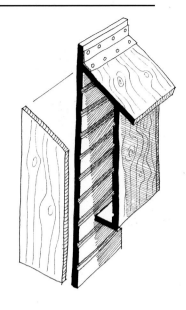

It's best to put up more than one box in each site, so that bats can move around and adjust their temperature.

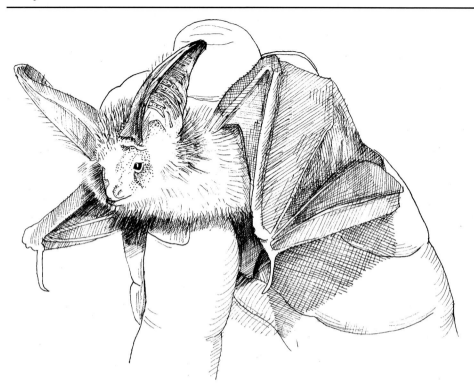

Brown long-eared bats' hearing can distinguish between a moth and the leaf it's on. They like roof spaces and, rather than old belfries, half of today's bats roost in modern houses.

roosts – and wait above or below the flight path from a suitably high vantage point, such as a roof. Bats can also be found on the ground. Pipistrelles, for instance, often choose flat roofs for their maternity roost site and all kinds of bats sometimes fly low, or crawl around in the grass, especially when grappling with a large insect. Domestic cats are, in fact, far more of a threat to bats than other predators, such as birds of prey, weasels, foxes and stoats.

If you own a cat, it may be possible to protect the bats' flightpath and entrance/exit using high plantings (e.g. tall thorny bushes, dense creepers), tight-weave netting (e.g. plant insulation matting) or even chicken wire, to provide a shield or underhang that will block predator access, while still allowing bats safe passage and a clear flightpath. The BCT (Bat Conservation Trust), has free advice leaflets on the problems of bats and cats, with practical suggestions. These include bringing your pet in half-an-hour before sunset, keeping it in at night as a priority between mid June and the end of August, and fitting a bell collar. The Royal Society for the Protection of Birds found that a cat's kill rate (birds and mammals) was reduced by over a third through wearing this kind of collar.

(also see *Useful Organisations* on how to proceed.) Injured or displaced bats will need to be attended to first. It may be possible to restore the roosting site or transfer uninjured animals to a suitable alternative position elsewhere in the area. Otherwise, surviving casualties (e.g. young which are not yet ready to live independently) will need to be treated or hand-reared in captivity and found suitable release sites later. This work, carried out by volunteer bat handlers and wildlife rehabilitation specialists, is labour-intensive, expensive and, for the most part, entirely avoidable.

Cats

Bats are frequently caught, or clawed in passing, by cats. Cats are skilled predators and get to know when and where bats regularly enter and exit from their

Many catted bats have to be **euthanased** (often because of severe internal injuries). Others may be saveable, after lengthy care and treatment. They are given **prophylactic** antibiotic cover (amoxycillin) which must be given **orally**. Although it is possible to give bats **anaesthetic**, with minimal mortalities, it has to be administered as an inhaled gas mixture, not an **injection**. It cannot be given as a "local", either, because of the nature of bat **metabolism**.

FRACTURES

These are most common in the bat's wings and usually the result of being caught by a cat. They may be surgically repaired, but results would need to be excellent if the bat were to stand any chance of surviving, and hunting, on release. While the bat's "finger" bones were healing, its wings would be lightly, but firmly, bound and the bat confined to a small cage.

WING TEARS

These often heal naturally, within a week or so, while the bat is given supportive care in captivity. Larger, more ragged tears may be sealable, according to their severity and position, and various methods of taping and surgically glueing have been tried. But a bat that failed its pre-release flight assessment (in an enclosed space), or which had needed to have a partial or full wing amputation, would need to spend the rest of its life in captivity. Long-term captives do best when housed with other bats – although the sexes may need to be separated to prevent the "colony" expanding.

SHOCK

Sometimes, bats are found by daylight, usually lying on the ground or just clinging to a wall. Such animals will usually be in shock (i.e. they will feel cold and be dehydrated) although they may not always show physical signs of traumatic injury. They should be taken into care, to be rehydrated and their condition stabilised, before being released in the area where they were found. A bat should only be released back to the wild when it is in good health, of good body weight,

able to fly continuously for several minutes and to land and take off at will. It must be released in mild weather – and, if in autumn, must have sufficient body fat to enable it to hibernate.

PARASITES

Sick or weak bats often carry a large parasite load (fleas, ticks, bat flies) which can be removed, either by daily brushing with a soft paintbrush, or by sparing use of a permethrin-based flea powder dotted between the shoulderblades (to stop the bat grooming it off).

ORPHAN BATS

Orphans that may have fallen from the roost, or got left behind when a colony moved, may be rehydrated and kept warm. An attempt would be made to return them to the site at dusk, to see if the mother came to collect them. Otherwise, a baby bat may be hand-reared, initially on bat-milk substitute, later on beetle larvae (mealworms). Great care must be taken to get the growing bat's diet right, or it will develop with deformed finger bones. Ideally, the young need to be socialised with other bats and encouraged to learn how to hunt, by example, in large pre-release enclosures where flying insects are available, before being set free near an established colony.

POISONING

Using pesticides to kill insects will have a highly damaging effect on all creatures who rely on insects for their food. Many compounds are very long-acting and while some – such as lindane, which used to be used in wood treatments – will kill in a day or two, others will cause slow-burn harm, making the animal chronically sick and debilitated and preventing it breeding.

Killing flying insects in your garden and around your home will deprive bats – and many birds – of their food supply. You may not like midges, but a pipistrelle will typically be eating up to 3,500 in one night.

REHABILITATION AND CARE

Bats being held and treated in captivity need a very specific environment and are usually cared for by specialist bat handlers. If the housing is too dry, for example, this can cause wing tissue to dry up and slough off permanently. If it is too humid, the bat may suffer from fungal and bacterial infections. Bats must also be minimally handled with extreme care to avoid fractures and dislocations – the usual bat holding position is gently held in the flat of the hand, behind the thumb. Bats must never be held by their wing tips, or held by their wings behind their back.

Bat casualties being cared for in captivity temporarily are fed on the innards of (cleaned) insect

Long-eared bats cannot match the speed of some other types, but their broad wings enable them to hover over prey.

larvae – usually headless mealworms, or waxworms and buffalo worms, and they may be trained to take these complete, from a bowl. They are given water in a small, shallow container or a caged bird's drinking fountain. A small amount of canned dog or cat food may be given in an emergency. Care has to be taken over bat diet and not just because bats are not used to anything other than self-catering. Beetle larvae which are beginning to mature produce a natural toxin, for instance, and this has been suggested as the trigger for the fur-loss which besets bats in captivity. Even when pre-release conditions have been fine-tuned to the extent of housing previously hospitalised bats in a large, heated open-air but escape-proof unit with its own insect-attracting lamp, feeding can be a problem. Some bats won't attempt to begin hunting unless insect density reaches a certain level.

Before going back to the wild (or setting out for the first time) a bat must demonstrate that it can fly vigorously for at least ten minutes. One rehabilitation unit has a sophisticated smooth-sided, fan-assisted wind tunnel, equipped with observation window and microphone link to a bat detector to assess fitness for release. The detector monitors the bat's use of echolocation to see if it conforms to the norm for its species. Fit, fed and warmed-up bats are released after dusk in fine weather, as near to a known old roost as possible, or **soft-released** with support feeding for a considerable time, if the bat is a misplaced orphan. Few follow-up studies have been done (bats are hard to mark and track satisfactorily without impeding their flight) but one Daubenton's with a wing band has been recorded, in good health, nine years after its release.

How Should I Deal with a Bat Casualty?

1 It is rare, but possible, for a bat handler to contract a form of **bat rabies** from a bite. The bat species found to be carrying the bat rabies **virus** in Britain were Daubenton's, a species that represents only 0.25% of all bats roosting in buildings and one that has very little natural contact with people. The rabies virus is fragile and its transfer route, from infected animal to person, would be via a bite or scratch that punctured the skin and made contact with the recipient's nervous system, or from infective saliva entering a cut or crossing the human handler's mucous membrane, (e.g. if you got saliva on your hand, then absent-mindedly rubbed your eye or touched your mouth lining). However, Natural England now insists that all its registered volunteer bat workers be immunised against rabies.

2 Personal disinfection for anyone who has handled a suspected rabies carrier includes thorough washing of the area with soap or detergent and hot water (which destroys the virus), plus repeated flushing of any wound with running water and application of iodine tincture or 40–70% alcohol. Prompt post-exposure treatment is believed to be completely effective. Anyone who is worried that they may have been in contact with an infected mammal, such as a bat, should immediately seek medical advice.

3 Rescuers are advised not to pick up bats with their bare hands. A pair of leather gardening gloves will offer sufficient protection from a possible bat bite, scratch or saliva contact. (Latex gloves can be punctured by a bite, but will protect from saliva – but take care when removing them.)

4 You don't have to touch an injured, grounded bat with your hands at all. Instead, try to get it into a small *escape-proof* upturned box, (cardboard shoebox or ice-cream carton with some small airholes pierced into it). You may be able to gently slide a thin card or stiff paper underneath the bat and then turn the container over, holding the card on the top, to carry it away. If the bat is hooked onto a cloth, put both bat and cloth in the container.

5 Some bats "play dead" if handled, tightly pulling in wings and legs and remaining immobile. Give them the benefit of the doubt. Transfer them to a container to be examined later.

6 If you have no box, place a lightweight cloth or piece of kitchen towel over the bat, taking care not to totally obstruct the airflow, and lift it, wearing your gloves. Be careful: bats are small, their bones are delicate and you don't want to cause further injury. Keep the container lightly covered (but adequately ventilated) to prevent the bat crawling out. Give the bat a "curtain of privacy" to hide behind: a piece of cloth, crumpled paper, or section of kitchen towel inside the container will do. Water, if provided at all, must be in a very shallow container, such as a milk bottle top or plastic drinks bottle lid. Anything deeper and the injured or shocked bat could topple in and drown.

7 Place the container in a safe, enclosed place such as a closed, quiet room or garage, or your car boot, for a brief time while you telephone for further advice and help, or notify the veterinary practice of your impending arrival. Make an accurate note of the position in which you found the casualty and notice what its injuries are so that any clinical treatment can be made ready. If the bat is hanging high up against a wall, and you don't think the above method of transferring it to a container is practicable, ask someone to stand guard while you seek help.

◆ How to Get Involved »»»»»»»

◆ Their speed and nocturnal habits make bat-watching a more problematic hobby than bird-watching. Bats traditionally like to roost in natural holes, like hollow trees and undisturbed caves, but they have also taken to shimmying into man-made crevices and crannies in buildings – even high-rise flats and offices in cities. If you get to recognise signs of roosts near where you live, such as the stains of droppings deposited on the wall immediately below the entrance/exit, and know the bats' working hours and hunting ranges (watercourse, alleyway, sports field margin, street lighting zone) where they go regularly to vacuum up insects, you can wait nearby and watch the show. The bat-watching season may be relatively short (i.e. the theatre really will be "dark" from November to the end of March) but in the warmer evenings, the open air acrobatics are a thrilling performance. There is a device (an electronic bat-detector box or "batometer") which picks up bats' cries which would otherwise be outside the range of human hearing and translates them for us – another means of finding out where bats live in your area. Go on a bat walk with someone who has a detector. Get trained to use one yourself and lead walks locally.

◆ **Put up bat boxes** – they should face south-east or south-west, away from extremes of weather. Hang them high (at least eight metres above ground), with clear flightpaths (e.g. approach is along a fence or line of a hedge, or garden wall). Make sure they are not in the way of neighbourhood cats and provide several, in slightly different locations.

◆ **Join your nearest bat conservation group**. Few people take the trouble to understand bats. Modern farming and landscape management methods (e.g. hedgerow removal) and over-busy garden and home "improvements" are contributing to their decline. The more informed we become, the less chance of bats disappearing. A burgeoning bat population is an indicator of a healthy eco-system.

Useful Organisations:

Bat Conservation Trust

Unit 2, 15 Cloisters House, 8 Battersea Park Road, London SW8 4BG

020 7627 2629; UK Bat Helpline 0845 1300 228; www.bats.org.uk.

Countryside Council for Wales

08451 306 229; www.ccw.gov.uk

Natural England

1, East Parade, Sheffield, S1 2ET

0114 241 8920; www.naturalengland.org.

Scottish Natural Heritage (SNH)

Great Glen House, Leachkin Road, Inverness IV3 8NW

01463 725000

www.snh.org.uk

The Vincent Wildlife Trust

An independent trust engaged in wildlife research focusing on British mammals.

3+4 Bronsil Courtyard, Eastnor, Ledbury, Herefordshire HR8 1EP

01531 636 441; www.vwt.org.uk

The Royal Society of Wildlife Trusts (RSWT)

The Kiln, Waterside, Mather Rd, Newark, NG24 1WT

01636 677711; www.wildlifetrusts.org

Bat Boxes

Bird boxes, insect, amphibian and hedgehog protection. *Schwegler* make wood and concrete models which have both warm and cold weather sections. www.schwegler-natur.de

FROGS AND OTHER AMPHIBIANS

Amphibians are cold-blooded creatures which can exist both on land and in water. They can breathe through their thin skins and, when they have developed into their adult form, they can also breathe through their lungs, but they cannot control their body temperature by internal means, as mammals do. In Britain, there are three groups of amphibians: **frogs**, **toads** and **newts**.

COMMON FROG

You are most likely to encounter this native frog. If you have a wildlife-friendly pond in your garden it will probably be awash with common frogs in spring. Other frog species introduced in the last 150 years include edible frogs and marsh (or laughing) frogs. Other non-natives are tree frogs and North American bull frogs – which will eat native common frogs, so don't introduce them as tadpoles into your pond!

TOADS AND NEWTS

The two species of UK toads are common toads and natterjacks (much rarer and legally protected, they live in sandy places). The three types of UK newts are the smooth or common newt, the palmate and the great crested – which is rare and requires a licence to handle it.

IDENTIFYING AMPHIBIANS

COMMON FROGS come in a variety of shades from grey to olive-green, yellow and brown. In Scotland, you might find red and black ones, and the odd yellow, red-eyed albino turning up occasionally. Frogs' skins are normally mottled with dark blotches, and they can lighten or darken their skin tone to match their environment. Frogs may be distinguished from toads by the *texture* of their skin, as well as its colour. Frogs have smooth, moist-looking skin (protected by mucous secretions).

TOADS have drier, knobbly (warty) skins and their colouring is a more uniform shade of brown or khaki. Other differences between the two include size and gait. Common frogs can be from 6 to 10cm long, weighing on average 22.7g. Females tend to be slightly bigger than males. Toads are bigger when fully grown, and less streamlined in appearance. While frogs favour the long, powerful springboard leap as a means of getting around speedily and avoiding predators, toads often amble along, crawling on all four legs (their legs are shorter than frogs' legs), relying to some extent on unpleasant skin secretions to avoid being eaten. Toads also have a large, protruding gland behind each eye, and frogs don't.

NEWTS look like little swimming dragons – especially those with large frilly crests along their backs. Newt skins are leathery, their bodies long and tubular, and much of their length consists of tail. Newts range in colour from light olive to darker brown, with paler skin on throat and belly and a variety of streaked and

Frogs try to return to water they were born in to breed. They rely greatly on garden ponds, migrating on mild, damp early spring evenings - so help them across roads and place them out of traffic danger.

mottled markings, according to species. During the breeding season, their coloration can change – male common newts develop bright orange and turquoise strips of colour at this time. Newts range in length from 7–15cm. Their tadpoles look like miniature adults, but with large feathery external gills.

HABITAT AND BREEDING

Frogs, toads and newts all spend the bulk of their lives on dry land, but they must return to the water to reproduce. All the species will breed in garden ponds, provided there is sufficient submerged water plant cover, e.g. water weed, and no abundance of fish to eat the eggs and young. Amphibians pick familiar sites in the spring, toads migrating in their hundreds and thousands to their chosen breeding area. Frogs and toads mate while the males tightly clasp the females and ride piggyback, waiting for eggs to be laid. Males develop special blue-black pads on their front fingertips to help them grip. Frogs, toads and newts all lay eggs which develop into swimming **embryos** called tadpoles. Frog eggs (spawn) are laid in a big jelly-like clump – each female depositing 1,000 to 3,000 eggs. Toad eggs are equally numerous, but they come in long strings. Newt eggs are fertilised inside the female's body after she takes

The biggest of the British newts, great-crested newts could live for 27 years, but because of pond and lake habitat destruction and pollution, they're now endangered. (Only the males have a crinkly skin ridge on their backs).

in a sperm capsule deposited by the male. The eggs are laid, then wrapped, one at a time, in water plant leaves.

Frog tadpoles take about 12 weeks to turn into little frogs, by which time their tails have been absorbed and their lungs are developed. Toads leave the water looking like miniature versions of their adult selves after only six weeks. Newt tadpoles grow their front legs before their back ones – frogs do it the other way round.

Very few tadpoles survive to adulthood. For frogs and toads, the proportion of those that will make it is reckoned to be 5%, at best. Their predators in early life include water beetles, ducks, fish – and other amphibians (e.g. a newt will eat a frog tadpole, and I have seen an adult common frog swallow a tiny froglet in my pond).

HIBERNATION

Amphibians hibernate – e.g. under a rock, or buried in the ground. Some frogs choose to hunker down in the mud and leaf litter at the bottom of a pond over the winter instead, so don't clear your pond debris until the frosts have finished (but do it before mating begins).

COMMON HAZARDS

Frogs tend to get caught and injured by gardening tools, such as forks, lawn mowers and strimmers. They also get injured by becoming entangled in nylon netting. Frogs and toads are often road accident victims – presenting with crush injures to their legs and pelvic areas – and they are particularly vulnerable during their annual spring **migration** to find breeding sites. Toads can also suffer damage after exposure to heavy road "salting" during migration (this can prove fatal, although less affected toads may be helped by being washed down with clean water).

Amphibians often get "catted", too. Whereas a fox, or other wild predator, will usually eat any amphibian it catches, most domestic cats injure and leave.

AMPHIBIAN DISEASES

Amphibian diseases are not fully understood. It is believed that they may fall victim, en masse, to bacterial and viral infections. "Red leg" in frogs – a condition in which red **lesions** appear on the underside and back legs – may be a symptom of more than one different disease. The first sign of a problem is usually a mass of frogs found dead, or dying, in or around a pond. Because of the danger of inadvertently transmitting diseases between populations, do not transfer clumps of spawn and tadpoles out of their original pond. There are two views over the "rescuing" of spawn and the rearing of tadpoles in a fish tank, if their original habitat has become life-threatening (e.g. full of goldfish, poor oxygen quality of the water). Although such a move may successfully result in the release of healthy froglets in your garden, some experts believe that this unnaturally inflates the local population size – even taking into account predation of youngsters on land. Another difficult decision for the amphibian rescuer to grapple with!

TREATMENT AND REHABILITATION

Using a hand lens will make examination of amphibians' injuries easier, because wounds such as cat bites or claw penetrations can be hard to spot. Amphibian bones are a mix of true bone and cartilage.

Breaks will heal, but usually take a long time because the animal is ectothermic (its body temperature takes its cue from the surrounding air or water temperature). Fractures may be stabilised (with water-resistant materials), hind leg breaks can be **splinted**, front legs **sutured**. Tissue injuries have also been successfully treated with water-based gels, aloe vera, etc. Even open tear wounds which have displaced the intestines have been treated with success.

Frogs may be given an anaesthetic dissolved in water. Treatments involving the absorption and excretion of a dose of medication are all reliant on that particular amphibian being kept at the correct temperature for its metabolism to function properly. Injured, sick or dehydrated amphibians may be given subcutaneous fluids at 10% of bodyweight.

Frogs in captivity tend to lose weight and condition, so they are released (ideally, near where they were found, otherwise into a suitable pond already used by frogs) as soon as possible after treatment. Toads, however, are easier in-patients (e.g. in a temperature-controlled glass or plastic vivarium, with access to dry land as well as water) and will continue to eat well.

Amphibians are all carnivorous as adults and will only feed on moving **invertebrate** prey. In captivity, they are given **worms**, cleaned maggots and crickets, plus powdered vitamin and mineral supplement. These may be obtained from a pet shop or live-food supplier. Tadpoles are herbivorous when they are young, feeding on vegetable matter (chopped lettuce in captivity). Later they become meat-eaters, taking a little fresh meat, or cleaned earthworms – they will also eat fishfood – and, occasionally, each other.

How Should I Deal with an Amphibian Casualty?

1 Amphibians do not like being handled. Their bodies are adapted to adjust to the temperature of their surroundings, and your hand may feel uncomfortably hot and dry for them. Many amphibians have thin skins which are normally covered by a protective layer of secretions, e.g. frogs are coated with a thin mucous film which helps protect them from bacteria. Handling them can rub this off, causing skin tears and dryness. Toads produce a toxic glandular secretion, especially when stressed. So keep handling to a minimum. (This will also minimise chances of catching any zoonotic bacterial infection from the casualty.)

2 If you do need to touch an amphibian, make sure your hands are clean (with no soap or detergent residue) and keep your hands moist and cool for handling. Use a wet teacloth, towel or soft net, if possible.

3 For transportation, use a well-ventilated, cool, waterproof box with some damp vegetation, such as moss, inside (or clean, damp sponge) that they can rest on. Tadpoles must be transported in water (e.g. pond water) with some air at top of the container.

Useful Organisations:

Froglife

9, Swan Court, Cygnet Park, Hampton, Peterborough, PE7 8GX

Wildlife Information Service: 01733 558960

www.froglife.org.uk

Schwegler

Bird boxes, insect, amphibian and hedgehog protection.

www.schwegler-natur.de

>>How to Get Involved >>>>>>>>>>>>>>>>>>>>>>>>>>>

◆ More than a million – 75% – of Britain's ponds have been lost in the last 100 years, largely as a result of development and intensive agriculture.

◆ Make a new pond, or bog garden, which has all the features that wildlife – including amphibians – need and like, e.g. well-oxygenated, clean water (use a pump, if necessary), no goldfish/carp, a shallow end with a gradually shelving "beach", good diverse selection of surrounding and overhanging marginal vegetation and a cat-proof border – wobbly stones, logs, prickly rose and hedge cuttings.

Create the right environment, and it will soon be naturally colonised by pondlife, which will return year after year.

◆ Campaign for a cleaner environment: nitrates and nitrites, the main substances in fertilisers, get into ponds and streams as run-offs in areas of intensive agriculture. Once they enter an animal's digestive system, they reduce to highly toxic nitrites. Frogs exposed to the chemicals develop severe deformities, become paralysed and die.

◆ Don't fill in your pond – redesign it as a bog, or cover it with a grille if there are very young children around.

REPTILES

Giant reptiles once dominated the Earth. Some of their descendants still live amongst us – in Britain, our native ones are snakes and lizards, but they are small in size and number. Reptiles are vertebrates with tough, waterproof scaly skins and cold blood. Like amphibians, they cannot independently maintain a constant body temperature, although they vary it by making changes to their metabolism. Some British reptiles reproduce by laying eggs, others (smooth snake, slowworm and common lizard) retain the eggs inside until they are ready to hatch and then give birth to live young. All Britain's reptiles hibernate.

From the health and rescue point of view, this means that reptiles must be kept in the right temperatures (ideally, at between 22 and 30°C) and correct environment if they are to stand a chance of recovery, and they should be handled as little as possible, to avoid causing them pain and stress.

IDENTIFICATION

GRASS SNAKE

These are the biggest of the three British snake species. They can be a metre or more in length and you might come across one in or near water. Although British reptiles all live on land, most can swim – and grass snakes, in particular, like to eat fish and amphibians. The body is olive-grey, brown or green with black dots and it has a yellow band around its neck area. There is no dark zig-zag marking.

ADDER

Also called the viper, this is the only poisonous snake found in Britain (not in Ireland) but its venom is unlikely to cause serious or fatal harm other than to someone very young, elderly or physically debilitated, or to a small dog. Adders are best identified by a bold, black zigzag line of scales that grow in diamond formation and run down the whole of the centre of its back. Their body is relatively short (53–60cms) and thickset and the iris of their eye is coppery red. Males tend to be grey, cream or light olive in background colour, females are usually of a darker golden, or reddish brown colour. Occasionally, one is found that is rich black. Adders often live in heathy places like moors and commons. They eat mostly lizards, plus some small mammals and birds. Adders are poisonous – but very shy – and you are unlikely to see an uninjured adder unless you surprise one resting on a sun-warmed rock surface or log. It will quickly disappear as soon as it becomes aware of your presence (via scent or vibration).

SMOOTH SNAKE

This rare snake is most likely to be found around the New Forest and in some parts of Dorset, Surrey, Berkshire and Wiltshire. Its skin surface is smooth to the touch and, although the markings are very similar to those of the grass snake, it is smaller (seldom longer than 46cm in Britain). It lives on heaths, stony areas and wooded hillsides and takes to water readily. Like

Snake Eyes: an adder's pupil is a vertical slit. Smooth and grass snakes have round pupils.

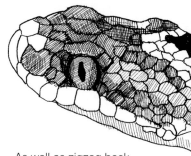

As well as zigzag back markings, adders have an "arrowhead" pattern on the top of the head. An adder also has a distinct neck between head and body.

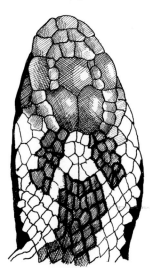

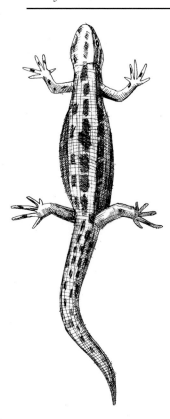

Female common lizards give birth to up to 8 young in thin transparent shells.

the grass snake, it gives off an unpleasant smell if captured (and like other snakes, often "plays dead" when picked up).

All snakes have a similar body structure, including a ribcage and mouth that are flexible enough to expand to take in quite large prey and swallow it. There is no escape, once the prey is in the snake's mouth, because all its teeth (which are renewable should any get broken) point backwards. Snakes have no eyelids – so if you see a slowworm and wonder if it's a lizard or a snake, wait for it to blink and prove that it's no snake! Snakes use their long, forked tongues to smell their surroundings and it appears that each body scale is equipped with nerve sensors.

Common lizards won't hang around for a close examination, shooting horizontally from one safe haven to the next in a flash. But you can see their markings if they linger to bask in the sun. They are roughly as long as an adult human's hand, the males being more slender and tapering than the females. The body is a shade of brown, with black stripes and dots, and often bright orange, red or yellow underneath. They favour sandhills and heaths, and eat chiefly insects. The species is in decline due to habitat destruction.

Sand lizards are found only in restricted sites, mainly heathland locations in Dorset and Hampshire. Markings include irregular dark brown or black spots, each with a white centre, on a background of purplish or greyish-brown. This lizard eats insects and spiders, worms and slugs. It, in turn, is eaten by smooth snakes with which it tends to share its habitat.

Slowworms may look like snakes because they have no legs, but this lizard's skeleton reveals traces that show that it once possessed them. Slowworms average 30cm long, are metallic brown in colour and feel very smooth to the touch, as if they had no scales (although they do). Because they have a very small mouth, they mainly eat very small slugs and snails, along with small insects, worms and spiders. They spend the day under flat stones or logs, or hiding inside burrows (they are eaten by hedgehogs and adders). They tend to feed soon after sunset or after it has rained, and often hibernate in garden compost heaps.

A rescuer may come across other varieties of snake, or lizard, which are likely to be escaped exotics. Do not pick up any reptiles that have not been identified.

COMMON PROBLEMS

WOUNDS CAUSED BY CAT ATTACK AND DOG BITES. Iodine preparations are often used to treat reptilian skin lesions.

FRACTURES, usually in the backbone. These may be the result of trauma or an infection such as **salmonella**. Advice would normally be taken from a vet specialising in reptiles before any treatment (or euthanasia) decision was made. Antibiotics would normally be given by injection or by mouth. Snakes are sometimes admitted after being attacked by people (with spades, etc.) in the mistaken belief that all types of snake pose a poison-bite danger. Such casualties will need to have any bleeding controlled and reptile casualties are given anaesthetic gas when necessary. Pain control is still in its infancy, as far as reptiles are concerned, but casualties may benefit from being placed in an environment with optimum humidity and temperature conditions for the species, to offset the effects of stress and shock. Surgical techniques are based on those used on reptiles in captivity – but healing can be protracted in these species.

DEHYDRATION The classic symptom of dehydration is tenting of skin. The reptile will benefit from rehydration fluids, given orally via a stomach tube. Fluids may also be administered under the skin in sinuses along a snake's side.

DISEASES AND WRONG ENVIRONMENT

Reptiles suffer from a range of diseases and can also become ill as a result of being subjected to unsuitable temperatures. They may experience problems when trying to slough (scrape off) their old skin (e.g. causing blindness, or tissue die-off at tail tips). Reptiles of various kinds can also spread bacterial infections to people – particularly if a handler has an open skin wound. So err on the side of safety and use disposable surgical gloves.

IN CAPTIVITY

Snakes and lizards kept in captivity are housed in a temperature-regulated vivarium, with special lighting and water provided, and fed on a variety of specialised diets (including dead mice, flies, maggots, crickets or slugs) according to species. Reptiles' body temperature matches that of their surroundings and care must be taken to keep them in correct conditions, or they will not eat or their food will decompose in their stomach, leading to fatal infection (see *Useful Organisations* p. 220).

Natural England will advise on release sites for reptile casualties (a licence is needed for adders under the Dangerous Wild Animals Act 1976).

HOW SHOULD I DEAL WITH A CASUALTY?

1 Don't – until you know for sure what you are dealing with. Experienced handlers use sticks and tongs to move snakes, but it may be possible to gently scoop or sweep an injured snake, including an adder, into a suitable container, such as a bucket or small swing-bin. It would be better to wait until expert help arrives because the casualty may be a poisonous exotic pet that has escaped from someone's collection. Some lizards from abroad have venomous bites.

---

2 Reptiles are best transported inside a bag, or cloth, then placed inside a solid container which will prevent escape should they bite through the cloth. Care must be taken not to let the reptile become shaken and scuffed. The bag should be cleaned after each use.

Reptiles should be handled as little as possible to avoid causing them pain and stress. Some reptiles, like the adder in the UK, have a venomous bite, so take great care with anything you don't recognise. Leave handling to the experts.

INVERTEBRATES

Last, but not least – the really tiny casualties. There is no need to itemise all the insects, **molluscs** and worms you may encounter. Not everyone will even consider them worthwhile "rescues". But it is worth removing them from harm's way – and some can even be revived and released, like other wildlife casualties!

EARTHWORMS – which do such sterling work in aerating the soil – often end up on pavements when they have escaped their flooded burrows in heavy rainstorms. Spare a thought for them and move them out of range of commuters' feet – a nearby patch of garden soil, hidden beneath some leaves, will do.

SLUGS AND SNAILS may be unwelcome on your plot. But they can always be transported in a small bucket to areas of vegetation where they will disgruntle no gardeners but continue to perform their useful task of consuming dead, rotting vegetation.

STAG BEETLES are our largest native beetle. They spend the first five years of their lives as larvae, underground, in dead wood "nurseries", then briefly emerge into the summer sunlight to mate, fight and enjoy the freedom of flight. All too often, though, they land awkwardly and end up crushed beneath people's feet. Their pincers may look menacing (they're supposed to intimidate rivals). But they won't hurt. Put stray beetles onto trunks of big, mature trees (such as oak, lime and apple) or onto an old fallen log, in a less populated place, out of harm's way. Leave them plenty of dead wood in the garden to breed in.

BEES. As any bee-keeper will confirm, bees sometimes become exhausted or too cold to fly back to the hive after a day's foraging. They can be kept in a jar overnight, with a little water (in a very shallow miniature container) and some runny honey, then released, revived, when the sun is stronger the following day. You can even help a bee that has become overrun with mites; they can be removed manually (working very gently with the aid of plastic forceps and a magnifying glass) or dusted off with cornflour, which will make the mites lose their grip.

Maybe the neighbours will think you are barmy to bother with such small-scale rescues – but what does that matter? You will not only be giving an invertebrate a second chance of life, but you will be helping the environment, too, by understanding the roles of its most often overlooked components. And that affects us all.

When earthworms (there are 3000 kinds) digest dead organic matter, like leaf litter, they aerate soil and make it fertile.

Male Stag beetles use their "antlers" to intimidate rivals. Gardens, especially in south London, are great places to spot this threatened species.

Bees may carry 75% of their body weight in pollen back to the hive. No wonder their energy sometimes flags.

Casualty Kit

✔ Small, plastic see-through box with ventilated lid, from a pet shop – as carrier and temporary housing
✔ Small, soft net
✔ Handheld magnifying glass (or screw-top container with a magnifying lid)
✔ Small houseplant spray, filled with water (e.g., from a rainwater butt)
✔ Lightweight, disposable rubber gloves (optional)
✔ Lightweight gardening gloves (optional)
✔ Small towel or cotton face cloth (use dampened for transporting amphibians)
✔ Canvas or cloth bag, (to be used inside a solid container, if carrying reptiles)
✔ Miniature pot of runny honey (for reviving bees – or rescuers!)

USEFUL ORGANISATIONS:

Buglife – The Invertebrate Conservation Trust

170a Park Road, Peterborough PE1 2UF

01733 201 210; www.buglife.org.uk

The Herpetological Conservation Trust (HCT)

655a Christchurch Road, Boscombe, Bournemouth BH1 4AP

01202 391 319; www.herpetofauna.co.uk

The Royal Society of Wildlife Trusts (RSWT)

The Kiln, Waterside, Mather Rd, Newark, NG24 1WT

01636 677711; www.wildlifetrusts.org

TRUE OR FALSE?

1 Deer can hear people approach from five miles away.

2 Frog tadpoles sometimes delay changing into frogs until the following year.

3 Bats keep the nests they've built clean by making sure that they always defecate outside the entrance instead of on the bedding.

4 It's OK to pick up a big stag beetle with bare hands; you won't get a nasty nip from its pincers.

5 A diving otter can stay submerged for ten minutes at a time.

ANSWERS

1 False. But, on a windless day, they can rotate their ears in all directions and pick up sounds of people a quarter of a mile away. They are particularly sensitive to high-pitched noises.

2 True. In certain conditions (water temperature too cold, not enough nutrients) tadpole growth can be retarded and individuals will successfully shelter in mud at the bottom of a pond before metamorphosising the following season.

3 False. Bats don't build nests, or use bedding. Instead, they hang upon, or crawl inside, existing cracks and crevices in trees and buildings.

4 True. Stag beetle pincers (huge extensions of their mouthparts, shaped like stag's antlers and bigger on males) are "for display purposes only" and they cannot hurt you. But if handling these beetles, take care not to hurt them (their legs can accidentally snag on clothing or "stick" to fingers).

5 False. Dives usually last between ten and 40 seconds, 45 seconds maximum.

A Frog He Would a-wooing Go

Amphibians keep a low profile for most of the year, concealing themselves under damp vegetation, stones and empty flowerpots to hunt for food or escape weather extremes that could dry them out or freeze them to death. But when it comes to breeding, frogs, toads and newts must come out of the undergrowth and make for water in which to mate. It is a stressful and dangerous time, not eased by the continuing disappearance of breeding ponds nationally. Toads, which may have been using the same mating pool for centuries, can get squashed en masse, or fatally harmed by anti-ice salting, on the busy roads they have to cross trying to get there once a year. Frogs are often caught (but not necessarily eaten) by cats on their journeys on damp spring nights.

"Freddie", as rescuers inevitably nicknamed him, was one such clawed victim, brought into the wildlife hospital with intestines protruding from a wound in his side. The clinical staff might have opted for a lethal injection at that point, but decided instead that an operation would give this frog a second chance.

Frogs make tricky surgical patients and not just because of their size. Their smooth, sensitive mucus-covered skin provides a wonderful barrier to the potentially harmful pathogens they encounter on land or in water in everyday life, but it is easily damaged by physical (or chemical) assaults. Frogs don't tolerate hot, dry conditions – such as being held in human hands – for very long, for example. Their skin is also difficult to surgically stitch because it is tough and slippery. But there is one important plus: it allows the frog's body to absorb liquid. That means it can be an effective route for rehydration fluids, as well as any therapeutics, painkillers and anaesthetics necessary during treatment.

"Freddie" was prepared for surgery, which would be carried out inside a sterile iodine "bath". First, his misplaced innards were thoroughly rinsed with sodium chloride solution. Then, with the aid of a magnifying lens to help locate the claw puncture wound without inadvertently enlarging it, a sterile probe was used to painstakingly ease all the intestine back where it belonged. A single surgical staple was put in place and "Freddie" was given a five-day course of antibiotics. His recovery ward was a light-humidity- and temperature-controlled, glass-sided terrarium (an adapted aquarium) complete with clumps of cool, damp moss, pieces of wood and bark and stones under which he could hide.

One week later, the wound had healed nicely, and a lively frog was released onto an adjacent nature reserve, still in time for the mating season.

Rescuers and The Law

The Veterinary Surgeons Act 1966 states that only a registered veterinary surgeon and veterinary practitioners registered with the Royal College of Surgeons have the right to practise veterinary surgery and treatment, including diagnosis, on mammals, birds and reptiles. Veterinary nurses, under supervision, may carry out medical treatment and minor surgery on casualties, including wildlife, provided it does not entail entering a body cavity.

So where does the layman stand when giving preliminary care to a sick or injured wild animal? The above Act recognises some exceptions to the general rule – and an emergency may be one of them. It states: "Anyone may give first aid in an emergency to save life or alleviate suffering." The term "first aid" has not been legally defined but is generally interpreted in these circumstances as being the provision of care to a wildlife emergency until a veterinary surgeon can attend to the animal.

The Act also states: "Owners of animals (and their employees and families) may give minor medical treatment." Temporarily, a wildlife rescuer becomes the legal "owner" of whatever they have rescued while the animal is in their care. This responsibility ends when the rescuer signs over the patient to a wildlife hospital, sanctuary or veterinary surgery.

As a rescuer, you will have to use your common sense. If you think that the animal requires urgent medical attention, your first priority must be to get it to a vet or rescue organisation as quickly as possible. You should carry out only those minimal first aid procedures that you believe are vital to keep the casualty alive, stable and as pain-free as possible until you can get qualified veterinary advice and help.

Obviously, you won't be contemplating carrying out any invasive medical procedures meanwhile. Nor should you consider administering drugs, although in some situations you may judge it safe to offer (never force-feed) rehydration fluids to a conscious casualty. Few veterinary drugs are licensed for use on wildlife, anyway. Even the drugs prescribed by your vet for a wildlife "rescue" will have been licensed for domesticated animals. These drugs are, in turn, often dosage-adaptations of ones commonly used on human patients.

Apart from worrying about being too "hands-on" in your rescuing, one of the most important legal issues to consider if carrying out a rescue is that of personal safety – your own and that of other people. Never take short cuts that could compromise this.

On a lesser legal note, be aware that if a wildlife casualty is on private land, permission should be sought from the landowner for access, otherwise you could be committing trespass for which you could, in theory, be sued (not prosecuted because it is a civil, not a criminal offence). Think, too, in the heat of the moment before parking a vehicle while engaged in a rescue. Don't stop in a place where you are likely to cause an accident and endanger life. Remember, too, that not all traffic wardens are soft-hearted enough to make an exception for a wildlife "ambulance", although some may be, particularly if you leave an explanatory sticker or notice behind the windscreen while dealing with an emergency callout.

Wildlife and The Law

All wild birds and those particular mammals, amphibians, reptiles and invertebrates specifically referred to have legal protection against a range of harms, under the Wildlife (Protection) Act 1996. Some species are not included, however, e.g. foxes, hedgehogs and weasels.

Some casualties you encounter may have been victims of cruelty, or other illegal activity, and if you suspect that this is the case, you should contact your area's local police wildlife protection unit (some forces share a Wildlife Liaison Officer) and report what you know. The RSPCA can also bring prosecutions, if there is sufficient evidence for there to be a case to answer.

WHO WILL PICK UP THE TAB?

No veterinary surgeon is obliged by law to treat a wildlife casualty. But if they do so, their professional guidelines advise that the first visit should be treated as an emergency admission and should not be charged for. Emergency cover entails immediate first aid and pain relief and this should not, according to the profession's Guiding Principles, be "unreasonably refused", even for those species not normally seen by the practice, "until such time as a more appropriate emergency veterinary service accepts responsibility for the animal."

However, all subsequent visits, after this emergency consultation, are entitled to be billed. In practice, by the time a surviving wildlife casualty has reached the stage of a second trip to the vet's, its care costs are likely to be borne by an animal welfare charity, such as the wildlife hospital, sanctuary, etc. to which the casualty was taken. Such organisations have regular access to veterinary care. Although there is no charge as such when a rescuer hands an injured, sick or displaced orphan wild animal over to such an organisation, they all appreciate donations to help offset their huge annual running costs. Even with high memberships and good levels of volunteering help, these are a constant source of anxiety.

It is not usually the cutting-edge technology that blows the biggest hole in the bank balance, either (although bone repair work on a badger might run into several hundred pounds). It is the in-house, round-the-clock feeding, watering, cage-cleaning and nursing care and subsequent convalescence and pre-release arrangements that costs the most. Sometimes, animals can be cared for relatively inexpensively and satisfactorily by private individuals on their own premises (many young hedgehogs are over-wintered, for example, by local members of the Hedgehog Preservation Society). But, in most cases, it is better both for the wildlife patient and for its rescuer if the animal is cared for in a dedicated wildlife unit with others of its own kind. Not only will such a place provide customised accommodation and access to expert advice and hospital facilities, but it will have its own experienced workforce, so guaranteeing the patient the best attention. It will also work out cheaper than DIY care by the individual rescuer because regular donations and the unpaid efforts of a largely volunteer workforce will have spread the expenses load.

GLOSSARY

a

abrasion – wound caused by skin being scraped off; graze

abscess – localised pocket of pus produced in soft tissue in any part of body as a result of infection

acaricide – substance used to kill a group of skin-irritating animal parasites that includes mites and ticks

activated charcoal – substance used in emergency treatment of poisoning, given via digestive system

acute – describes symptom that comes on suddenly (may or may not be severe). Also see *chronic*

airways – breathing passages leading to lungs, i.e. nasal passages, mouth, throat, windpipe, bronchi

amino acids – compounds that make up all of body's proteins, "building blocks of life". Some amino acids are made by body itself, others must be obtained via diet. They play a key role in chemical reactions inside cells

amputation – surgical removal of all, or part, of a limb (or tail in mammal). Surgical removal of an internal organ is an "excision")

anaemia – lack of red blood cells and/or haemoglobin in blood

anaesthetic – drug used to produce effect of insensibility, often used to relieve pain during surgery. Administered as gas or injected liquid. A local anaesthetic does not entail loss of consciousness. An overdose of anaesthetic is commonly used by vets to euthanase an animal

analgesic – painkilling (drug or treatment)

antibacterials – synthetically-produced drugs used to treat disease caused by harmful bacteria

antibiotics – a group of drugs, originally derived from moulds and fungi, but now made synthetically, used to treat infections caused by bacteria

antidote – remedy used to neutralise effects of a poison. A poison may be any substance given in such quantities, and on such a timescale, that the liver cannot process or detoxify it

antifungals – substances used to treat infections caused by fungi (e.g. ringworm, candidiasis/"thrush"); may be in tablet or cream form, or by injection

antihelmintic – drug administered internally to kill or paralyse internal worms, such as tapeworm, so that they can be excreted

anti-inflammatory – drug designed to reduce signs and symptoms of inflammation (pain, swelling), e.g. the non-steroidal anti-inflammatories (NSAID) group. They work by damping down the effects of a natural chemical released by the body after injury

anti-larval powder – topical treatment used to kill maggots colonising external wounds

anthrax – serious bacterial infection of livestock. Anthrax spores can stay dormant in soil for many years. Can be fatal if spreading to bloodstream

artery – thick, pliable blood vessel that carries oxygentated blood from heart to body tissues, under pressure

artificial litter – young, unrelated individual animals put together in naturally occurring numbers/ratio, so that they can be reared and released back to the wild as a social group

aspergillosis – life-threatening illness in birds caused by spores of a fungus (aspergillus) which grows in decaying vegetation. Balls of fungal overgrowth may block lungs

asphyxia – suffocation; may be caused through insufficient oxygen in surrounding air or by blockage of a large airway

asthma – lung condition in which airways become oversensitised to certain stimuli; bronchial asthma produces inflammation, breathlessness, wheezing.

asymptomatic – producing no noticeable signs in body of active disease, although disease may be present

attenuated (vaccine) – vaccine derived from altered form of an original infecting organism which renders it reduced in strength (though of sufficient strength to trigger antibodies in recipient)

avian diphtheria – bacterial illness affecting birds

b

bacillus (pl. bacilli) – rod-like micro-organism (bacterium), only visible under microscope. Various types cause disease by entering and multiplying in body tissues (flesh)

bacterial action – when harmful micro-organisms invade a body and multiply inside it, they release poisons that are harmful to mammal cells

bacterium (pl. bacteria) – single cell organism; three different types, grouped according to shape. A bacterium that causes illness is a "pathogen" (germ). Some thrive where there is no oxygen, e.g. in deep tissue wounds

barrier-nursing – patient is isolated while in care to prevent spreading infection

biopsy – diagnostic test in which cells are removed and examined under a microscope

biting flies – flat/louse flies. Blood-feeding parasites with flattened bodies which may be found on birds. Possibly implicated in blood-borne disease, also anaemia in nestlings when present in large numbers (e.g. in swifts' nests)

blackfly – variety of dipteran fly

blowfly – the "meat fly" or bluebottle

bluebottle – variety of dipteran fly

blood poisoning – serious, often life-threatening condition caused by build-up of toxins, released when harmful bacteria multiply in bloodstream. A complication of wound infection

body salts – also see *electrolytes*: minerals (sodium, chloride, potassium) that occur naturally in body. Derived from foods eaten, they are important for maintaining fluid balance between liquid inside a cell and that which surrounds it. Dehydration and illness dangerously upset their chemical balance

botulism – poisoning caused by bacterial toxins, resulting in progressive paralysis

bovine – relating to cattle

bovine tuberculosis – disease of cattle that may affect a wide variety of other mammals, caused by mycobacteria

breeding season – time(s) of year when mammals are fertile and during which young are normally produced. Both male and female mammals may be fertile only at particular times of year

bronchodilator – drug used to improve breathing. These drugs work by relaxing muscles around the lung branches

broncho-pneumonia – see *pneumonia*

broad-spectrum (antibiotic) – commonly-used class of drugs used to combat a wide range of illnesses caused by pathogens

brown fat – specialised kind of fat found in human infants and some mammals. Energy source that helps maintain body temperature

brucellosis – a rare bacterial infection which may be caught from contact with farm animals and dairy products. The bacteria enter the bloodstream, via a cut in the skin, or may be breathed in. Symptoms are fever, sweating, loss of appetite and weakness. Untreated, it may lead to possibly fatal complications, such as bronchitis or meningitis. Humans at highest risk are farm workers, vets and slaughterhouse workers.

c

calculus – mineral concretions which may build up, e.g. on surface of tooth

callus (bony) – the first lumpy growth of new, soft bone that forms around a break; later replaced by harder, stronger bone

campylobacteriosis – infection by campylobacter micro-organisms, found on farm and pet animals; a zoonosis, it causes diarrhoea

candida – fungus which can affect mucous membranes if immune system is not functioning properly

canid – a member of the dog family (Canidae), which includes domestic dogs, wolves, jackals, foxes, coyotes, African Painted dogs and dingoes.

canine teeth – the strong, pointed teeth between incisors and molars

cardiovascular – relating to the heart and blood circulation system

carnivore – meat-eating mammal

carrion – dead putrefying body of animal, bird, etc.

cerebro-spinal – relating to brain, backbone and its central nervous canal

cerebro-spinal fluid – liquid containing dissolved glucose, proteins and salts, plus some white blood cells, that washes around central nervous system and acts as a natural shock-absorber

chick crumb – processed, complete bird food, used in poultry rearing

chlamydia – bacteria strains, producing illnesses in birds and mammals (a zoonosis that can infect people). Transmitted by inhalation of infectious dust and droplets, and by ingestion.

chloramphenicol – antibiotic, often used topically for eye and ear infections. (In human patients, it may be injected to treat acute life-threatening infections elsewhere in body when other antibiotics have failed, but it can trigger life-threatening side-effects in rare cases.)

cholera (avian) – infectious disease of birds, not linked to epidemic cholera in humans

chronic (of illness) – lasting a long time

clinical (signs) – signs of illness or injury used to make diagnosis

clinical shock – see 'shock'

coagulation – blood-clotting mechanism

collapse – sudden loss of strength; semi-consciousness

colostrum – first milk produced by a mammal after giving birth; helps set up newborn's immune system

coma – deep unconsciousness; often ends in death

corvid – bird member of the crow family, the grouping which includes ravens, rooks, magpies, jackdaws and jays.

d

dander – animal or bird body debris, such as dandruff, fur, feathers, dried saliva particles

dehydrated – a condition in which the body has become dangerously short of water contents, including circulating body salts. The "tenting" skin-pinch test can be useful in diagnosing dehydration

Defra – Department of the Environment, Food and Rural Affairs (formerly Ministry of Agriculture, Fisheries and Food)

depression – noticeable loss of vitality (in animal)

dipteran fly – a two-winged member of a zoological order of insects (Diptera) that includes the fruit fly, house fly and certain kinds of mosquito

drip – system for administering drugs, vitamins, etc. into vein very gradually, at blood temperature, via a hollow nylon line

e

eclipse – a specialised term for a time of year when ducks moult all their wing feathers (various times from mid-July to end October according to type of duck)

e-coli – short for Escherichia coli; some forms of this bacterium are part of normal "good" gut flora in people and animals, but other rarer varieties cause sickness, diarrhoea and bleeding. Infection may be picked up from eating contaminated animal produce, or via animal faeces, if hands are not washed after handling animals

ectoparasite – parasite that feeds and lives outside body, e.g. flea

electrolytes – also see *body salts*: mineral compounds that normally exist in finely balanced proportions in healthy body, regulating blood acidity, water balance, nerve impulses, muscle contraction, etc. They are lost through vomiting, diarrhoea and bleeding

emaciation – severe wasting, often signals disease

embryo – fertilised egg cell in earlier stages of pregnancy

emetic – substance given to empty stomach by vomiting

endoparasite – parasite that feeds and lives inside body, e.g. tapeworm

endotoxic shock – a life-threatening condition triggered by poisons produced in the body by invading staphylococcus aureus bacteria. Although they can be harmlessly present on the skin, these bacteria pose considerable danger if they enter the bloodstream and become trapped inside body tissues. Toxins are released when the bacteria die. Signs and symptoms of endotoxic shock include fever and a serious drop in blood pressure (caused by fluid leaking from blood vessel walls into surrounding tissue).

enteritis – gut inflammation caused by infection of small intestine, leading to pain and diarrhoea

enterobacteria – part of normal gut flora in healthy animal (or human)

epiglottis – small flap of cartilage that seals off airway during eating and swallowing to stop fluids and solids seeping into lungs

epileptic fit – sudden loss of consciousness, convulsions; may be caused through injury or disease that affects brain or by disturbance to metabolism

euthanase – veterinary term for "putting to sleep". i.e. humanely killing an animal, usually by an injected overdose of anaesthetic

f

faeces – solid waste from digestive system

femur – thigh bone

fever – state of high body temperature

fluid therapy – intravenous (or oral) treatment to restore normal body fluid balance and volume in a casualty

flystrike – effect of flies laying eggs on animal's body (e.g. in wounds); hatching maggots eat flesh, bacterial action releases harmful toxins

fluke – kind of parasitic worm that lives inside animal's body

foetus – developing unborn mammal in womb, at latter stages of pregnancy

foot-and-mouth – infectious disease of hooved animals, including deer; produces ulcers in mouth and inner hoof areas

foraging – looking for food and water

force-feeding – a relatively non-invasive method of artificial feeding, often used for larger bird casualties unable to feed themselves; uses flexible, lubricated tubing to access stomach quickly

g

gavaging – *see force-feeding*

gestation – pregnancy period from conception to birth

gizzard – muscular first section of bird's stomach

gland – group of specialised cells which make and release body chemicals, such as hormones

granulation – first-stage scar tissue, contains ingredients of collagen and small blood vessels

h

habitat – natural home of animal or bird, etc.

haemorrhage – medical term for bleeding

helminth – any kind of parasitic worm

herbicide – substance that kills plants

hibernation – seasonal extreme slowing-down of heart rate and metabolism, with bodily temperature drop, to conserve energy in cold weather conditions when food is short

host – living organism used by a parasite (which feeds and lives off it)

host-specific – refers to parasite that only targets certain species (during particular stages of its life)

hypersensitivity – extreme bodily reactions to certain stimuli

hyperthermia – extremely high body temperature (as in fever)

hypothermia – extremely low body temperature (as in shock)

hypoxia – condition in which not enough oxygen is reaching body tissues

i

immune reactions – body's natural responses to infection by viruses, bacteria, fungi, etc. Involves activities of specialised cells which may isolate or engulf invading micro-organisms

immune system – (see *immune reactions*). The action of the body's cells and proteins in protecting the body from harmful invasion by infectious agents, such as viruses, bacteria and funghi. Healthy, unbroken skin, the body's biggest organ, is its first-line immunity defence

imprinting – process by which a young mammal, bird etc. bonds with the person that feeds and rears it. In wildlife rescue and rehabilitation, it is important to avoid very young or orphan casualties bonding with humans, instead of their own species, through over-handling at this crucial stage of social development.

incubation – (i) keeping eggs warm until they hatch(ii) time in which an infectious disease produces characteristic signs and symptoms

infection – occurs when mammal's cells are invaded by viral, bacterial, fungal, protozoal, parasitic micro-organisms

infective – able to infect others

inflammation – immune system response at site of injury or infection which increases bloodflow to damaged area. Side-effects are pain, redness, swelling and heat. Defender white blood cells are attracted to the inflammatory chemicals and accumulate at the site

infusion – slow introduction of a liquid into a vein

inhalation pneumonia – lung infection following inhalation of foreign material

injection – fast introduction of a liquid into a vein

insecticide – insect-killing substance

intravenous – inside a vein

invertebrate(s) – this translates, literally, as "without a backbone" and it is the catch-all biological term for all creatures, from snails and worms to flies and jellyfish, that do not possess vertebrae or a spinal chord

irrigate – to flush (deep wound) with liquid, usually sterile water or surgical saline solution

ivermectin – a generic drug used to kill parasitic worms (e.g. in cattle, sheep, horses), also used against sarcoptic mange mites in other mammals

j

jaundice – yellowing of eye whites, gums, mouth lining; chief sign of liver and spleen malfunction. Caused by failure of liver to absorb brown pigment containing old red blood cells from circulatory system

k

kaolin – aluminium compound used in some anti-diarrhoeal treatments; may absorb toxins, viruses and bacteria from gut

keratin – fibrous protein in outer layer of skin, nails, claws, hair and fur

kidney failure – extremely serious condition in which kidneys can no longer filter body waste products properly. May damage kidneys irreversibly

l

laceration – torn, ragged, irregular wound

lagomorph – a member of the zoological group of mammals that includes rabbits and hares. The name comes from two Greek words meaning "hare" and "shape"

lavender oil – the only essential oil which can be used without a 'carrying oil' to dilute it; natural antiseptic and insect repellent

leech – blood-sucking worm; may live on land or in water

leptospirosis – bacterial-borne disease causing acute illness, with life-threatening kidney and liver damage. Weil's Disease in humans. Can be treated by antibiotics, if promptly given

lesion – catch-all term for any bodily abnormality, e.g. wound, tumour, infection, abscess or biochemical abnormality

louse (pl. lice) – small wingless insects with flattened bodies that feed on blood

Lyme disease – bacterial illness transmitted by tick bite. Causes fever, joint inflammation and complications may damage heart or nervous system. First diagnosed in USA in 1975

lymph node – organ along route of lymphatic system (e.g. in groin); contains white blood cells and forms antibodies to fight infection

m

malaise – feeling bodily discomfort

mange – (also see *sarcoptic mange*) infectious skin condition caused by burrowing microscopic mites which feed on host's dead skin cells

membrane – very thin barrier layer of body tissue that covers an organ or lines its surface

metabolism – natural process in which living creature absorbs food and nutrients and breaks them down so that they can be used by the body to provide energy

metaldehyde – (blue-coloured) poison used in slug pellets; ingested, it increases heart rate, and causes damage to nervous system

methiocarb – a pesticide. As with organophosphates and polychlorinated biphenyls (PCBs), accidental exposure causes muscle paralysis, seizures, abdominal pain, vomiting and diarrhoea and may lead to death by respiratory failure

microscopic examination – examination under microscope or electron microscope used to investigate diseased tissue

migration – mass seasonal movement of animals or birds, usually to warmer climate for a while, for breeding and food-finding

mineral supplements – powder-form (veterinary-use) food additives containing mix of vitamins and minerals, such as iron and calcium

mite – small, spider-like animal with eight legs. Many mites are parasites, living on host's blood

mollusc – group of animals with soft bodies and, often, hard shells, living on land and in water. One branch, the gastropods, includes slugs and snails

mustelid – mammal belonging to a species grouping that includes badgers, weasels and otters; distinguished by strong scent-marking

myiasis – see *flystrike*

n

nares – nostrils

nasal discharge – body fluids draining from the nostrils, which may signal illness or injury. In wildlife casualty, this may be mucus, blood or leaking cerebro-spinal fluid from head injury

nebuliser – device that administers a bronchodilator (lung tube-opening) drug, automatically pumped as a fine aerosol, so that it can be breathed in by patient via a face mask or chamber

necrosis – death of the body's cells resulting from loss of blood supply

nervous system – cells and tissue through which information is conveyed from brain to organs, and back again. The brain, spinal cord and network of nerves throughout the body make up the nervous system

neural – to do with nervous system

neurotoxin – chemical that damages nervous tissue, causing weakness and paralysis

NSAIDs – non-steroidal anti-inflammatory drugs group, used to provide pain-relief and reduce post-traumatic swelling in joints, muscles and soft tissue. They work by blocking production of naturally-produced body chemicals (prostaglandins) that trigger pain signals to the brain which then give rise to inflammation and swelling as part of the immune reaction to infection and /or injury

nursery – nest, hole, etc., in which young are born and reared away from animal's main living quarters

o

oedema – an abnormal build-up of fluid which has leaked into the body's tissues from the network of tiny, thin-walled blood vessels (capillaries) which would normally contain it. Oedema is commonly associated with localised traumatic injury and may be signalled externally by swelling

oral – (treatment given) by mouth

opioids – narcotic drugs originally derived from poppy plant extract, now also made synthetically, used in pain control. They work by depressing brain function

organochlorines – pesticides; many accumulate in the environment

ornithosis – bird disease; a type of chlamydial infection, causing feverish illness. It is a zoonosis (can be transmitted to humans)

oxygen therapy – treatment in which oxygen-enriched air supply is given when insufficient oxygen is reaching body tissues

p

pancreas – long gland (behind stomach) which secretes digestive enzymes and sodium bicarbonate (which neutralises stomach acid)

pangolin – scaly ant-eating mammal. Its name is Malay for "roller"

paralysis – loss of controlled body movement, due to muscles' failure to contract

parasite – organism living in or on a living creature. Some do so harmlessly, others cause disease and eventual death

parvovirus – viral infection of dog-family animals; virus mutated from similar virus in cats. Causes acute enteritis and, without intensive symptomatic treatment, death is likely within 24 hours; young animals that have lost their maternally-given immunity are most vulnerable and, in UK, virus may survive off animal's body in environment for many months. There is no cure but vaccination of young target species is advisable. The virus is highly resistant to disinfectants, although bleach solution may be effective for use in animal hospital environments

pathogen – any agent that causes disease, e.g. harmful micro-organisms

pelvis – wide girdle of bone that protects internal organs and to which tops of leg bones are attached

perturbation – (viz. badger culling and bovine TB): theory, confirmed by Krebs Randomised Badger Culling Trial, that killing badgers increases bovine TB spread in badger population, probably by disrupting badgers' otherwise stable social order and increasing amount of contact they have with cattle

pesticide – any poisonous chemical used to kill pests (plants, insects, fungi, etc)

phenol – an antiseptic (used, for humans, in throat lozenges and sprays)

pinning – method used in orthopaedic surgery to stablise a broken bone. A metal rod or pin is placed inside a long bone

plating – surgical repair technique in which a metal plate (which will not react adversely with body fluids) is used to hold a fractured bone together while it heals. New bone tissue forms around the plate

pneumonia – infection of lungs causing inflammation (also see *inhalation pneumonia*)

poison – any substance that disrupts cell function in the body

post-mortem – after-death examination of a body

potassium permanganate – antiseptic, astringent drug used topically, on skin

poultry – domestic fowls (e.g. farmed chickens, ducks, geese)

predation – preying upon other animals

preen – to trim with beak; birds need to rearrange and clean their feathers constantly to keep them water- and chill-proof and to maximise flight efficiency

prophylactic – drug, treatment or equipment used to prevent disease

prosthesis – artificial replacement for a body part

protozoa – microscopic simple, primitive animal consisting of only a single cell. Some are **parasites** of larger animals during various stages of their life-cycles and can transmit blood-borne diseases

pseudo – like, similar to, another disease (e.g. pseudotuberculosis)

pus – destroyed blood cells (which have been fighting infection), plus some dead and live micro-organisms. A lining normally forms, so that pus is isolated from surrounding tissue

pyrethrum – organic pesticide made from chrysanthemum flowers (usually contains piperonyl butoxide to increase efficiency) used in organic gardening to kill aphids, whiteflies and other small insects. Poisonous to fish and to some beneficial insects. Supposedly less lingering in environment than most other pesticides. May also be used to kill fleas on animals

r

rabies – acute viral infection of nervous system

rehabilitation – whole process of treating a wildlife casualty and returning it to the wild

rehydration – emergency method of administering fluids (e.g., plasma volume expander, drugs) and nutrition into a collapsed casualty. This is usually done via a catheter introduced into a vein (in unconscious mammal) or via a needle inserted into a bone cavity (in birds). A fully conscious casualty would be encouraged to drink rehydration fluids for itself.

respiratory failure – life-threatening condition that occurs when there is a lack of oxygen and a build-up of carbon dioxide in the blood

rickets – deformation of bones owing to nutritional deficiency (lack of calcium and phosphate)

rickettsia – micro-organisms that live inside lice, fleas, ticks and mites; passed into mammals' bloodstreams, can transmit diseases such as typhus

ringworm – fungal disease of skin, producing itchy, blistery patches

rodent – animal belonging to species grouping that includes various types of mice, rats, voles, squirrels

roundworm – group of internal parasites with long, cylindrical bodies living in intestines. May be picked up by host via swallowing worm eggs, by larvae penetrating skin (in tropics) from host eating larvae in cyst form in meat, or blood-to-blood via an insect bite

RTA – (abbr) road traffic accident

s

salts – see *body salts*

saline solution – liquid containing sodium chloride in same quantities as natural body fluid; given in large amounts to replace lost body fluids in cases of dehydration

salivation – production of saliva (spit)

salmonella – bacterial organism that produces the feverish illness plus diarrhoea of salmonellosis; affects animals and people and can lead to blood poisoning in the very young and very old

sarcoptic mange – infectious skin disease caused by a parasitic mite that feeds on skin cells and burrows below upper skin layers

secondary bacterial infection – opportunistic invasion by harmful micro-organisms of an original problem caused by illness or injury

sedation – drugs used to relax and keep quiet a casualty or patient

seizure – epileptic fit; sudden uncontrolled electrical activity in brain

septic – a condition in which a wound or body tissues are infected with bacteria, leading to a production of pus

septicaemia – multiplication of harmful bacteria in body and presence of bacterial toxins in the blood; may lead to highly dangerous septic shock

shock – dangerous reduction in blood flow; leads to collapse/coma

signs – indications of disease or injury which are noticeable to an observer, as opposed to symptoms, which are noticed and described by sufferer

soft-release – gradual reintroduction back to the wild, after temporary housing in accommodation at release site; aims to allow acclimatisation and includes encouragement to animal to return for supplementary support feeding and security, as needed

space blanket – a light foil blanket designed to retain heat

spasm – involuntary, often painful, contraction of muscle or organ lined with muscular tissue

spleen – sponge-like organ that removes and destroys outworn red blood cells and helps fight infection; part of lymphatic system

splint – device used to immobilise part of body (e.g. broken bone); in emergency, may be made from piece of wood, or rolled-up newspaper or magazine

spores – seeds released into the air by a fungus in order to reproduce

stabilisation – immobilisation of broken bone; or management of a medical condition

stapling – method of closing wound using small surgical metal staples

sterile – "germ-free"

steroids – drugs that resemble natural hormones

styptic – substance that checks bleeding

suture – surgical stitch

symptoms – see *signs*

systemic – affects whole body

t

tapeworm – ribbon-shaped parasitic worm that lives in intestines

territory – fixed area that an animal, bird, etc. defends from intruders of its own or other species. May be defined by scent-markings

thiamine – vitamin B1; plays key roles in functioning of nerves, muscles and heart through enzyme activities using carbohydrates

tick – tiny eight-legged parasitic animal that feeds on blood

tissue – group of specialised cells (e.g. muscle, mucous membrane) that perform a particular function in body

tissue death – death of living tissue cells, e.g. as result of infection or loss of blood supply

topical – describes use of drug or treatment only at particular site on body's surface

tourniquet – device put around limb to restrict blood flow; in emergencies, pressure bandaging is now used instead to control excess bleeding because there is less danger of too-prolonged use causing tissue death (see above) and gangrene

toxic shock – extreme reaction to toxins released by overgrowth of harmful bacteria invading body

toxin – poisonous protein produced by disease-causing bacteria

trauma – acute physical injury (e.g. result of road traffic accident, shooting, snaring, bite, etc)

tremors – rapid, involuntary muscle movements; twitches

tuberculosis – infectious disease cause by a mycobacterium

tumour – swelling, any abnormal mass of overgrown tissue. Malignant tumours are those that spread elsewhere in body, i.e. are cancers; benign ones are non-cancerous, but their growth can also be life-threatening if their increasing size interferes with other organs, e.g. pressing on brain.

typhoid fever – illness caused by ingestion of salmonella typhi bacteria

u

ultraviolet light – invisible light from sun's rays in that part of electromagnetic spectrum ("rainbow") beyond violet (at visible end of spectrum). UV light is responsible in nature for production of vitamin D through action of sunlight on skin surface.

Light may be produced artificially (e.g. by a mercury vapour Wood's lamp, used to diagnose some skin conditions such as ringworm, when it causes infected areas to fluoresce)

umbilical cord – cord containing vein and two arteries that connects growing embryo to placenta in mammals, through which embryo (indirectly) obtains oxygen and nutrients. It is severed after birth (e.g. animal bites it off) once young are breathing independently

urine – fluid produced by kidneys as they filter waste products and remove excess water from the blood. It includes urea, uric acid and creatine, variable amounts of sodium chloride, hydrogen and other ions. Excretion of urine adjusts the body's healthy salt and acid-base balance

V

vein – generally, a blood vessel that sends blood back to heart from body's organs and tissues

vertebra (pl. vertebrae) – cylindrical bones that protect the nerve fibres within the spinal cord and which join together to form the backbone/spine

viral – connected to actions of a virus

virus – smallest known infective agent, invades cells of other living organisms

vitamin K injection – may be given to offset effects of diarrhoea, which can affect natural vitamin K absorption. Vitamin K is vital for liver production of substances that make blood clot

vitamin supplements – contain range of vitamins and trace elements (A, E, D, B complex, folic acid, magnesium, copper, iodine, iron, calcium, zinc, potassium, selenium, etc); given with food to boost recovery in patient suffering deficiencies owing to malnutrition or disease, or one that is recovering from surgery or traumatic injury, or is a growing youngster

W

warfarin – drug used to prevent blood clotting; may be used to kill rodents; works gradually. Signs of poisoning include bloody diarrhoea

Weil's Disease – human form of leptospirosis; disease spread by bacteria, causes acute, potentially fatal illness if not treated promptly, with fever, severe head- and muscle-ache, skin rash, eye inflammation. Causes liver and kidney damage

worm – (i) earthworm or (ii) internal parasite

wound management – series of processes to control bleeding, aid and accelerate healing; includes removal of any foreign material and dead tissue from wound, keeping wound clean (e.g. by bandaging), closing it, or deliberately leaving it open, in case of deep wound, to avoid high risk of infection, plus possible specialised surgery where bones and nerve tissue are involved

Z

zinc – trace element essential for normal growth and body development and wound-healing. In human health, zinc compounds are often used in treatments for skin disorders

zoonosis – infectious or parasitic disease of animals that can pass to humans. This may occur through close association, e.g. handling livestock, pets or wildlife casualties, through ingestion via eating meats, or by blood-to-blood transmission via insect bites. (Adj: zoonotic)

INDEX

S